THE SILENT
REVOLUTION

'Tools, or weapons, if only the right ones can be discovered, form 99 per cent of victory . . . Strategy, command, leadership, courage, discipline, supply, organisation and all the moral and physical paraphernalia of war are nothing to a high superiority of weapons . . . at most they go to form the one per cent which makes the whole possible.'

Major General J F C Fuller,
Armament and History, 1946

THE SILENT REVOLUTION

The Development of Conventional Weapons
1945–85

Guy Hartcup

Brassey's (UK)
London • New York

First English edition 1993

UK editorial offices: Brassey's, 165 Great Dover Street,
London SE1 4YA
UK orders: Marston Book Services, PO Box 87, Oxford OX2 0DT

USA orders: Macmillan Publishing Company,
Front and Brown Streets Riverside, NJ 08075

Distributed in North America to booksellers and wholesalers
by the Macmillan Publishing Company, NY 10022

Guy Hartcup has asserted his right to be identified as author of this work.

Library of Congress Cataloging in Publication Data
available

British Library Cataloguing in Publication Data
A catalogue record for this book is available
from the British Library

ISBN 0 08 036702 X Hardback

Typeset by M Rules
Printed in Great Britain

To
the memory of
Edward Lovell, OBE,
Defence Scientist, 1940–65
and to
Alexander
in the hope that he will grow up
in a safer world

CONTENTS

Force multipliers – and their converse – Science and the Cold War –
Time scales and expense in weapon research and development –
Remedies for controlling weapon programmes

New German weapons – Equivalent Allied developments – Radar, radio
countermeasures and proximity fuses – Aircraft propulsion – The birth of
mechanised warfare and the development of anti-tank weapons – Land
mines – Developments in artillery and chemical warfare – Anti-
submarine warfare – Advent of the computer

Post-war development of American and British computers – Invention of
the transistor: developments in the US and UK – Invention of the
integrated circuit – Employment of computers in US and UK air
defences – Computers in the Soviet Union – Advances in ground and
airborne surveillance radars – Millimetric radar – Radar and infra-red
guidance of tactical missiles – Lasers as illuminators of targets – Inertial
guidance – Missile propulsion

PREFACE

The weapons of armed forces have been affected by the advent of the computer and the microchip as much as any other form of human activity. Weapons, however, must conform to strategy and to the requirements of each service. They are also subject to the financial constraints of governments. By the mid-1970s, some years after the abandonment of the strategy of mutual assured destruction, it was apparent that the so-called 'emerging technologies' were transforming weapons used on the ground, in the air and on, or more significantly under, the sea. In fact, this transformation had begun as early as the last year of the Second World War with the initial development of all kinds of unorthodox weapons by the Germans.

This book attempts to provide a survey of the main technological changes that took place in the years following the end of the Second World War. Some three-quarters of the book had been completed when the dramatic events that led to the end of the Cold War took place. Far from upsetting the original aim of the book, the new situation in Eastern Europe allowed a deeper perspective to the changes described and confirmed the value of conventional, as opposed to nuclear, weapons whether strategic or tactical, which have no place in the uneasy peace that now exists.

For the genesis of many of the new generations of weapons and the reasons that were given for developing them, it was possible under the Thirty Years Rule to draw on original documents held by the Public Record Office at Kew. For more recent years, it was necessary to follow clues in a variety of journals or scientific papers dealing with advances in defence technology published in the West.

Of greater value have been the detailed comments of those who have read individual chapters namely: Derek Barlow, a computer systems consultant; Handel Davies, at one time Director General of Scientific Research and

Development in the Ministry of Supply; Major General David Egerton, a former President of the Ordnance Board who also acted as Chief of Staff to the Air Defence Working Party, 1963–64 under Professor R V Jones; Basil Lythall, a Chief Scientist of the Royal Navy; Richard Ogorkiewicz, Visiting Professor to the Royal Military College of Science, who is also a friend and next-door neighbour; and Donald Tomlin, for many years an Experimental Officer of the Radar Research and Development Establishment and later of the Royal Radar Establishment. I am greatly indebted to them all. Any errors of fact which remain are my own.

I am also grateful for information, supply of books and scientific papers from Professor R V Jones, who sent me his paper on Air Defence and the Falklands; Gordon Bussey, Historical Adviser to Philips Electronics; Patricia Keen, Historian of the US Photo Reconnaissance Association; Dr Gabriel Khoury of the Imperial College of Science, Technology and Medicine; Arnold Nayler, Technical Manager of the Royal Aeronautical Society, for many demands on his time and patience; Brian Riddle, Librarian of the Royal Aeronautical Society; and John Leather of the Royal Institute of Naval Architects.

My thanks are due to the staffs of the Public Record Office at Kew, the Science Museum Library, and the Library of the International Institute for Strategic Studies.

I wish to express my gratitude to my publishers and in particular to Major General Anthony Trythall and Jenny Shaw who gave me the idea for the book, and Brigadier Bryan Watkins, my Editor, for his enthusiasm and for many constructive suggestions which have improved the text. Finally, to my wife for her patience over the past three years.

East Sheen, 1993   *Guy Hartcup*

LIST OF ILLUSTRATIONS

Plates

Figures

Table

GLOSSARY OF ACRONYMS AND ABBREVIATIONS

Committees, Organisations and Titles

ACE	Allied Command Europe
ACAS	Assistant Chief of Air Staff (UK)
AORG	Army Operational Research Group (UK)
BTL	Bell Telephone Laboratories
Caltech	California Institute of Technology
CIA	Central Intelligence Agency (US)
CIGS	Chief of the Imperial General Staff (UK)
DCAS	Deputy Chief of Air Staff (UK)
DRPC	Defence Research Policy Committee (UK)
DSIR	Department of Scientific and Industrial Research (UK)
GEC	General Electric Company (UK)
MIT	Massachusetts Institute of Technology
MWDP	Mutual Weapons Development Programme (UK/US)
NAMMA	North Atlantic Treaty Organisation Multi-role Combat Aircraft Development and Production Agency
NPL	National Physical Laboratory (UK)
ORDCIT	Ordnance Department – California Institute of Technology
PPBS	Planning, Programing and Budgeting System (US)
PSAC	Presidential Scientific Advisory Committee (US)
RAE	Royal Aircraft Establishment
RCA	Radio Corporation of America
RNSS	Royal Naval Scientific Service
RRDE	Radar Research and Development Establishment (UK)
RRE	Royal Radar Establishment (UK)
RSRE	Royal Signals and Radar Establishment (UK)

SERL	Services Electronics Research Laboratory (UK)
SHAPE	Supreme Headquarters Allied Powers, Europe
SRDE	Signals Research and Development Establishment (UK)
TRE	Telecommunications Research Establishment (UK)
UDE	Underwater Weapons Development Establishment (UK)
USAF	United States Air Force
VCAS	Vice Chief of Air Staff (UK)

Strategy

| ALB | AirLand Battle |
| FOFA | Follow on Forces Attack |

Computer Systems and Semiconductors

ACE	Automatic Computing Engine (UK)
AWDATS	Artillery Weapon Data Transmission System (UK)
BATES	Battlefield Artillery Target Engagement System (UK)
DIANE	Digital Integrated Attack Navigation System (Air-US)
DIP	Digital Image Processing (UK)
DME	Distance Measuring Equipment
EDVAC	Electronic Discrete Variable Calculator (US)
ENIAC	Electronic Numerical Integrator and Calculator (US)
FACE	Field Artillery Computer Equipment (UK)
MIDAC	Military Data Processing and Computing (US)
VHPIC	Very High Performance Integrated Circuit (UK)
VHSIC	Very High Speed Integrated Circuit (US)

Radar, Radio and Infra Red

AEW	Airborne Early Warning
AI	Aircraft Interception
AM	Amplitude-modulated
ASV	Air-to-Surface Vessel (radar)
AWACS	Airborne Warning and Control System
BLADES	Buffalo Laboratories Application of Digital Spectra (radio-US)
C^3	Command, Control and Communications
C^3CM	Command, Control and Communications Countermeasures
ECM	Electronic Countermeasures
ECCM	Electronic Counter Countermeasures
EHF	Extremely High Frequency
ELF	Extremely Low Frequency

ELINT	Electronic Intelligence
ESM	Electronic Support Measures
EW	Electronic Warfare
FLIR	Forward Looking Infra Red
FM	Frequency-modulated
HF	High Frequency
H2S	Airborne radar for target detection (UK)
HOBOS	Homing Optical Bombing System (US)
IC3	Integrated Communications System (RN-UK)
IFF	Indentification, Friend or Foe
INTACS	Integrated Tactical Communications Studies (US)
JSTARS	Joint Surveillance and Target Attack Radar System (US)
JTIDS	Joint Tactical Information Distribution System (US)
MIMO	Miniature Image Orthicon
MTI	Moving Target Indicator
NADGE	NATO Air Defence Ground Environment
NICS	NATO Integrated Communications System
NWCS	NATO-wide Communications System
OTH	Over the Horizon (radar)
PPI	Plan Position Indicator (radar)
RCS	Radar Cross Section
RHAW	Radar Homing and Warning (US)
RITA	*Résau Intégré de Transmission Automatique (FR)*
SAGE	Semi-automatic Ground Environment (US-radar)
SIGINT	Signals Intelligence
SIF	Self Identification System (US)
SS	Spread Spectrum
TERCOM	Terrain Contour Matching System (UK)
TOBIAS	Terrestial Observation Battlefield Intruder Alarm System (UK)
TWT	Travelling Wave Tube
UHF	Ultra High Frequency
VHF	Very High Frequency
VLF	Very Low Frequency

Explosives, Guns, Missiles and Vehicles

AAM	Air-to-Air Missile
ALARM	Air-launched Anti-radar Missile (UK)
APC	Armoured Personnel Carrier
APDS	Armour-piercing Discarding Sabot (shot-UK)
APFSDS	Armour-piercing Fin Stabilising Discarding Sabot (shot-UK)
AQM	Air-launched, drones, guided missile (US)

ARM	Anti-Radiation Missile
ATGM	Anti-Tank Guided Missile
CEP	Circular Error of Probability
FMBT	Future Main Battle Tank
FNAL	Fabrique Nationale-Fusil Automatique Légère
FV	Fighting (BE) Vehicle (UK)
GPMG	General Purpose Machine Gun (UK)
HARM	High Speed Anti-radiation Missile (Air-US)
HEAT	High Explosive Anti-tank
HESH	High Explosive Squash Head
ICBM	Inter-continental Ballistic Missile
LARS	Light Artillery Rocket System
MLRS	Multiple Launch Rocket System
PGM	Precision-Guided Munition
RAP	Rocket-Assisted Projectile pulsion
RPG	Rocket-Propelled Grenade
SAM	Surface-to-Air Missile
SSM	Surface-to-Surface Missile
TOW	Tube-launched, Optically-guided Weapon (US)
V-1	*Vergeltungs-Waffe 1* (Retaliation Weapon 1 – flying bomb (GE))
V-2	*Vergeltungs-Waffe 2* (Retaliation Weapon 2 – long range rocket (GE))

Logistics

CEPS	Central European Pipeline System

Chemical and Biological Warfare

DNA	Deoxyribonucleic Acid
G-A	Tabun (nerve gas)
G-B	Sarin (nerve gas)
G-D	Soman (nerve gas)
G-E	Subsidiary nerve gas (UK)
G-F	Subsidiary nerve gas (UK)
N	Anthrax (UK)
NAIAD	Chemical warfare detector (UK)

Aircraft, Reconnaissance, Satellites, Surveillance

ADV	Air Defence Variant
CCD	Charge-Coupled Device

EORSAT	Elint Ocean Reconnaissance Satellite
IDS	Interdiction Deep Strike
MRCA	Multi-role Combat Aircraft
PR	Photographic Reconnaissance
RORSAT	Radar-equipped Ocean Reconnaissance Satellite
RPV	Remotely-piloted Vehicle
SCOT	Light Weight Satellite Communications System (RN-UK)
TSR	Tactical Strike Reconnaissance
U-2	Utility 2 (Long range high altitude reconnaissance aircraft – US)
V(/S)TOL	Vertical (/Short) Take-off and Landing
WCA	Wing-controlled Aerodyne

Sea Warfare

HTP	High Test Peroxide
LAMPS	Light Airborne Multi-Purpose Sonar System (US)
MAD	Magnetic Air Detection
RDSS	Rapidly Deployable Surveillance System (USN)
ROV	Remotely-Operated Vehicle (mine hunting)
SOSUS	Sound Surveillance Underscan (US)
SURTASS	Surveillance Towed Array Sensor System (US)

INTRODUCTION

The latter part of the Second World War provided a foretaste of how warfare would evolve in the future. The development of radar as a means of surveillance, detection and control of weapon systems was a major advance and made the electromagnetic spectrum a new area of conflict where measure was confronted by countermeasure. Computers, then clumsy infants, nevertheless proved that they could not only be used as super calculating machines but indispensable tools for rapidly decoding enemy signals. Guided weapons were used for the first time and improvements were made to every type of conventional weapon as will be described in Chapter 1.

Force Multipliers – and their Converse

No sooner had the war ended than the new technology of microelectronics, stemming from the inventions of the transistor and the integrated circuit, began to transform the accuracy of surveillance systems, guided missiles, armoured vehicles, communications, artillery, underwater weapons and the avionics of military aircraft. Hitherto technical superiority over the enemy had been achieved by quantitative means; production of guns increased fire power on land, fleets were assessed by the number of battleships, and air power was wielded by squadrons of bombers returning repeatedly to the same targets with loads of high explosive bombs.

With the technology of microelectronics, superiority over the enemy was obtained by *qualitative* means. For example, in all kinds of warfare, the ability to see in the dark or in fog is a great asset. This stimulated the development of thermal imagers which provide a pilot with a picture on his head-up display in his cockpit hardly different from that in daylight, while a tank commander is able to observe and sight his gun at night or in fog. These are examples of what are now known as *force multipliers*. So too, are digital communications which enable commanders on the battlefield to make decisions derived from 'real time' intelligence; in other words, they can receive or transmit orders and act on data received as events take place. Conversely there are countermeasures which are designed to parry or frustrate the functioning of radio communications or the operation of radar and infra red and sonar equipment. These lead to further changes, so that the same equipments can adapt themselves to the latest hostile ploy: activities in this field are known as electronic warfare (EW). EW has been succinctly defined by the Americans as the use of electromagnetic energy to 'determine, exploit, reduce, or prevent hostile use of the electromagnetic spectrum and action which retains friendly use of the electromagnetic spectrum.' EW now overshadows every kind of warlike activity.

At the same time, while new technology has put greater destructive power into the hands of individuals and reduced the numbers required to man major weapon systems, their sheer complexity increases the need for logistical and technological support, thereby cancelling out any manpower advantage gained. To take but two examples: the maintenance back-up needed to support a *LIGHTNING* squadron in the 1960s involved nearly 200 per cent more men than the number required to service a wartime *SPITFIRE* squadron. Nearly every type of weapon must now be fitted with some form of electronic equipment and this annually becomes more expensive. In the 1970s, the French devoted over a quarter of their defence expenditure on electronic equipment, over 2½ times more than they spent on air frames and over 20 times the amount spent on artillery and small arms.

Science and the Cold War

The start of the 'Cold War' between the Western Alliance and the Soviet Union and its satellites in 1947 followed by a 'hot' war in Korea in 1950 led to rearmament and a mobilisation of supporting science in the West, made all the more urgent by the explosion of the first Soviet atom bomb in August 1949; the launching of *Sputnik* eight years later again set alarm bells ringing in scientific establishments. Most of the scientists who had worked in defence establishments during the Second World War had returned thankfully to their civilian occupations. Now scientific manpower was needed for developing new types of weapons. As we shall see German scientists had already begun to develop rockets and guided missiles during that war and many of them had been tempted to leave their homeland for a more comfortable life with good pay in the United States. The Soviet Union meanwhile, had either cajoled or forcibly extradited German scientists and technicians to work on military projects. The British and French, while making use of German expertise, were less keen to pay for or retain them for more than a limited period.[1]

Plate 1 Sir Henry Tizard, first Chairman of the British Defence Research Policy Committee (by William Dring RA). One of the early protagonists of radar, he set the post-war course of future weapon development for the British Services. (*The Oxford Times*)

British research and development for the rearmament following the beginning of the Korean war owed much to Sir Henry Tizard, who had been responsible for introducing radar as the backbone of the air defence of Great Britain four years before war began in 1939 and who, in January 1947, became the first chairman of the Defence Research Policy Committee (DRPC), responsible for advising on priorities for future weapon systems. Tizard was succeeded by a number of eminent scientists, of whom probably the most influential was Sir Solly Zuckerman, Chief Scientific Adviser when the three Service ministries were integrated within the Ministry of Defence in 1964. Formulation of operational requirements, which hitherto had suffered from inter-Service rivalry and duplication of effort, was now given a more rational and responsible framework and became closely associated with the reductions in defence expenditure that became necessary with Britain's relinquished imperial role.

The American Services had gained much from the exchanges of scientific information with the British during the war, but for some time had cultivated close relations with the universities and academic foundations like the Massachussetts Institute of Technology (MIT). Now that the North American continent was exposed to attack from long-range aircraft or missiles, new extra-governmental institutions were set up, like the Rand Corporation,[2] to make independent investigations into air defence and other areas of defence science. Commercial organisations, like the Bell Telephone Laboratories (BTL), which had been heavily engaged in war work, began to make important contributions in the field of microelectronics. Other commercial companies, now that radar was no longer secret, began to develop aircraft, guided weapons and various forms of electronic equipment to sell to the military. Vannevar Bush, who had ably led the United States scientific effort in the war, set the course for post-war research and development. A Research and Development Board became responsible to the Department of Defense for new projects. American Presidents, according to their inclinations, were able to draw on advice from personal scientific advisers or from the Presidential Scientific Advisory Committee (PSAC) – a much less formal body than the British DRPC.[3]

One of the most remarkable aspects of post-1945 Europe was the revival of French science through the leadership of scientists and engineers like Frédéric Joliot, Raoul Dautry and Paul Dassault. Taking advantage of German technicians, the French began to specialise in anti-tank guided weapons. In addition, they were soon producing aircraft and electronic equipment on a par with that of Britain and the United States.[4]

The armed forces of the Soviet Union, relying on a command economy, made a great leap forward in the development of conventional weapons after the death of Stalin and the subsequent relaxation in the exchange of ideas. By

Plate 2 Vannevar Bush, first Chairman of the Joint Research and Development Board of the US Joint Chiefs of Staff. In the Second World War he had been Head of the Office of Scientific Research and Development. (*Karsh/Ottawa*)

the mid-1970s, it appeared to the West that the Soviet Union was actually producing more artillery, weapons for chemical warfare and anti-ship missiles than the United States. The Soviets achieved their success not, as popularly supposed, by building cheap, simple to operate equipment, but by spending more than the Americans on military equipment and much less on manpower. Whereas the United States spent more than half of its defence budget on manpower, the Soviet Union spent less than a quarter of its budget on that item.[5]

Time Scales and Expense in Weapon Research and Development

As weapons became more and more sophisticated, the time needed for research and development (R&D) grew ever longer. A minimum of five to seven years became the norm, though it was not unusual for ten or more years to elapse before an equipment became operational. In consequence, the costs of R&D soared alarmingly.

In Britain, for example, the expenditure of the Ministry of Supply rose from £30m in 1945 to some £214m in 1958, in which year the Admiralty's demands were for £18m. A further £20m went on the development of atomic weapons. In the United States huge sums were being committed by the government to R&D. In the 1970s, 32 major systems, ranging from surface-to-air missiles (SAMs) and anti-tank guided weapons (ATGWs) to AEGIS (a US Navy combined early warning, tracking and fire control system) to the airborne warning and control system (AWACS), cost the Department of Defense over $100 billion in R&D, production and initial support. Western governments were also committed to their electorates to finance extensive programmes of civil expenditure. In Britain, where the economy was still severely strained by the paralysing costs of the Second World War, the government was under constant pressure to reduce the cost of defence.[6]

In direct contrast, unfettered by any considerations of democratic control, the Soviet Union's defence spending rose steadily until, by 1982, it totalled no less than 12–14 per cent of Gross National Product (GNP).

Remedies for Controlling Weapon Programmes

Britain, on account of her prodigious spending during the Second World War, was least able of all the nations in the Western Alliance to afford new weapon systems. Tizard, in a paper on R&D programmes written for the War Office Weapons Development Committee on 31 August 1949, doubted whether the capacity of the United Kingdom

'. . . will be able to meet the demands made upon it. In peace our limitation is money, and the more elaborate, and therefore expensive, our equipment becomes, the less of it we can afford to buy. In war, man hours of skilled and unskilled labour become the limitation, and, again, we cannot hope to get our full requirements, either in quantity or in quality. Our starting point must be to suit our tactical methods to the realities of the equipment position, and not to try to design our equipment to meet ideal tactical methods.'[7]

Tizard's advice was largely unheeded as, for example, in the decision to embark on three types of SAM, one for each service, and three types of strategic (V) bombers. Britain's unsound economic position in the late 1950s and 1960s was an unfavourable environment in which to launch ambitious weapon programmes. Over-optimistic forecasts lengthened time scales, causing rises in expenditure. Demands for financing civil programmes led to projects for new weapons being abandoned. It was estimated that, up to 1967, some 32 major projects had to be cancelled costing the government a total of £500m. The famous (or infamous as it appeared to many at the time) Defence Budget of 1957 was merely the first of a series of reviews designed to make Service ministries more realistic in their choice of weapons. It was not until the early 1970s that the ordering of new equipment was taken on by a single agency called the Procurement Executive. At last, committee decisions were replaced by accountable management.

Whether the reforms of British weapon procurement were effective or not is open to question. Zuckerman, who had been in a good position to observe, thought not. 'Millions of pounds are still being wasted', he wrote in 1988, citing the cancellation of the RAF NIMROD AWACS aircraft abandoned in favour of the US version after a long period of development. He continued, 'It is hardly surprising that to the layman the way R&D resources are distributed never seems to reflect a rational appreciation of what might or might not be best in the national interest.'[8]

A significant attempt to make such a 'rational appreciation' was, in fact, carried out by President Kennedy's Secretary of Defense, Robert S McNamara who had formerly been chairman of the Ford Motor Company.[9] The United States had been no less prone to military project cancellations than the British – to mention only three: the nuclear-powered aircraft, the NAVAHO ballistic missile, the SKYBOLT stand-off missile. But whereas Britain had to shed her pretensions to be a global power, the United States sought to expand, or at least to retain her global commitments in response to the Soviet threat; while from 1964–72 she was engaged in a costly and unpopular war in South-East Asia.

McNamara diagnosed the problem as being the lack of 'essential management tools needed to make sound decisions on the really crucial issues of national economy.' He introduced two such tools. The first was the Planning-Programming-Budgeting System (PPBS) which provided information and a control device linking long range planning and shorter range budgeting through programmes costed over a five year period. The second tool was systems analysis (akin to operational research, used by the British in World War 2) which was the means by which data were compared as a way of determining the cost of various options. It also provided the means for judging the logic of the many (often conflicting) proposals that were submitted by the services.

Although the PPBS and systems analysis were resented by the services as being interference by civilian 'whizz kids' and, indeed, there were failures as well as successes, notably the lengthy and expensive development of the F-111/variable geometry aircraft (discussed in Chapter 7), McNamara's PPBS endured and systems analysis was transformed into an analytical mode of thought throughout the Pentagon.

The British likewise found that operational analysis was a useful tool for assessing cost effectiveness. They began to use war games and computer models to explore the consequences of adopting different options.[10] For example, either one-on-one engagements or more complex scenarios could be studied. In the former, a simulated aerial combat could provide information for aircraft design and the best trade-off between capability and cost could then be selected. In the latter, the best mixture of, for instance, SAMs and fighter aircraft to be deployed against an enemy bomber formation could be assessed, given a fixed total sum for procurement. Of course, a number of external factors, such as changes in international relations or prolonged time scales in weapon development, cannot be formulated and operational analysis rarely provides prescriptive answers.

Finally, collaborative projects helped to alleviate expense. In the 1950s and early 1960s a number of expensive European military equipments were met by US-licensed production projects and by financial support provided by the Mutual Weapons Development Programme.[11] The NAT0 powers then learned to be more self-sufficient by spreading the cost of a weapon system between two or more states. These arrangements were called a Memorandum of Understanding. Design, development and production were contracted to two or more companies separately, for example, a company in one country would produce the wings of an aircraft and another company the fuselage. Alternatively, contracts would be placed with a new company which was a consortium of the individual companies taking part. Although the *overall* cost of production of a co-operative project will be higher than if undertaken by a single nation, the *unit* cost of each equipment will be lower because of the longer production run involved. Co-operative projects also offer better prospects for export since purchasing nations often select systems whose potential is reflected in the number of nations who already have those systems in service.

A number of successful weapon systems have been brought into service in this way. Among them were the JAGUAR strike aircraft, the Multi-Role

Combat Aircraft (MRCA) later known as the TORNADO, and the FH70
155mm towed gun. On the other hand, attempts to collaborate in developing a
new main battle tank have so far been unsuccessful, either because of differ-
ences in national policy, or because of disagreement on the choice of
equipment to be fitted.

THE SILENT
REVOLUTION

. 1 .

A NEW ERA IN WARFARE

Most of the advances in military technology since 1945 – the 'Silent Revolution' – originated during, and in some cases before, the Second World War. An understanding of these changes must include at least a brief account of the developments in radar, sonar, submarines, tanks, ballistic rockets and flying bombs (the progenitors of guided missiles), and even computers, in the years 1939–45.

New German Weapons

On 25 August 1943 a small Allied convoy was attacked by a formation of Heinkel bombers operating over the Bay of Biscay and carrying radio-controlled missiles developed by the firm of *Henschel* and known as the HS293 A1. One of these winged projectiles narrowly missed the destroyer, HMS *Bideford*.[1] A second, more successful attack took place two days later, sinking the destroyer HMS *Egret* and the Canadian sloop *Athabaskan*. On 8 September, another new missile was used by the Germans in the Mediterranean. This was the *FRITZ (FX)*, an armour-piercing radio-controlled bomb designed by the firm of Ruhrstahl for attacks on capital ships or cruisers. It was nearly 11ft long and could attain supersonic speeds and had a range of over 400 yards. The *FRITZ X* sank the Italian battleship *Roma* and about 80 other vessels before suitable radio countermeasures were devised to render attacks of this nature abortive. The appearance of these forerunners of contemporary guided missiles was overshadowed by the appearance less than a year later of the *FZG76*, a small unmanned aircraft (popularly known as the V-1) with a warhead containing a ton of high explosive, and the *A-4* ballistic rocket (known to the Allies as the V-2) also carrying a ton of high explosive.

Thanks to good intelligence and to effective air attacks against their launching sites and supply lines, these weapons failed to upset the Allied landings in Normandy. While the damage inflicted on London and its surroundings and on targets on the continent was relatively slight, the effect upon a war-weary civilian population was much more marked, giving them a foretaste of what 'push button warfare', as it was popularly known, might be like.

The development of German rockets and guided missiles was remarkable considering that by the time it got underway, the *Wehrmacht* had been driven back on the defensive on both the Eastern and Western fronts, and the centres of industry and the communication systems connecting them were then being bombed relentlessly. Indeed, it could be argued that had greater priority been given to surface-to-air missiles rather than to the V-weapons, which were essentially morale-breaking systems, the German air defences could have been greatly improved. Backed by the already formidable radar network, they might have presented an insuperable obstacle to the Allied combined bomber offensive.

Fortunately for the Allies, the Germans were unable to coordinate weapon research and development. There was no supervision by a central authority of the successive stages from the design on the drawing board to the final stages of production, inspection and acceptance by the user. By 1943, the war production ministry under Albert Speer, the most technically-minded member of Hitler's entourage, formed a special commission of Service officers, scientists and industrialists to organise the development of new weapons. However, after only a year, it was replaced by a more streamlined committee under the rocket chief, General Walter Dornberger. Jealousies between the Services, each dealing independently with the armament manufacturers, and the lack of trained technical personnel, combined to induce inefficiency and slow output.[2]

The leading producers of guided weapons were the firms of *Henschel* and *Ruhrstahl* which had made the *HS293* and *FX* glider bombs already mentioned. More advanced was the *SCHMETTERLING* (Butterfly) from the Henschel stable, a surface-to-air missile (SAM) with a range of about 20 miles, a ceiling of 50,000 ft and top speed of 625 mph. Trials began in 1944. Although primitive by post-war standards, it could have wreaked havoc in the slow-moving heavy bomber streams of the Allies.

Even the well-known *Messerschmitt* company, fully engaged in turning out fighters, managed to develop a missile. Known as *WASSERFALL* (Waterfall), it was 25 feet long and had a wing span of over nine feet. Its maximum range was over 30 miles and it was intended to engage hostile aircraft at heights of around 40,000 feet. However, after its propulsion and guidance systems had been tested at the great rocket experimental centre at Peenemunde on the Baltic, the conclusion was reached that *WASSERFALL* was too large and too expensive for operational use. Another ambitious missile was made by the armament firm of *RHEINMETALL BORSIG* and called *RHEINTOCHTER*

(Rhine Daughter). It was a two stage rocket weighing one and a half tons, over 20 feet long with six wings each 7 feet long. Guidance was provided by radio and two radars, one directed at the target and the other giving warning of intercepting aircraft. *Rheinmetall Borsig* produced several interesting missiles which never passed beyond the experimental stage, but which were a foretaste of future weaponry. One of these, called *ENZIAN* (Gentian), had swept back wings and was designed to reach supersonic speeds; another was *FEURELILIE* (Fire Lily). Like *ENZIAN*, it was a SAM and capable of supersonic speeds. *TAIFUN* (Typhoon) was, for that time, more practical, being an unguided rocket reaching a height of 50,000 feet and with a range of over seven miles. It was later adapted by the Americans to contain a liquid propellant. In a short while, however, unguided rockets were abandoned for guided missiles.[3]

Greater difficulties were experienced with designing air-to-air missiles (AAMS) to be launched from fighter aircraft. The most successful again came from the designers of *Ruhrstahl*. This was designated *X-4* and was controlled by a fine wire which unwound from the tail and was unjammable by electronic devices.

The Germans made a belated, but vain, attempt to coordinate all these individual projects into what was called the Fuehrer's Emergency Programme early in 1945. The weapons earmarked for continued development were *WASSERFALL*, *RHEINTOCHTER* and *ENZIAN*. But with the Americans and the British poised on the west bank of the Rhine, and the Red Army driving on Berlin, such advanced technology could not turn the tide.

British and American Developments

Compared with the German advances in the guided weapons field, the Allied effort was tentative and cautious. The British decided at an early stage in the war to concentrate on the development of unguided rockets which would supplement the scanty stocks of anti-aircraft guns. It was hoped to achieve accuracy with proximity fuses, but as development of the latter had to be undertaken by the Americans and involved a lengthy period of trials before production, the rockets did not achieve the expected results. Much better value was given by rockets equipped with a 60 pound warhead and fired by fighter bombers against land and sea targets. These rockets, too, left much to be desired, but when used in the latter stages of the Battle of Normandy had a decisive effect on German tanks, setting them on fire or otherwise disabling them. Rocket attacks were similarly successful against German U-boats. Impressed by the V-1 and V-2 attacks, the British drew up quite detailed plans for guided missiles, priority being given to anti-aircraft defence. But proposals were also made for medium and short range weapons for the Army and Navy to be used for bombardment. The first meeting of a guided anti-aircraft projectile committee met on 10 March 1945 to discuss methods of propulsion, aerodynamic problems at supersonic speeds, radio and radar guidance and gyro stabilisation and servo mechanism problems.[4] But little progress was made before the end of the war.

Enjoying more ample resources, the Americans were able to embark on a more ambitious programme. As early as February 1945, the British Commonwealth Scientific Office in Washington reported that 'The Americans are putting a very big research and development effort into guided missile investigation'. Consequently 'progress is likely to be very rapid over here'.[5] The United States already had quite a strong interest in rocketry due to the pioneer, R H Goddard, who had fired the first liquid-propelled rocket in 1926. But it was not until 1936 that military-sponsored experiments with rocket motors began at the Guggenheim Aeronautical Laboratory in the California Institute of Technology (Caltech) under the direction of Theodore von Karman, the Hungarian aeronautical engineer who had been employed by the German Army in the First World War before emigrating to the United States. His team of young scientists led by F J Malina and John Parsons embarked on a programme of research with the object of discovering whether rocket engines could be driven more efficiently by solid rather than by liquid fuels. In the spring of 1942, Parsons proposed that a solid fuel, using potassium perchlorate as an oxidiser, could give a thrust of a million pounds and assist the take-off of an aircraft. But in 1944, the US Army revived its interest in military rockets (dormant since the 19th century) and that June arranged that Caltech should start a programme for long range rocket-propelled missiles. Seven months later, the Army ordered the construction of a surface to surface rocket with a payload of 1000 lb and a range of 150 miles. This programme was given the title of ORDCIT (Ordnance Department-California Institute of Technology).[6] With these investigations in train, the Americans were better placed than the British to take advantage of the latest German rocket technology when the war was over.

The Russian scientific effort devoted to rocket research, like the British and the American, was limited, but proceeded on rather similar lines. In October 1933 the first state-controlled rocket research establishment was founded. As in America, this was primarily for the purpose of jet-assisted take-off for aircraft. It was called the Jet Propulsion Research Institute and experiments with liquid and solid fuel rockets took place there up to 1939. Some time before the Soviet Union was invaded by the Germans, the possibility of using rockets for saturation fire was investigated by the scientist, I I Gvaay.[7] It was appreciated that the inherent inaccuracy of unguided rockets required them to be used in large numbers. This was the genesis of the famous multi-barrel rocket batteries, or *KATYUSHA* batteries, mass-produced from 1940 onwards and used so effectively in the battles on the Eastern Front. The Russians, too, were more than receptive to the potential of rockets and missiles when the end of the war gave them the opportunity to exploit their enemy's technology. Even more important, according to some of their scientists, a team of designers, scientists, mathematicians and technicians had been trained to take on post-war projects.

Radar, Radio Countermeasures and Proximity Fuses

Early in the war, a leading British defence scientist predicted that it would be won by the side producing the shortest wave length.[8] Both sides sought to exploit centimetric wave lengths which would give them the accuracy to detect small targets. The Allies were fortunate enough to benefit from the British discovery of the magnetron – a small device which could produce bursts of power of over 100 kilowatts, thus enormously extending the range of radar sets without overloading the valve. The means was now available for night-fighter pilots to detect and intercept bombers, for bomber crews to identify their targets far more accurately and for maritime aircraft crews to be able to detect surfaced submarines in the featureless ocean. A joint Anglo-US production effort became responsible for equipping the air forces with the magnetron. The Germans had also joined in the search to obtain centimetre waves, but it was only after the discovery of a British blind bombing aid called H2S in February 1943 that they realised how far behind they were. Steps were immediately taken to fit German night fighters with centimetric radar and to devise countermeasures against centimetric anti-surface vessel radar for their U-boats.

The magnetron was possibly the most important of the devices presented to the Americans by the British Scientific and Technical Mission, popularly known as the Tizard Mission because of its leader, in August 1940 when a German invasion of Britain was anticipated any day. American scientists, already preparing for the eventuality of war, were not slow in appreciating its possibilities. Before long, they had developed the best fire control apparatus of the war – the SCR 584 used for the control of anti-aircraft guns. The SCR 584 in combination with an electrical predictor – the M9 (of which more later) – and shells fitted with the proximity fuse (another device taken to the States by the Tizard Mission) were responsible for virtually halting the V-1 attacks on Southern England in August 1944. On account of the danger of revealing its secret to the enemy, the proximity fuse was not made available for use in land operations until the German counter-attack in the Ardennes at the end of 1944. Even then, its employment was restricted by adverse weather conditions. The radio-operated fuse was based on the Doppler principle and was activated when a signal was reflected from the target aircraft or, when fitted into shells, at a pre-estimated distance above the ground. Its extreme sensitivity made it liable to fail in cloud or rain and, of course, it was susceptible to enemy radio interference.[9]

Indeed, the greater the use of radio waves and of radar aids for target identification or aircraft interception, the more both sides intensified measures to counteract their effect. These measures included the jamming of radar by 'window', or 'chaff', as it was later called, and the use of radio decoys and a host of jamming or deceptive equipments designed to protect aircraft or submarines or to deflect bombers from their targets. Another way of avoiding electromagnetic jamming was to use infra-red equipment which could detect radiation emitted from a target in the form of heat, or, alternatively, pick up radiation reflected by a target from a subsidiary source. Even so, infra-red could be counteracted by the use of special paints and was inoperable in certain weather conditions. Infra-red was used on a very limited scale by the Germans after the Allies had begun to jam their best airborne interception radar called *LICHTENSTEIN*. The beneficiaries of this work were the Russians, who captured most of the German research equipment after the war.

Improvements in Aircraft Propulsion

One indisputable requirement of the Second World War was the need to gain air superiority whether operations were being conducted on land or at sea. The need to increase the performance of all types of aircraft, especially interceptors and ground attack aircraft was paramount. Investigations into the possibility of designing an efficient gas turbine had taken place for many years, but the production of a practical aircraft engine did not become possible until the 1930s. In Britain, as is well known, it was a young RAF officer, Frank Whittle, who hit on the possibility of combining a gas turbine with jet propulsion. Less well known is the work of A A Griffith, who was employed by the Royal Aircraft Establishment and who, by 1929, had designed a compressor of sufficient efficiency to make a gas turbine a practical engine for driving a propeller, Close behind was a young German physicist, Hans Joachim-Pabst von Ohain who, by 1934, had patented a turbojet engine. In contrast to Whittle, whose long drawn out attempts to interest the British Air Ministry only began to bear fruit in the summer of 1939, Ohain, who had succeeded in becoming employed by *Heinkel*, the German aircraft manufacturers, had already had his engine fitted in the first experimental jet plane built in August of that year.

Intelligence reports emanating from Germany concerning the development of unconventional power plants for aircraft at last gave the touch of the governmental spur to the production of the first British jet-propelled aircraft – the Gloster METEOR powered by the Whittle W2 B/23C engine. No more than a handful of these interceptors were available to complement the TEMPESTS and SPITFIRES despatched to shoot down the V-1s, themselves propelled by small pulse jet engines as they streamed across the Channel from their launching pads in northern France. In due course METEORS were attached to the

6

British tactical air force, then operating in support of the British army on the west German frontier, but no combats took place with their German counterparts.

The Germans had, in fact, failed to take advantage of their early lead. An urgent requirement for a fast-flying fighter to counter the American daylight bombing offensive was the reason for the development of the Me 262. It was powered by Ohain's engine now called the *Junkers JUMO* 004 (actually much less reliable than the W2 B/23C), but it was the first jet-propelled military aircraft to become operational. Equipped with four 33 millimetre machine guns or cannon and having a top speed of over 500 mph, it was a formidable addition to the German fighter defences. But Hitler's decision to convert it into a fighter bomber in support of the army was a blessing in disguise for the Allied day bomber formations and their fighter escorts. Jet propelled aircraft, then, had no significant effect on operations in the latter part of the war.[10]

Experiments were made with rocket-propelled aircraft on both sides of the Atlantic. Again it was the Germans who led the race. The *Me* 163, designed by the Bavarian, Alexander Lippisch, was intended to intercept high-flying Allied bombers. It had a maximum speed of just under 600 mph and could reach a height of about 30,000 feet in three and a half minutes. Armament consisted of two 30 millimetre cannon. It had originally been intended to be a high-speed research aircraft for rocket-assisted take-off of heavy bombers and was the outcome of many years work by Lippisch on tailless aircraft. The power plant was designed by the marine engineer, Helmuth Walther, who was interested in rocket propulsion for torpedoes. Unfortunately the *Me* 163 could only remain airborne for eight minutes and was extremely dangerous to fly and even more hazardous to land on account of the volatile nature of its fuel. It also needed very long runways for take-off and in the last months of the war few of them remained undamaged. Nevertheless the *Me* 163 did destroy some Allied bombers and, more significantly, it provided a model for post-war rocket-propelled aircraft development.

Another stop-gap against the introduction of guided missiles by the Germans was the *NATTER* (Viper), a piloted rocket-propelled fighter with radar guidance, able to take off vertically without a runway and climb at a speed of over 35,000 ft per minute with a load of 30 rockets in its nose. Unlike the *Me* 163, it never became operational but several pilots were killed during experimental flights.[11]

Like the Germans, both the British and the Americans saw possibilities in using rocket propulsion to enable heavy aircraft to take off from limited runways or from aircraft carriers. The British made use of such assisted take-off to enable naval fighters to operate from the escort carriers built during the war. In the States, the rocket experiments conducted by the Guggenheim Laboratory, already mentioned, included rocket-assisted take-off for aircraft

7

operating at sea. The first jet-assisted take off took place on 23 August 1941, but the technique was never used operationally the US Navy.[12] At least American research gave an insight to British workers in the field who were then able to appreciate that large rockets using liquid fuel and travelling for distances of about 200 miles with a war head of over one ton were feasible. Such information in the autumn of 1943 provided British intelligence with evidence that the threat of attack by German rockets was far from being imaginary.

The Birth of Mechanised Warfare and the Development of Anti-Tank Weapons

Tanks had made their first cautious appearance in the First World War, primarily as trench-crossing vehicles. There was no time to discover whether they would be able to make a break through a static front like armoured cavalry and exploit the ensuing confusion that their protagonists had hoped for. Lieutenant Colonel (as he then was) J F C Fuller's 'Plan 1919', designed to produce a war-winning blow by vast numbers of tanks penetrating deep into the enemy's rear areas and shattering his system of command and control, although never effected, sparked off a general move towards the development of mechanised warfare. It inspired such radical thinkers as Guderian in Germany, Tukhachevsky in the Soviet Union, and Broad and others in Britain to foster the concept of deep penetration and to urge the development of the tank to this end. So it was that in the 20 years between the two world wars, despite all the economic and political difficulties, a dramatic change occurred to the whole conception of war on land.

Although the tanks produced by both the Germans and the Western Allies in 1939 were hopelessly undergunned, and mostly underprotected, they at least possessed sufficient fire power and mobility to make possible the sweeping and dramatic German victories in Poland in that year and in France and the Low Countries in 1940. Furthermore, they paved the way to the first great tank battles between the British, Italians and Germans in the Western Desert, and between the Germans and the Russians on the plains before Kursk and Kharkov in 1943.

In the Second World War there was no time to pay attention to improving tank design and instead the main effort was concentrated on improving the ability of weapons to penetrate armour. This could be done either by improving the high velocity gun firing conventional, or kinetic energy, projectiles, or by increasing the penetrative force of the projectile itself, without regard to its velocity or weight.[13] As ever, first in the field, the Germans began to increase velocity by firing a tungsten-cored shot through a tapered or squeeze bore barrel. The shot emerged at 4,600ft per second; it was the fastest velocity achieved by any gun in the war. But the Germans were forced to abandon this method because they were unable to obtain the tungsten. Their conventional high velocity guns (75 millimetre and 88 millimetre in particular) both tank-mounted and wheeled, were of the highest quality.

The British too developed a squeeze-bore version of their 2pr gun but sought to increase velocity mainly by the use of lengthened gun barrels and increased bore size. Perhaps the best example of this was the 17pr anti-tank gun, which was mounted on a limited number of Sherman tanks and also used extensively for a self-propelled version, the M-10. Later, in order to reduce cost they decided to retain the normal length of the barrel, but increased velocity of the muzzle by streamlining the shot with a ballistic cap. Next, instead of increasing muzzle velocity, the British began to make the round itself lighter and introduced a new munition with the lengthy designation of armour piercing discarding sabot shot (APDS). The shot, made of tungsten-carbide and so both dense and very tough, was held in a sabot, or light case, which fell off after the round had left the barrel. A much greater velocity than that provided by the ballistic cap was the result. The sabot shot only became available in the latter part of 1944 and was not used in the tank battles in Normandy.[14] Meanwhile both sides had discovered that armour plate could be penetrated more effectively, not by using the principle of kinetic energy, but by the employment of a hollow charge round or high explosive anti-tank (HEAT) as it later became known. This was a shaped charge of high explosive packed into a coned warhead. The charge was so designed that it exploded at a short distance from the armour being attacked. This allowed a high velocity jet to form and burn its way through the plate, followed by the debris from the cone. This new method of disabling tanks only began to be exploited in the last 15 months of the war when the Germans introduced their *PANZERSCHRECK* and *PANZERFAUST* anti-tank weapons, usually used by the infantry at very short range: they were ideal weapons against armour in the Normandy *bocage*, German forest areas, and in the scrub and vineyards of Northern Italy. Some indication of the power of hollow charge weapons may be seen from an analysis of tank casualties in north west Europe. Before the Rhine crossing in March 1945, only about 10 per cent of losses were due to hollow charge weapons, but after the subsequent advance beyond the Ruhr this figure jumped to 34 per cent and evidence suggested that the rate of advance of Allied armoured units was reduced by about one third.[15]

Another German weapon which was a forerunner of post-war anti-tank weapon technology was the X-7, a small wire-guided missile that could be launched either against tanks or aircraft. A few of these missiles were produced but they never emerged from the development stage. However, they did serve as a prototype for the first anti-tank guided missile devised by the French with German technical help not long after the war. On the Eastern Front the

9

Germans, like the British, used airborne rockets against tanks, but in their case they were fitted with hollow charges.

The new anti-tank weapons naturally put tank designers on their mettle. Obviously, the best way of defeating the hollow charge was to increase the thickness of armour plate, but this merely increased the overall weight of the tank and made it less mobile and presented problems where bridging equipment was required. Several solutions were investigated. The fundamental requirement was to defeat the action of the jet by upsetting its 'focus'. This could either be achieved by the use of spaced armour – so that there was an air gap between the point of the explosion and the main plate under attack or by the application of a crude form of plastic armour which, again, distanced the cone from the main plate. Of course neither of these measures were of any help against kinetic energy attack. As will be seen, no substantive progress would be made in that respect until advances were made in the use of new technology in plastic materials.

Land Mine Warfare

Yet another threat to the tank was the land mine, neglected by the British but anticipated by the Germans who had both anti-tank and anti-personnel mines in service at the outbreak of war. They became a dominating feature of land-based operations, particularly in the desert and on the mainland of Europe. The Germans were past masters in the rapid laying of barrier minefields and prolific broadcasters of mines in areas where movement off the roads tended to be difficult. This development was virtually unheard of before 1939 but by about 1942 mine warfare was a major feature of most campaigns. Not only did mines actually impede movement but, perhaps more importantly, the threat of them slowed down the tempo of an advance. It was soon realised that unless minefields were properly charted, they could be as much of a hindrance to the layers as their enemy, once the flow of operations changed and the defending troops began to advance. The scale of the effort put into the development of mineclearing devices – from hand-held detectors to regiments of flail tanks – was proof enough of the seriousness with which the mining threat was seen by the Allies.

Developments in Artillery and Chemical Warfare

Changes in other types of weapons used in land warfare were less revolutionary than those just described. While the German infantry tended to be more liberally supplied with automatic weapons than the Allies, the latter on the whole had to make do with weapons that were little more than advanced versions of those brought into service in the First World War. The Germans

10

deserve a mention for their development of light artillery and for the introduction of recoilless guns which were used for the first time in the airborne
landings in Crete. In the field of artillery, the most striking advances made
were in the use of radio to control massed artillery fire. The barrage, which was
such a dominating feature of First World War battles, tended to be replaced by
the concentration. Immense weights of fire could be brought down very
rapidly, thanks to the greatly improved communication which reached down to
gun positions. The quality of ammunition too was much improved. A reference
has already been made to the Russian *KATYUSHA* rocket batteries installed on
the back of trucks and which had a devastating effect when fired in salvoes.

Throughout the war there was always the possibility of chemical weapons
being introduced either in shells or in bombs dropped from the air. Research on
new agents was actively pursued by both sides as was research on antidotes.
Not long before the outbreak of war examination of organic phosphorus compounds at the Bayer research laboratories at Leverkusen (the scene of chemical
warfare research in the First World War) had led to the production of the nerve
gas. The scientists responsible were employed by the German army to develop
what became known as Tabun intensively. In 1942 large scale production
began at a plant in Silesia. Tabun was intended to be delivered to the target
area by shell or rocket. Another nerve gas called Sarin was being developed by
the Germans. It was 30 times more toxic than phosgene – the standard gas used
by the British and the Germans at the end of the First World War. As the plant
where it was manufactured fell into Russian hands at the end of the Second
World War, the need for the Western Powers to protect troops in the field
against nerve gases, and against bacteriological agents which had also been
subjects for research by both sides, assumed a high priority.[16]

Anti-Submarine Warfare

Naval actions in the Second World War resolved any doubts about the end of
the day of the capital ship (although a single battleship like the German *Tirpitz*
posed a serious threat to convoys and diverted many aircraft in attempts to sink
it). Its place was effectively taken by the aircraft carrier. The pattern of future
naval warfare could be discerned in the threat to shipping posed by the submarine and the vulnerability of naval surface craft to air attack. The use of
radar, not only to detect hostile enemy vessels, but to provide long range early
warning of enemy fleet and aircraft movements had only just begun to be
appreciated. Thus the most important technological advances were, firstly, in
defensive and offensive measures against hostile submarines (these were
almost exclusively Allied) and, secondly, the development of homing torpedoes, the initiative in this case being taken by the Germans. As in the war in the
air, the war against the submarine was similarly a ding-dong battle of measures

and countermeasures. The U-boat itself was no more than a 'drab, scantily-equipped craft', virtually a submersible, diesel-engined torpedo boat , hardly superior to the types of boats that had so nearly tipped the scales of victory towards the Germans in the First World War and did so again in the Second.[17]

The submarine continued to be dependent on long distance radio communications with its headquarters for intelligence reports, navigational fixes and for meteorological information. German U-boats operated many thousands of miles from base, but maintained contact with base through powerful radio transmitters. The most advanced of these was called *Goliath*, operating on very low frequency wave lengths which could be picked up by U-boats even off the coast of South America. But all radio transmissions were vulnerable to interception by the Allied high frequency direction finders, already established in the First World War and greatly improved by the 1940s.

However, the most important changes were in techniques designed to protect convoys or units of the fleet from marauding submarines. Asdic, or echo ranging, equipment now known as sonar (to use American nomenclature) had been developed painstakingly by British and American naval scientists in the inter-war years and by 1939 it had become possible to detect submarines in favourable conditions at ranges up to 5,000 yards. The most effective set produced in the war was probably the British TYPE 144 which came into service in the summer of 1942. It was a distinct advance on previous British and American sets in that it was partly automated, the echo-ranging system was electrically-controlled and, above all, it could be used with ahead-thrown weapons (electrically-fired mortars) which were an improvement on the old system of stern-released depth charges.[18]

When a submarine was on the surface, centrimetric radar was an efficient means of detection, especially when operated by a searching aircraft and it was to become the most important factor in winning the Battle of the Atlantic for the Allies. In contrast to echo-ranging equipment, the most potentially valuable passive listening device was the expendable radio sonobuoy developed by the Americans. It consisted of a radio transmitter and a directional hydrophone and was dropped on to the surface of the sea from an aircraft. Employing a complicated electronic system, the sonobuoy was able to transmit to the aircraft above the bearing of a hostile submarine. By using a number of aircraft, large areas of ocean could be covered and, as each buoy had a different code signal, the progress of the submarine could be tracked.

The Germans' response to these improved detection methods was to equip their submarines with the *schnorkel,* a breathing tube fitted to the diesel engine which enabled them to charge batteries while submerged. The *schnorkel* was very difficult for radar to detect and was easily lost in the spurious reflections caused by waves. Its disadvantage was that the submarine commander had to keep his craft at a constant depth, which was an extremely tiring procedure.

Some years before the war, the Germans began to experiment with homing torpedoes. They operated acoustically, but serious problems had to be overcome before they became effective weapons, particularly in reducing the noise made by the torpedo motor. Nevertheless due to the development by the firm of *Atlas Werke* in Hamburg, a number of acoustic torpedoes were brought into service by the German Navy. The most formidable was known by the Germans as *ZAUNKÖNIG* (Wren) and designated GNAT by the Allies.[19] It was introduced shortly after the HS 293 guided missile and accounted for 45 naval and merchant vessels. Allied scientists had already anticipated this form of attack and had prepared suitable anti-torpedo devices chiefly in the form of noisemakers, the object being to create a noise louder than the target vessel. Several mechanical or explosive noisemakers were introduced in due course in addition to a self-propelled noise decoy released from a submarine torpedo tube. Rather less progress was made by the Allies in development of homing torpedoes, but new designs for both underwater and air-launched torpedoes took shape and provided the basis of post-war development.

Frustrated by their inability to cut the Allied transatlantic lines of communication, the Germans turned in the last months of the war (after the Normandy landings) to designing new types of U-boat which could evade radar detection by travelling for long periods underwater with the help of the *schnorkel*, and with novel, and sometimes hazardous, forms of propulsion. Even the *schnorkel* was omitted in the TYPE XXVI U-boat which was fitted with a turbine burning fuel combined with hydrogen peroxide which enabled it to travel underwater for six hours at 25 knots. It had been designed by Helmuth Walther, head of *Germania-Werft* in Kiel, whom we have already met in connection with the power plant of the Me 163. Plans were even afoot to use this submarine to tow floating platforms into the Atlantic for launching V-2 rockets at targets on the American continent, but they were a long way from being realised by the end of the war.[20] Naturally, Walther and his colleagues were eagerly sought by American and British scientists for interrogation after the war has already been noted. The slightly less revolutionary, but speedy, TYPE XXI fitted with the latest sonar equipment and homing torpedoes and the hull coated with sound-absorbing synthetic rubber became the model for the first post-war generation of submarines.

Advent of the Computer

The Second World War was responsible for stimulating the development of the electronic computer that in the long term would probably change the conduct of future warfare more than anything else. The possibility conceived by the Victorian engineer, Charles Babbage, of devising a machine to relieve the human brain of having to work out laborious mathematical calculations was carried a long stage forward in the 1930s when a handful of academics appreciated that, by applying the new technology of electronics, a 'thinking machine' might be evolved which could provide mathematical decisions: the solution of the *entscheidungsproblem*, as they called it.[21] It so happened that some of the British mathematicians and scientists interested in this abstruse problem were enveigled into applying their skills to solving an extremely important military problem: the deciphering of signals transmitted by a highly sophisticated mechanical encoding machine. The substitution of mechanical techniques for human calculators using pencil and paper led to the building of the forerunner of the modern programmable computer (though there were other valuable military applications for which it could be used).

Before the Second World War the German armed forces were already using a cipher machine called *ENIGMA* which had been put on the market in the

Plate 3 British *ENIGMA* cipher machine. Brought to Britain by Polish cryptanalysts and used to break the German *ENIGMA* ciphers. (*Royal Signals Museum*)

1920s but which their technicians had greatly improved. At about the same time, the British Government Code and Cipher school had cracked an earlier and less secure model used by the German and Italian services and by General Franco's Nationalist forces, but the more sophisticated version appeared to be unbreakable. The work of the cryptanalysts at Bletchley Park in Buckinghamshire, where the Government Code and Cipher School was evacuated at the outbreak of war, is now well known. Perhaps less well-appreciated has been work, crucial to the establishment, of a team of mathematicians under Professor Maxwell Newman from Cambridge which included the young mathematical genius, Alan Turing, then a Fellow of King's College Cambridge, whose advanced ideas on realising artificial intelligence had been sketched out in his so-called Universal Turing Machine.[22]

The first task of Newman's team at Bletchley Park was to improve on the electro-mechanical scanning machine called a Bombe, on account of the loud ticking noise it made, originally devised by a group of Polish scientists for the purpose of breaking the German *ENIGMA* encoding machine. The Bombe was able to 'find' the *ENIGMA* keys by the 'rapid automatic testing of several tens of thousands of possible combinations'. It was extremely successful and became the main code breaking device for the Government Code and Cipher School throughout the war.[23]

Newman's section, now called 'Hut F', then began to work on more advanced aids for cryptanalysis. The first versions of these machines were called Heath Robinsons (after the well known cartoonist who had a gift for designing humorous solutions to apparently impossible situations); they were able to read two paper tapes at a rate of up to 2000 characters a second, and they had a primitive automatic line printer for producing decimal output. A faster and more reliable machine called COLOSSUS was then built in eleven months and became operational at Bletchley in December 1943. It incorporated 1,500 valves and operated in parallel arithmetic mode at 5,000 pulses per second. The main purpose of this machine was to break the German teletype ciphers which were even more impenetrable than the *ENIGMA*. In the event, it provided very important information about the latest German anti-invasion preparations which required last minute readjustment to the Allied plans for a landing in Normandy. A COLOSSUS Mark II machine five times faster than the original model, because it had temporary memory storage, was assembled in anticipation of the increased signals traffic that would be generated during the fighting on the continent and, after last minute rewiring had been completed, was serviceable five days before D-day, 6 June 1944.[24]

COLOSSUS, clumsy and primitive though it was, has been claimed as being the first programmable computer to be used in war. (It was not, it should be emphasised, a stored programme computer; that had to wait the development of a high speed memory capable of holding a large number of binary

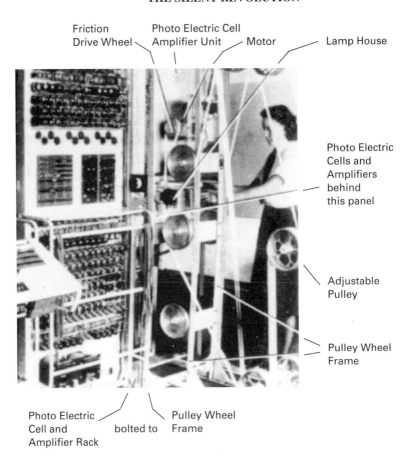

Friction Drive Wheel — Photo Electric Cell Amplifier Unit — Motor — Lamp House

Photo Electric Cells and Amplifiers behind this panel

Adjustable Pulley

Pulley Wheel Frame

Photo Electric Cell and Amplifier Rack — bolted to — Pulley Wheel Frame

Plate 4 COLOSSUS: the first British electronic computer. Assembled at Bletchley Park in 1943, it incorporated 1500 valves. It provided mechanical techniques for the solution of problems hitherto resolved using paper and pencil. (*Public Record Office*)

digits.) In the meantime, American physicists and engineers had been working for some years on large calculating machines. They, too, appreciated that these machines would be useful for the military. One machine, designed for the rapid production of range tables for new weapons, was the Electronic Numerical Integrator and Calculator (ENIAC); it was assembled at the University of Pennsylvania from May 1943 onwards, but was not actually ready for use until 1945, after the war was over. ENIAC was a larger and faster machine than COLOSSUS and contained 18,000 valves; it could perform about 5,000 additions per second, about 500 to 1000 times as many per second as an electromagnetic relay computer.[25] Development of the latter was a speciality of BTL in New Jersey, and in particular of one of their engineers, Claude Shannon, who applied his knowledge of telephone relay circuits to the fire control of anti-aircraft guns. His most valuable contribution to military technology was the M 9 gun director, already mentioned in connection with the SCR 584 radar set. After being supplied with information by the gun crews on the range and position of the target, the M 9 aimed and gave firing signals to the guns.

Surprisingly perhaps, the development of computers in Germany was rather more restricted than the Allied experiments. At least Konrad Zuse, a physicist from Munich, did pioneer work on relay circuits similar to that carried out at BTL and he later went on to design a 1,500 valve computer, but his proposal was rejected by the German government on the grounds that more urgent projects needed attention.[26] But when the development of rockets and other kinds of missiles with guidance systems got under way, the need for computers became more apparent. Helmuth Hoelzer, head of the Flight Control and Guidance Division at Peenemunde, was the leading pioneer. He built an electronic computer for calculations on the flight path simulation of the V-2s and surface to air missiles like *WASSERFALL*. Hoelzer, like other leading scientists at Peenemunde , went to the States after the war.[27]

All these diverse activities provided the launching pad for the modern analogue and digital electronic computer with which we are familiar to-day.

Operational Research

The new weapons and techniques that have been described above brought scientists and engineers out of their 'small back rooms' into the headquarters and operations rooms of the fighting forces. New weapons had to be evaluated to discover how well they performed on operations. Secondly, operations had to be analysed to find out how the weapon fitted the tactics or, alternatively, to what extent tactics dictated the form of weapon that was chosen. As the war lengthened, scientific prediction of the outcome of future operations, either in the tactical or strategical fields, became necessary in order to determine the correct policy. Finally, it was necessary to make studies of military organisations to improve their efficiency in battle. Such activities were known as 'operational research' by British and Commonwealth forces and as 'operations analysis' by the American forces. Although scientists had been consulted on a somewhat haphazard basis in the First World War, such close collaboration between scientists (either in or out of uniform and in or outside the battle area) was truly novel. The term 'operational research' was first used to describe the activities of a party of civilian scientists (a number of them from the Cavendish Laboratory in Cambridge) whose task it was to study and recommend improvements for the whole aircraft reporting system of Britain from the coastal radar chain back to Fighter Command headquarters where decisions were made on the movement of interceptor aircraft. This first 'operational research section', as it was called, was described by the officer-in-charge at the height of the Battle of Britain as being unique in that it was 'not under the command of any fighting service' and yet 'maintained such a close and amiable relationship with and at the headquarters of a commander-in-chief'.[28]

Operational research spread from the RAF to the Army, where similar teams of scientists of different disciplines improved the performance of anti-aircraft guns, tanks and field artillery, and to the sailors and airmen responsible for anti-submarine warfare where problems such as the optimum number of vessels for convoys and the correct setting of depth charges for the destruction of U-boats were evaluated. Later, when senior scientists were established and accepted by senior commanders at their headquarters, it became possible to advise on high level policy. An historic example was the 'transportation plan' proposed by Zuckerman prior to the Normandy landings in which, on the basis of operational research studies made during the early days of the Italian campaign, it was discovered that heavy air attacks on rail centres with the locomotives, rolling stock and repair facilities were more effective than bombing small targets such as rail bridges and signal boxes in the vicinity of the battle area, or, indeed, targets in Germany beloved of the strategic bomber commanders. The verdict of those who were aware of what had been done was that the relatively small amount of operational research in the war had made 'a contribution having a value out of all proportion to the staff involved.'[29]

. 2 .

THE ELECTRONIC REVOLUTION

Before the Second World War solid state physics, which was to bring about the virtual demise of the thermionic valve, was an esoteric field hardly considered useful for practical application. However, the exception to that rule was a handful of, mainly American, physicists working on new designs for telephone relay circuits. Nevertheless, the development of microwave radar and the major physical problems requiring solution in the evolution of nuclear fission weapons promoted a keen interest in what was to be called electronics.

This chapter will sketch the origins of the 'electronic revolution' in the 1950s and 60s which threw up inventions such as the transistor and the semiconductor integrated circuit and so transformed the primitive computers of the time. One of the first, and very important, military applications of the computer was to enable the control and reporting systems of national air defence to cope speedily and comprehensively with attacks by supersonic aircraft and later by ballistic missiles. Computers also revolutionised radar development and the guidance systems of missiles. Finally, the discovery of lasers and their employment as target illuminators will be described. The transformation of communications by computers will be described in Chapter 3.

At the time, these developments attracted little public attention and, oddly enough, they were, to some extent, unanticipated by the scientists and engineers themselves. Harvey Brooks, a Professor of Applied Physics at Harvard, reviewing recent military innovations in 1975 admitted that the 'rapid advances of the 1950s–60s were not anticipated until they were almost upon us.'[1] Scepticism manifested itself in the most unlikely places. A list of proposals unlikely to yield positive results compiled in 1950 at the Lincoln Laboratory (set up specially, as we shall see, to deal with the possibility of air attack on North America) included thermonuclear bombs, high speed digital computers, supersonic aircraft, short range guided missiles, inter-continental ballistic missiles, inertial guidance, satellites and radiation weapons – all of which would soon be realised.[2]

Post-War Development of Computers

In mid-1945 the team working on ENIAC at Pennsylvania University was reinforced by the outstanding mathematician and pioneer of operational research, John von Neumann, who was well able to appreciate the possibilities of using computers for purposes other than calculation. He proposed a faster, more sophisticated machine called EDVAC (Electronic Discrete Variable Computer) which would contain radical changes in the programming and logic of computers including the use of binary arithmetic involving only 1's and 0's.[3] This became the model for the digital computer which, in addition to being a calculator, can use successively the results of computations developed in its programme or stored in its memory. Digital information for the memory may be recorded on tapes, disks, drums, cores, banks of solid state devices, and by other means.

In Britain, the moving spirit in initiating computer development) was John Womersley, head of the Mathematical Division of the National Physical Laboratory (NPL) who had worked on calculating machines at Manchester University. In the spring of 1945 he visited America to obtain information about ENIAC.[4] Shortly after his return, he met Turing, the Bletchley genius, and persuaded him to join the NPL. In March 1946, largely due to Womersley and Turing, the Executive Committee of the NPL decided to build a small digital computer. It was called ACE (Automatic Computing Engine) in acknowledgement of Charles Babbage's Analytic Engine and received a modest sum from the Government for its construction. Its design was to some extent based on the wartime COLOSSUS machines but no accommodation was made for data storage. ACE was considered to be a 'powerful and effective tool for science but unlikely to revolutionise industry.'[5] This cautious approach was in marked contrast to the confident and positive policy adopted by the Americans.

The lack of adequate facilities at NPL prevented the working stage of the pilot model being completed before mid-1950 and some years elapsed before it was operating satisfactorily. By then more advanced machines had made it redundant.

Luckily, computer development had begun at two British universities. At Cambridge, M V Wilkes, who had worked on coastal defence radar during the war, was responsible for designing a machine called EDSAC (Electronic Delay Storage Automatic Computer) from 1947–49. Wilkes's machine was strongly influenced by von Neumann's EDVAC.

The second project was sponsored by Manchester University, birthplace of the 'Differential Analyser' on which Womersley had worked, and which had recently acquired two important scientists. One was F C Williams, who had played a leading role in radar development at the Telecommunications Research Establishment, the famous wartime centre for radar research, and now wanted to find peaceful applications for the electronic skills he had acquired. The second was Maxwell Newman from Bletchley, who was appointed Professor of Mathematics. Fortified by a grant from the Royal Society for Fundamental Research, design of a computer could begin. Drawing on his wartime knowledge, Williams adapted a small cathode ray tube for memory storage and, on 21 June 1948, operated the first stored programme electronic digital computer in the world.[6]

The following month, Sir Henry Tizard, chairman of the DRPC, saw Williams's machine, pronounced it to be of national importance and instructed that development 'should go forward as speedily as possible.'[7] He promised full support in the supply of materials, which would be given priority (industry was still handicapped by post-war shortages). Several months later, the Ministry of Supply placed an order with Ferranti, the Manchester electronics manufacturers, to 'construct an electronic calculating machine to the instructions of Professor F C Williams.'[8] Work on the first model (the Manchester Mark I) began in October 1949; it started to operate on 12 February 1951, about the same time as the EDSAC prototype of Wilkes. By then Williams's team had begun to design a Mark II model and were thinking of replacing valves by a new device called the transistor.

Invention of the Transistor

Computers at this time were extremely large and cumbersome and dependent on quantities of valves. In a few years time, the point contact transistor radically transformed computer design, Its inventor was William Shockley, a theoretical physicist, who before the war had worked at BTL studying materials such as germanium and silicon which could be used as semiconductors (or 'chips'), with a view to replacing the valve (or vacuum tube as it was called in the US).

During the war Shockley worked on operational research and was awarded the Medal for Merit, the highest American civilian decoration for wartime service. Then aged 30, he returned to BTL to resume his pre-war studies on semiconductors.[9] Experience with microwaves in radar had shown him that silicon and germanium made excellent conductors, especially at low frequencies. Shockley wanted to use semiconductors to control the flow of electrons in a solid. He believed that it would be possible to control the electrons from outside the semiconductor without actually contacting the material. In company with two experimental physicists, Walter H Brattain and John Bardeen,[10] he

Plate 5 William Shockley, inventor of the transistor with John Bardeen and Walter H Brattain: one of the most significant inventions of the 20th Century. (*MIT Museum*)

began to conduct experiments to discover whether this could be done. They found that the electric field was unable to penetrate the semiconductor. Bardeen then tried using an electrolyte in a modified form of Shockley's amplifier in which a suitably treated small block of silicon was used. He thought that current flowing to a diode contact to the silicon block could be controlled by a voltage applied to the electrolyte surrounding the contact. Brattain put this idea into practice, but found that the operation was limited to very low frequencies because of the electrolyte.

Similar experiments were made with germanium but the sign of the effect was opposite to that predicted. Brattain and Bardeen then replaced the electrolyte by a rectifying metal contact and discovered that the voltage applied to this contact could be used to control, to a limited extent, the current flowing to the diode contact. Again, the sign of the effect was opposite to the predicted one. After analysing these unexpected results, the two physicists designed the point contact transistor which operated on a completely different principle from the one originally proposed. Current flowing to one contact is controlled by current flowing from a second contact, rather than from an externally applied electric field.* The experiments were very simple, the most expensive piece of apparatus being an oscilloscope.

The first point contact transistor was operated on Christmas Eve 1947. The immediate reaction of Mervyn Kelly, Director of Research at BTL, was to decide to keep the discovery secret for the next seven months, anticipating that the Service laboratories might be engaged in making similar experiments. The first intimation of the new device for the US Army Signal Corps came on 23 June 1948, the day after the entire technical staff at BTL had been treated to a private demonstration. The military implications of the transistor were immediately perceived; it would replace valves in the guidance systems of missiles, predictors, proximity fuses, mines and torpedoes, and it would be invaluable in signals equipment. The question arose whether it should be developed secretly like the atomic bomb in the Manhattan Project. But, because of its enormous commercial possibilities, the authorities agreed that the invention should not be classified. Nevertheless, the military wanted to have a finger in the pie and authorised financial support for the continuation of research and development in June 1949.

The original point contact transistor had a number of defects; it was noisy and unable to control large amounts of power, thus limiting the number of possible applications. It took another six years before transistors became reliable for service purposes. Even in 1957, US naval scientists working on missile

---

* In 1943 R H Kinman, responsible at British Thomson Houston for producing high quality 10 centimetre crystals, discovered the phenomenon of current enhancement, but this at the time was regarded as an unwarranted side effect.

guidance systems complained of difficulties known as the 'purple plague'; 'the junction of the lead to the transistor would start to rot, and under the right light, or maybe by bare eye, it turned purple, and you lost connection . . . it was like a disease that went through all the early transistors.' This was the junction transistor which Shockley developed to eradicate earlier defects and which provided the model for later types of transistor. But the breakthrough had been made and Shockley, Brattain and Bardeen were jointly awarded the Nobel Prize for Physics in 1956. By then, Shockley had left BTL and formed his own company which was a progenitor of California's 'silicon valley' and the electronics industry.

British Transistor Development

The BTL experiments were naturally followed with great interest in Britain, especially at TRE. Sir John Cockcroft, the nuclear physicist, then head of the Atomic Energy Research Establishment, had been keeping an eye on American transistor development during his regular visits to the States, After a visit to BTL in September 1951, he noted that very great improvements in noise level and longevity had been made. 'The compactness, low loss level, low voltage requirements are likely to produce a revolution in electronics',[11] he later wrote. He was told that mass production of the latest type of transistor was due to begin in 1952 at the rate of 20,000 a week.

Shortly after Cockcroft's return to the United Kingdom R A Smith, the head of the Physics Department at TRE, which had already begun to investigate semiconductor materials, urged the Ministry of Supply to initiate transistor research independently of the Americans. He foresaw that transistors would replace valves in

> many common circuits . . . It is already clear that where space and power dissipation are very limited, the transistor will have very great advantages. We, therefore, are forced to the conclusion that the transistor is likely to play an important part in circuit development for such applications as guided weapons.[12]

Although the British were hard put to mount a transistor programme on anything like the scale of the Americans (the United States invested around $930 million on semiconductor research and development between 1958 and 1974), a modest and not insignificant programme was launched at TRE. F E Jones, who had played a notable part in developing a wartime blind bombing system, formed an Experimental Physics Group of able young scientists to work on transistors in addition to infra-red and millimetre waves.

The key to progress in research was the acquisition of suitable crystals, especially silicon and germanium, and Jones arranged for small supplies to be obtained from the Standard Telecommunications Laboratory. By the spring of 1953, when he left TRE to become Deputy Director (Equipment) of RAE, Jones was able to tell STL that 'now we have verified that silicon transistors will undoubtedly meet certain military requirements, our one aim is to make them available.'[13]

Although germanium was unsuitable for certain Army requirements, if used in temperatures ranging from 60°–80° C, it was found to be capable of sustaining high current devices whereas silicon for a long time was a small signal, small current carrier. Only when extensive work had been done, firstly on the difficult process of silicon refinement and, secondly, doping, that satisfactory high current devices became feasible. It was for this reason that the Radar Research and Development Establishment (RRDE) (since 1950 responsible for the radar and electronics aspects of a new air defence system for the UK) decided to use germanium rather than silicon in its transistors, even though the latter would eventually become effective. It later argued that a change of direction half way through a long term military programme would have been disastrous and claimed that if the change to silicon had been made in 1972, the project would have taken another 10 years to complete and would have still failed to meet the exacting standards of reliability required. Computers of unspecified reliability would then have had to fill the gap.[14]

In order to increase the supply of semiconductors, it was decided to form a British subsidiary of Texas Instruments, one of the leading American electronics firms (representatives had already been trying to market their products in the United Kingdom). Texas Instruments was able to make silicon by a chemical process. In 1956, after negotiations with the Ministry of Supply and the blessing of the Board of Trade, Texas Electronics Ltd was formed to produce small quantities of silicon and germanium for transistors. In 1957 a factory near Bedford was opened for this purpose.[15]

Meanwhile the leading British electronics manufacturers such as Ferranti, Mullard, Siemens and the Standard Telephones and Cables Company were engaged on contracts for military semiconductors. The Mullard OC-41 series types were available in quantity from 1955. One of their first military uses was in the Army/RAF Digital Data Link Mark 1 and No I Mark 1 – the data transmission system developed by Ferranti in 1956–57 for the fire control radar which enabled the first generation of British SAMS from 1958 onwards to acquire a target.[16] The Digital Data Link Mark 1 was used for many other digital requirements until around 1980 when new processes for modulation and demodulation took over.

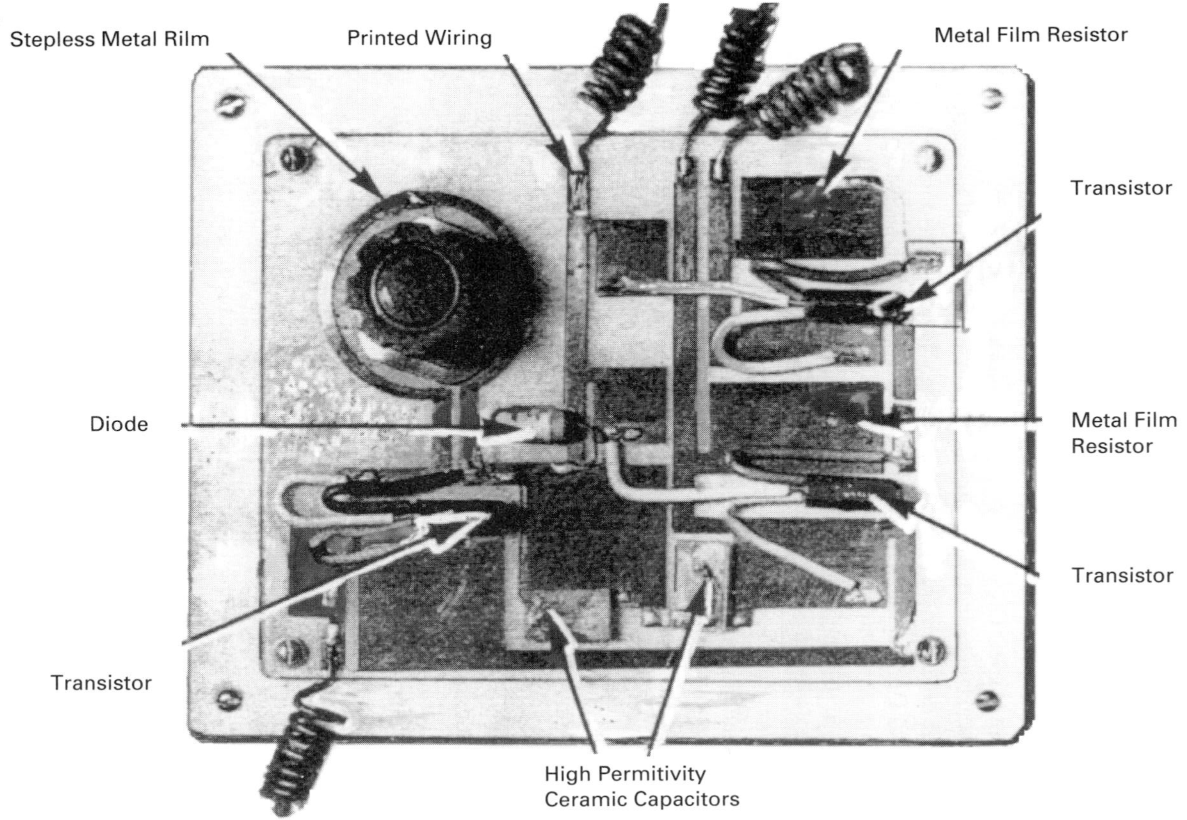

Figure. 1 Diagramatic representation of a complete circuit using an early transistor, developed by the Royal Radar Establishment

Metal Film Resistor

Transistor

Metal Film Resistor

Transistor

Printed Wiring

Stepless Metal Rilm

High Permitivity Ceramic Capacitors

Diode

Transistor

Invention of the Integrated Circuit

In 1958, another breakthrough in solid state physics research took place which led to the introduction of microelectronics. By the end of the war, electronic equipment had become so complex that it could no longer be assembled by the traditional technique of hand-soldering. Much military equipment (eg aircraft) required quantities of valves and passive devices. Although valves, used within their design limits, had long lives, when used in aircraft or tanks they were subjected to severe vibration. They were also large and expensive and dissipated an inordinate amount of power.

After the war, the Americans began to simplify the manufacture of valves, either using miniaturised valves, or small modules consisting of ceramic wafers such as the Tinkertoy concept sponsored by the US Navy, or the Auto-Sembly process favoured by the US Army Signals. These projects were either abandoned or modified after the appearance of the transistor.[17] Tinkertoy was replaced by the US Army's micro-module project and the US Navy sponsored the development of film resistors made on glass and ceramic plates, Similar developments were taking place in Britain.

The transistor also suggested the possibility of an all-solid circuit based on semiconductor technology. The first to appreciate this possibility was G W A Dummer who, like F E Jones, had been a wartime member of TRE and was now in charge of a group in the Applied Physics and Technical Services Division. At an American conference in May 1952, he said that:

> With the advent of the transistor and the work in semiconductors generally, it now seems possible to envisage electronic equipment in a solid block with no connecting wires. The block may consist of layers of insulating, conducting, rectifying and amplifying materials, the electrical functions being connected directly by cutting out areas of the various layers.[18]

Although Dummer was to let a small contract to a British manufacturer in 1956, a working device was not realised, mainly because the latest junction transistor technology was not used.

Thus the major advances in electronic circuitry took place in the States. The USAF, unlike the other services and possibly influenced by Dummer, decided to embark on a type of all-solid circuit. A more radical approach to the problem was made by Texas Instruments. A member of their staff, Jack St Clair Kilby, a specialist in radio and hearing aids, believed that transistors could be made more cheaply by only using semiconductors and that both active and passive components could be made from the same material to form a complete circuit. During the late summer and autumn of 1958, Kilby, using semiconductors, built and demonstrated circuits made of silicon and germanium.

Of the Services, only the USAF displayed any interest in Kilby's concept and even that was tempered by their earlier commitment to the molecular project. But one group of Air Force scientists appreciated that the integrated circuit 'eliminated the need to invent thousands of new devices which would be required for future equipments.' A number of contracts were therefore placed with Texas Instruments to enable the technique to be perfected.

When Kilby's circuit was made public on 6 March 1959, it was not immediately hailed as a breakthrough as anticipated. According to Kilby it was criticised on three counts:

1 it did not make the best use of materials;
2 manufacture would be difficult; and
3 designs would be expensive and difficult to modify. The leading electronics laboratories were therefore not prepared to exploit the design.

In the autumn of 1959, Texas Instruments began a serious marketing campaign. Fairchild Semiconductors, a new company, also took up the idea. In October 1961, the USAF bought a small computer from Texas Instruments with a memory made with semiconductors (Series 51). The following year Texas Instruments was awarded a contract to design and build 22 special circuits for the MINUTEMAN ICBMs. Fairchild's received substantial contracts for the APOLLO space programme. Although only a few thousand units were delivered in 1962, it marked the beginning of mass production.

In Britain, Dummer's group at the Royal Radar Establishment (as TRE had now become after amalgamation with the Radar Research and Development Establishment [responsible for ground radar] in 1953) actually anticipated Kilby's discovery by some 18 months. In April 1957, the Plessey Caswell laboratories received an RRE-sponsored contract to investigate the possibility of fabricating an integrated circuit in silicon.[19] (The other government laboratory where circuits were investigated was the Services Electronics Research Laboratory [SERL] at Baldock, but its interest was more in microwave electronics.) Yet it was not until 1960 that a group was formed at RRE specifically to study integrated circuits.[20] A probable reason for delay was the series of cutbacks in equipment development and procurement after the 1957 Defence White Paper. The British had also been buying American high velocity transistors for prototype application purposes. In due course Plessey, Texas Electronics, Standard Telephones and Cables and Ferranti obtained contracts for integrated circuit development.

By the mid-1960s production of semiconductor integrated circuits was in full swing.[21] This was a period of small scale integration with less than 100 components per semiconductor. In the 1970s, large scale integration began with the introduction of the calculator chip. Even so, the American services had hardly

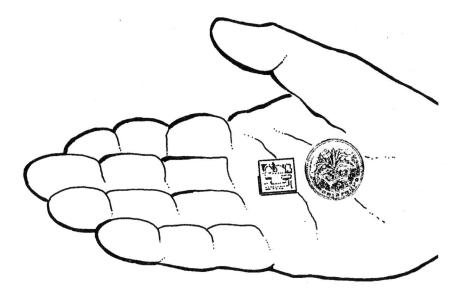

Figure 2 Diagrammatic representation of an integrated circuit developed by the Royal Radar Establishment in 1957. Note the size in comparison with a one pound piece.

taken advantage of the new technology. By the end of the 1970s, however, the Soviet Union was already rivalling the United States in the development of electronic equipment. In response the US Department of Defense approved the very high speed integrated circuit (VHSIC) programme in 1978 and which eventually got underway in 1980.[22] The British inaugurated their very high performance integrated circuit (VHPIC) programme at about the same time.

Employment of Computers in Air Defence

Computers were used for the first time to collect and assimilate information on a real time basis in the post-war air defence system of the United States. The explosion of a Soviet atom bomb in August 1949 made the USAF uncomfortably aware of the virtual non-existence of air defences in the North American continent, In December 1949, George E Valley, Professor of Physics at MIT, was appointed chairman of an Air Defense Systems Engineering Committee.[23] The Committee at once appreciated that the inadequate existing air defence system should be replaced by a network of large and small radar stations to provide nation-wide coverage with communications and centralised automated systems to handle raid information based on current computer technology.

In 1951, a study group called Project Charles was set up under F Wheeler Loomis, who had been Assistant Director of the wartime Radiation Laboratory, to make proposals. It was composed of scientists and United States and NATO air force officers, the most senior being Air Commodore G W Tuttle, who had commanded the RAF Photographic Reconnaissance Unit in the war and was now Director of Operational Requirements on the British Air Staff. In order to develop automated equipment, Project Lincoln was also now created, leading to the establishment of the Lincoln Laboratory at Harvard, in some ways a reincarnation of the wartime Radiation Laboratory.

Jay W Forrester, a wartime radar expert, was made responsible for developing a computer. Reliability was essential and Forrester decided to find an alternative to the cathode ray tube memory used by F C Williams. He used as a model the MIT WHIRLWIND, the first computer to have a magnetic core memory. Eventually his group developed the AN/FSQ-7 which had a memory core containing 65,000 words. This computer doubled the operating speed and quadrupled the input data rate of WHIRLWIND. It reduced the mean time between failure from four hours a day to two hours a week. The computers operated in pairs; if one failed, a redundant machine could take on the work load. It became the heart of the system called Semi-automated Ground Environment (SAGE).

In 1952, trials at Cape Cod confirmed SAGE's ability to track and control aircraft and its capacity for surveillance and weapons control. The threat at that time was the long range bomber which would need to be intercepted by fighter aircraft. In the late 1950s, surface-to-air missiles were introduced which were able to intercept targets at greater speeds and heights (NIKE/HERCULES). At the same time the very low altitude long range bomber remained a threat as it could not be detected by an aircraft carrying an interception radar.

SAGE was not fully deployed until 1963. By then the original computer had been replaced by the AN/FSQ-32 in which the core memory had been replaced by semiconductor integrated circuits. The Back-up Interception Control provided automation at the radar stations as well as at the direction centres thus ensuring an operational capacity if the SAGE direction centres were put out of action. SAGE could now assimilate information on ballistic missiles and receive data from satellites. Even as late as 1983, six SAGE direction centres (including two in Canada) were still in operation.

The cost of SAGE had been immense (one estimate put it at $8 billion) but the scientists who devised it believed SAGE to have been a model of its kind. Three factors contributed towards its success. First, the project was not conceived as a whole but developed in stages, enabling it to be adapted to the changing military situation; secondly, it took full advantage of rapidly improving computer technology; and thirdly, it was not restricted by rigid specifications and could be modified as its capability was improved.

Computers in the British Control and Reporting System

The British manually operated control and reporting system had, of course, been the backbone of the air defence of the United Kingdom throughout the war. But in the early 1950s, Britain lay open to attack from high altitude, high speed, hostile bombers carrying nuclear weapons; these had to be destroyed before the bombers crossed the coastline. Responsibility for designing a new system continued to rest with RRDE/RRE and the plans which emerged will be discussed in more detail in Chapter 9. Here the requirement for computers need only concern us.

The first plan (ROTOR) lacked any transistorised computers and the system continued to be manually-operated. In February 1959, the Air Council considered and approved a new system which would be less vulnerable to jamming, less dependent on human reactions to enable fighters and air-to-ground missiles to operate effectively and, finally, would be able to coordinate the operation of LIGHTNING interceptor fighters and the BLOODHOUND missiles. This proposal was called PLAN AHEAD.[25] Its main purpose was to protect the relatively small but vital area in central England containing the V bomber bases against attack by anything up to 30 hostile aircraft.

In the first stage, a main control centre and three radar tracking stations would be provided. Information from the latter would be transmitted in digital form to the main control centre outside Norwich where information from continental early warning radars would be collated. A concise picture of the enemy threat would then be provided for the Government, RAF commands and NATO headquarters. AHEAD was intended to come into operation in 1965, but it became clear that the proposals involved computer and data transmission far in advance of existing hardware. Overriding this factor was the Government's fear that the scheme had become too expensive (it was currently costed at £75 million).

In February 1961, PLAN AHEAD was superseded by LINESMAN as the future ground environment for the air defence system of the United Kingdom. The change over took place primarily because of the mounting expense of PLAN AHEAD. For this reason, the Government decided (despite the opposition of the RAF) to combine the military control and reporting system with the Civil Air Traffic Control Centre at West Drayton, near London. (As most civil air traffic entered the United Kingdom from the South and West and the probable direction of a Soviet attack would emerge from the North-East, a conflict of interests was considered unlikely.) Furthermore, as the Commander-in-Chief Fighter Command insisted that as it was 'impossible to control the LIGHTNING interceptors without the aid of a computer, [it was] unacceptable to consider anything less than fully-computed control at each radar tracking station',[26] full scale automation became essential.

LINESMAN was based on the new concept of the main frame computer proposed by Automatic Telephone Equipment (later Plessey). All equipment had to be ultra-reliable. As just noted, most development had been done on germanium transistors and these were accepted as the basis for design. RRE and Automatic Telephone Equipment set up a special quality control system which had to be observed by all manufacturers providing components for LINESMAN. Even the slightest change in manufacturer had to be reported and tested. The computer itself was overtaken three times during design and manufacture by significantly faster machines, leading to the long over-run of the project caused by these changes as well as by the inevitable under-estimation of the time of completion. When, at last, the computer went into operation in 1977 it proved to be reliable, though bulky. The mean time between failure which had been predicted by Dummer for every 14½ minutes proved to be more than seven days.[27]

Tactical Air Defence

At the same time, control systems for air defence in the battle area had to be devised. One of these was the US Army's MIDAC (Military Data Processing and Computing). It was based on discussions between members of the Radar Research and Development Establishment and American development teams from 1950 onwards. Due to the lack of funds and manpower on the part of the British, the project was completed by the Americans.

Military Computers in the Soviet Union

Like the Western Allies, the Soviet armed forces were not slow in appreciating how much automation would speed up control and communications. Much of their early knowledge of the subject was acquired through absorbing the writings of Norbert Wiener, the distinguished American mathematician, who had done so much to improve the accuracy of anti-aircraft weapons in the Second World War. Indoctrination of senior officers on the importance of computers was given high priority in military academies.[28]

However, even greater obstacles than those in the West were experienced in bringing computer programmes into operation. Prototypes of digital computers became available in 1953, at about the same time as in the West, and production began two years later. But progress lagged behind Europe and North America both in numbers and in characteristics such as operating speed and memory capacity. There were also serious shortcomings with the management of the computer industry, identified as a lack of interest shown by manufacturers in their customers and failure to provide a back-up service after installation and running in. A shortage of trained programmers further aggravated this situation. Although these observations, derived from studies made in 1970, related to industrial management, problems of a similar nature were believed to exist in military staffs, academies and research establishments. A great effort was made to overcome these deficiencies and resulted, as just indicated, by the Soviets rivalling the Americans, particularly in their RYAD series of computers, by the end of the 1970s.[29]

An important characteristic of phased array radars was their ability to provide hemispherical and omnidirectional coverage. This could be done by using a planar array facing upwards over which was placed a dielectric lens (able to refract radio waves in the same manner that an optical lens refracts light waves). The dielectric lens made the radar beam point either vertically or horizontally so as to achieve full hemispherical coverage. Lens arrays were introduced into ground radars in the early 1970s.

Advances in Ground Radar Surveillance

Computers and integrated circuits made it possible to increase the reliability and accuracy of ground radars. The threat posed by ICBMs was a spur for the development of large electronically-scanned phased array radars able to provide a variety of beam patterns for target acquisition and tracking. The first American phased array, which became operational in the mid-1960s, was called COBRA DANE, able to detect a target at 930 miles. It was supplemented in due course by PAVE PAWS, able to detect a target with a cross section of 10 square metres at a range of 2,800 miles.[30] In the East, the Soviet Union deployed two phased arrays, one for target acquisition and tracking and one for early warning on the Soviet Union's borders, In contrast, the British TYPE 80 surveillance radar (equipped with valves) was able to detect a 13 square metre target at 340 miles at an appropriate height, due partly to atmospheric bending, not anomalous propagation.*

As ECM became more numerous and complex, phased array radars were needed in tactical air defence systems on land and at sea and on the battlefield for the location of artillery and mortar positions. The cost of components was reduced when VHSICs came into service.[31]

A second important development was three dimensional radar (from 1953) enabling height as well as a plan position indicator (PPI) presentation of the situation to be given.[32] The British TYPE 82 set for home defence and the TYPE 984 set for the defence of the fleet were early examples. (It is worth noting that

* Anomalous propagation, or super-refraction, is the bending or refraction of radio waves in the lower atmosphere in certain conditions. It gives rise to abnormally long ranges at times that may roughly be compared to visual images in some special atmospheric conditions. These conditions seemed to vary with the wave length of the transmission.

the Americans were not developing a 3D radar but were proposing a fan beam search radar with one or more separate heightfinders.) At the end of the 1960s, the consensus of opinion in NATO was that future long range radars should:

1 be three dimensional;
2 they should have the maximum resistance against ECM; and
3 they should be mobile and reasonably transportable.

In answer to these requirements the British introduced MARTELLO;[33] the first type to enter service in the 1980s was the S713 designed by GEC.

A third innovation was the multifrequency radar used for search and lock-on-follow of which the British TYPE 83 set and the radar for the low level SAM RAPIER were examples.

Airborne Surveillance

Of great importance in the 'Cold War' was the need to take aerial photographs of enemy, or potentially hostile, territory without having to penetrate beyond the frontier. In the early 1950s, development began on both sides of the Atlantic of a sideways-looking radar (SLR). Even as early as 1941, pictures had been obtained from a primitive radar installed along the side of a WELLINGTON bomber. However, development was delayed by the need to solve a number of practical problems, mainly relating to obtaining good resolution; a number of techniques had been examined and discarded. In 1950, a team under J Clegg at TRE began to design a new equipment.[34] This was a long aerial mounted alongside the aircraft enabling it to look at right angles to the flight path for up to 100 miles. Signal returns from a scanning arc were projected on to a photographic film moving continuously at a rate proportional to the speed of the aircraft and parallel to the flight path, the resolution of the map being a function of the beam width along track and the pulse width across track. The use to which sideways-looking radar was put will be described in Chapter 6.

Moving Target Indicators

Hitherto radar had been unable to detect small moving objects such as tanks and vehicles, even less human beings because it was unable to differentiate between them and returns from the ground known as 'clutter'. This problem was overcome by the development of Doppler* radar which was able to distinguish between fixed and moving targets by detecting the apparent change in

*The Doppler principle was discovered by Christian Doppler, an Austrian physicist, in 1842. The Doppler effect has been compared to a train approaching an observer and emit-

frequency of the reflected wave due to the motion of the target or the observer. A moving target indicator (MTI) was able to provide a picture of a column of vehicles moving along a road. The characteristics required by the MTI were the opposite of those required by sideways-looking radar. Whereas the latter relied on ground returns for mapping purposes, such signals had to be eliminated in the MTI picture.[35] MTI radars were used by both air and ground forces for surveillance. In the latter case, it was first applied in 1944 in a British centimetric fire control radar for locating German mortars using pulse Doppler and a plan position indicator, but because of design difficulties, only a few sets were made.

Millimetric Radar

Although the subject for study since the late 1940s, millimetre waves were only used towards the end of our period. They possess a number of advantages over microwaves; in particular, they are less susceptible to jamming and detection because of their smaller beam width and low employment density, and their smaller antenna beam width and range resolution. They also have increased band width availability and range resolution. On the other hand, they suffer from low power and atmospheric absorbtion. Millimetre radars are potentially valuable in the battle area for surveillance target acquisition and low angle tracking and they provide reasonably good security against ECM.[36]

Radar Guidance of Tactical Missiles

Radar was first used for tracking aircraft targets for anti-aircraft guns in the early 1940s. From 1941 it was recognised that shells and mortar bombs could be tracked or detected by centimetric radar. When surface-to-air missiles (SAMs) or air-to-air missiles (AAMs) began to be developed in the late 1940s, more effective radar and infra-red techniques were needed. Air-to-surface missiles (ASMs) were also required for attacking enemy tanks or ships.

Development of types of missile employed by ground, air and sea forces will be described in the appropriate chapters. The three methods of missile guidance must now be described.[37]

1 *Beam riding*. The missile is launched into a radar beam immediately the radar tracker outside the missile locks onto the target. Pulses from the radar transmitter are received by the missile, correcting its course until it

---

ting a whistle. As the train passes the observer the pitch falls abruptly. Neither pitch, either before or after passing, is the true pitch of the whistle which lies between the two. This apparent shift in pitch (or frequency) is the Doppler effect.

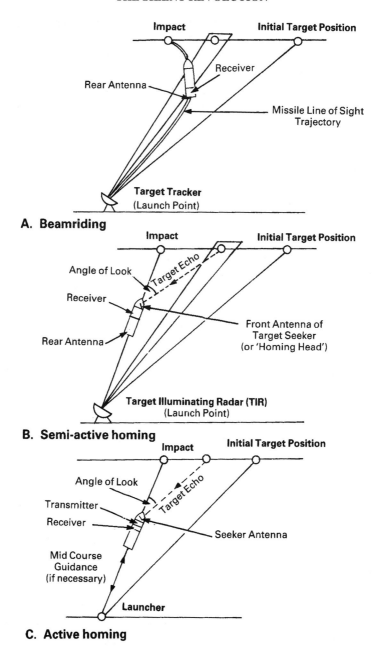

A. Beamriding

B. Semi-active homing

C. Active homing

Figure 3 Radar Guidance for Surface-to-Air Missiles.
Also applicable to Air-to-Air Missiles – see Table 1. (*GEC Journal of Research*).

intercepts the target. Although beam riding is relatively simple and has a strong received signal, it is not an efficient method of interception as it has to follow an assigned path.

2 *Semi-active homing.* Again the missile is launched when the tracking radar locks onto the target. The target is illuminated by the tracking radar throughout the flight of the missile. The reflection from the target is received by a 'homing head' in the nose of the missile. Semi-active homing is more effective than beam riding as it gives the direction of the target throughout the flight of the missile. The 'homing head' provides information which enables the missile to be steered onto the target.

3 *Active homing.* In this case the transmitter is inside the missile and with a track generation computer is able to provide an optimum interception path. It is therefore the most efficient form of guidance, but requires the most sophisticated equipment.

All these systems, it should be noted, are vulnerable to ECM. Continuous wave, or unpulsed radar transmissions were but one method of countering interference.

Infra-red Systems

Infra-red is the region in the electromagnetic spectrum lying between visible light and microwaves. The possibilities of using infra-red frequencies to detect targets was considered as long ago as the First World War. Like radar, infra-red is divided into passive or active systems. In the former case the system will sense the radiation emitted by the target; in the latter case the target is illuminated and the system senses the radiation that is reflected by the target. A further distinction may be made between active systems in which the illuminator is an integral part of the sensor system and semi-active systems that use a naturally-occurring illuminant.

As the development of radar had made such strides in the late 1930s, the military possibilities of infra-red detection were not pursued. The British had, nevertheless, carried out some successful experiments with airborne infra-red detectors as early as 1937 but the approach of war did not permit further development.[38] The Germans, on the other hand, became interested in infra-red fire control equipments for use at night and were even contemplating the use of infra-red-guided AAMs in the latter stages of the war because of the Allied jamming of their airborne radars. After the war, infra-red research was continued by all countries, primarily with a view to developing heat seeking infra-red-guided AAMs. In due course infra-red applications were extended to SAMs and ATGMs. Again, like radar, infra-red is subject to countermeasures and is affected by certain weather conditions.[39]

Aids to Optical Guidance

Electronic techniques have also helped optically-guided weapons such as ATGMs and short range SAMs (usually portable and operated by one or two men). In such cases the human operator can be partly or entirely replaced by using an automatic tracker to track either the missile (semi-automatic command to line of sight) or the missile and target (automatic command to line of sight).[40] A further aid to optical guidance is to place the target sensor in the missile itself (eg with a television camera) thereby avoiding the problem inherent in optical guidance of the missile obscuring the target with its brightly burning motor.

Terminally-guided Weapons

The increasing accuracy of air defence systems made it difficult for strike aircraft to approach and identify their targets. Moreover, accurate delivery of a bomb is dependent on the necessity to release the weapon from a precise point with the precise velocity required to hit the target. Free fall bombs are also affected by atmospheric factors such as wind. Bombing thus became wasteful in terms of aircrew and weapons. Terminal guidance, however, has the characteristic that absolute accuracy increases as the target is approached; and since many targets do not radiate signals or if they do, these may be turned off by the enemy to avoid destruction, the target must be designated. The laser, with its capability of high brightness illumination, provides a low cost and easily-used target designator.

The new technique was pioneered in the early 1950s by the physicist, Charles Townes, and two colleagues at Columbia University.[41] Their aim was to achieve even greater accuracy from microwaves and they found that a beam of ammonia gas molecules contained in a resonant cavity could emit energy for microwave oscillators and amplifiers. This new source of energy was made public in May 1954 and was named Maser (microwave amplification by stimulated emission of radiation). The American services especially the USAF were quick to see that masers could illuminate targets. The USAF had supported earlier experiments and continued to provide lavish financial aid, thereby giving the scientists the pretext to rename maser as 'means for acquiring support for extensive support research'. The success of the maser principle in the microwave frequency range prompted other investigators to examine the possibility of extending this principle into the infra-red and optical regions of the spectrum. One of them was Ted Mariman, working in the laboratory of the Hughes Aircraft Company; in 1961, he developed an 'optical maser' in the infra-red band. It was given the name of laser (light amplification stimulated by emission of radiation). Mariman used as a designator a neodymium yttrium

Table 1 Tactical guided missiles and bombs

Type	Name	Entered service	Guidance		Range (miles)	Nation	Remarks
			Initial/mid course	Terminal			
Surface-to-air (land)	BLOWPIPE	1968	Radio cmd/visual/TV	Radio cmd	1–3	UK	Man-portable
Low altitude (land)	STINGER	1979	IR	IR	2	UK	Man-portable
Low-to-medium altitude (land)	SCHMETTERLING	1940s			20	GE	Under development
	RHEINTOCHTER	1940s				GE	Under development
	WASSERFALL	1940s				GE	Under development
	CHAPPARAL	1966	IR	IR	10	US	
	RAPIER	1967	Optical/radar track/radio cmd	Optical/Semi-active radar homing (SARH)	3	UK	
	CROTALE	1968	Radio cmd/radar Track	Radio cmd/IR/ Proximity fuse	5	FR	
	ROLAND I	1977	Optical track/ Radio cmd/IR track	Proximity fuse	39	FR/GE	
	ROLAND II	1980/81	IR/Radio cmd Radar Beam rider		39	FR/GE	Also US version
	SA-7 GRAIL	1972	IR	Proximity fuse/IR	2–3	USSR	

39

Type	Name	Entered service	Guidance		Range (miles)	Nation	Remarks
			Initial/mid course	Terminal			
	SA–3 GOA	1961	Radio cmd	Radio cmd	15	USSR	
High-to-medium altitude (land)	NIKE/AJAX	1953	Radio cmd	Active radar	24	US	Initially for defence of USA
	NIKE/HERCULES	1958	Radio cmd	Active radar	86	US	
	HAWK	1954	SARH	SARH	21	US	
	HAWK (IMPROVED)	1972	SARH	SARH	21	US	
	BLOODHOUND	1958/64	Radio cmd radar track	SARH	49+	UK	
	THUNDERBIRD	1960/65	Radio cmd/radar track	SARH	46+	UK	
	SA–2 GUIDELINE	1958	Radio cmd	Radio cmd	24–31	USSR	
	SA–4 GANEF	1964	Radio cmd	Radio cmd	43	USSR	
	SA–6 GAINFUL	1967	Radio cmd	Radio cmd	37	USSR	
	PATRIOT	1981	Radio cmd/radar track	SARH	37	US	Multiple target capability using phased array radar
Surface-to-Air (sea)	SEA CAT	1962	Optical/radar track/radio cmd	Radio cmd	2	UK	Based on MALKARA ATGM

Category	Name	Year					Notes
Low altitude (sea)	SEA SPARROW	1967	Radio cmd/radar track	SARH	15	US	
	SEA WOLF	1978	Radio cmd/radar track	Radio cmd	3	UK	
Medium altitude (sea)	SEASLUG	1961	Radar beam rider	Radar beam/Proximity fuse	27–36	UK	
	TERRIER	1953	Radar beam rider	SARH	11	US	
	TARTAR	1953	SARH	SARH	10	US	
	MASURCA	1960	Radio cmd/radio track	SARH	31	FR	
High altitude (sea)	STANDARD I	1966	SARH	SARH	10	US	
	TALOS	1958	Radar beam rider	SARH	74	US	
	SEA DART	1967	SARH	SARH	49	UK	
	STANDARD II	1978	SARH	SARH	75	US	
Air-to-air (very short range)	SIDEWINDER	1956/79	IR	IR	6–11	US	
	MAGIC	1975	IR	IR	6	FR	First dog fight missile
Short range	FALCON family	1956/63	SARH/IR	SARH/IR	4–6	US	
	FIRESTREAK	1958	IR	IR	4	UK	
	RED TOP	1964	IR	IR	6	UK	
	ANAB	1961	SAR and IR versions	SARH/IR	6	UK	
	ATOLL	1970	SAR and IR versions	SARH/IR	12	USSR	

| Type | Name | Entered service | Guidance | | Range (miles) | Nation | Remarks |
			Initial/mid course	Terminal			
Medium range	SPARROW	1956/79	SAR	SARH	4–62	US	First AAM to use SA homing
	SKYFLASH	1977	SAR	SARH	31	UK	
Long range	PHOENIX	1970	SAR	Active radar	129	US	
Air-to-Surface	BULLPUP	1959	Radio cmd	Radio cmd	7	US	
	WALLEYE	1966	Radio cmd	TV camera image lock-on	15	US	
	PAVEWAY	1968/79	Free fall	Semi-active laser	–	US	
	ROCKEYE	197?	Free fall	Semi-active laser	–	US	
	HOBOS	1969	Electro-optical	Electro-optical	–	US	
	MAVERICK	1972	Automatic TV	Automatic TV	13	US	
	EXOCET	1974/77	Inertial	Active radar	23–46	FR	Also SSM version
Anti-radiation	*MARTEL*	1968	Autopilot cruise	Passive radiation searcher	37	UK/FR	
	SHRIKE	1964	Radiation homing	Radiation homing	7–10	US	
	HARM	1983	Radiation homing	Radiation homing	45	US	
	ALARM	1987	Active radar homing	Active radar homing	?	UK	

Category	Name	Year	Guidance	Homing	Range	Country	Notes
Surface-to-surface (land)	CORPORAL	1954	Autopilot = radar		80	US	
	SERGEANT	1962	Inertial		27–86	US	
	HONEST JOHN	1953/63	Inertial		4–22, 85	US	
	LANCE	1972	Inertial		93+	US	
Surface-to-surface (sea)	STYX (SS–N–2)	1955/60	Radio cmd + IR or ARH	IR/ARH	24–49	USSR	
	SIREN (SS–N–9)	1968/69	IR + ARH Mid-course guidance for long range	IR/ARH	68	USSR	
	GABRIEL (Mks I–III)	1975	Auto pilot cmd + IR or radar	IR/ARH	11–22	Israel	
	HARPOON	1976	Inertial sea skimmer	Active radar	68	US	
	OTOMAT	1978	Auto pilot/cmd	Active radar	62+	FR/Ital	
Anti-tank guided missile (Man portable)	SS-10	1955	Wire cmd/visual track		900 yds	FR	first post-war ATGM
	ENTAC (Engin téléguidé Anti-char)	1972	Wire cmd/visual track		1	FR	
	MILAN (Missile d'Infanterie Léger Anti-Char)	1972	Automatic wire cmd, IR track		1	FR	FR design but produced by FR/GE consortium.
	VIGILANT	1963	Wire cmd		600 yds	UK	
	COBRA/MAMBA	1960/72	Wire cmd		1	GE	Originally Swiss design

43

| Type | Name | Entered service | Guidance | | Range (miles) | Nation | Remarks |
			Initial/mid course	Terminal			
(Medium to heavy)	DRAGON	1972	Wire cmd		600 yds	US	First US man portable ATGM
	SS–11	1958	Wire cmd		1+	FR	
	SS–12	1962	Automatic wire cmd with IR track		1+	FR	
	SNAPPER	1963	Wire cmd		546– 2515 yds	USSR	
	SWATTER	1964	Wire cmd		646– 2734 yds	USSR	
	SAGGER	1965	Wire cmd		437– 2187 yds	USSR	
	MALKARA	1962	Wire cmd/wire track		492– 3500 yds	UK	
	TOW (Tube-launched, optically-tracked, wire-guided)	1969	Automatic wire and optical track		2	US	Second generation ATGM least demanding of operator's skill
	SHILLELAGH	1967	Automatic radio cmd/wire track		3	US	Launched from 152 mm tank gun

SWINGFIRE	1969	Wire cmd	2	UK	Turned through angles up to 45°
HOT (*Haut subsonique optiquement téléguidé tiré d'un Tube*)	1977	Automatic wire cmd/IT track	2	FR/GE	Also helicopter version

45

aluminium garnet emitting at a very narrow wave length of 1.06 micrometres. This was exactly what the Air Force needed to

> guide missiles, make communications more secure, and transform navigation, surveying and reconnaissance. The high angular resolution, narrow wave band and intensity of laser beams offered security and high directivity not available with microwave radar.

The other two services were not far behind in finding applications for lasers. The US Army realised that lasers would make excellent rangefinders and commissioned the Hughes Company to develop a rangefinder with a ruby designator for the M-60 tank which came into service in 1968. It is still regarded as the most accurate and fast method of rangefinding yet devised, perhaps justifying the prophecy made by a senior US Army officer that 'lasers may be the biggest breakthrough in the weapon area since the A Bomb.'[42] Certainly, the speed with which the rangefinder was developed appears to have been a model of close attention to application, competition for the best contractor to make the equipment, subsequent cooperation between contractor and military and, finally, selection of practical rather than over-elegant techniques.

Lasers were developed by the US Navy for space projects, improving navigation, the defence of warships and for making underwater communications more secure.

In the early 1960s, scientists investigated whether high energy lasers could be used to destroy incoming ICBM, using a glass laser. (Proposals for anti-ballistic missiles were then in vogue and it was hoped to develop at least a prototype weapon in the next decade.) But by the summer of 1962, it was evident that the solid state laser was a doubtful candidate for ground-based missile defence because of the high powers that would be required to shoot down re-entry vehicles. It would cost as much as one of the current anti-ballistic missile systems on its own and would be dependent on fair weather for successful operation.

The war in Vietnam diverted the military mind to more practical applications. US Army engineers had become interested in using laser beams to illuminate targets like tanks and to provide designators for guided missiles which would home on to the source of reflected light from the target. But the laser was still too bulky to use in the field as it required enormous amounts of energy for illumination.

This problem was solved late in 1962 when David Salonimer from US Army Missile Command argued that targets could be sufficiently illuminated by regularly spaced short bursts (pulses) of very high energy rather than by a continuous beam. Thus the size of the power plant could be reduced. Ironically, there had as yet been no tank actions in Vietnam and Salonimer's proposal was quietly shelved.[43] Undeterred, however, he managed to attract the attention of Colonel Joseph Davis, USAF, in charge of a small research group called Detachment 5 whose aim was to expedite procedures for low cost weapon developments. This was highly appropriate as the Vietnam war was threatening to become serious. Davis wanted to improve free-falling bombs and immediately appreciated that, once fitted with a guidance and control kit (in the manner of the wartime German radio-controlled bombs), they could be transformed into accurate weapons.

However another three years elapsed before the USAF asked for laser-guided bombs. Two designs were submitted by Texas Instruments and the Autonetics Division of North American Aviation, both with markedly different guidance systems. Here the technique of bombing by laser needs to be explained. The pilot must release his bomb within a 'basket' (defined by the field of view of the laser sensor and the manoeuvrability of the bomb) in order that the guidance mechanism may operate correctly. The prototypes of both the Texas Instruments and the North American Autonetics Division were designed around an optical assembly that gathered and focussed the reflected laser energy onto the surface of a detector that was divided into four quadrants. A preamplifier compared these quadrants to determine which received the most energy; this information was then used to initiate the bomb's guidance mechanism.

In TI's design, the seeker head was attached to the bomb's fin; in the NA-A design, guidance depended on 'proportional control' whereby the fins of the bomb were regulated during its descent. TI's design, compared with NA-A, was cheaper, less complicated but unproven. After feasibility trials, the concept of laser guidance was found to be viable and TI's design was seen to be superior to that of its rival. In September 1967, the USAF gave an operational requirement for a laser-guided bomb (PAVEWAY) which would have a circular error of probability (CEP)* of 25 feet. A production programme of 1000 kits was ordered and they were to be attached to 2000 pound bombs, a more powerful calibre than previously used in Vietnam.

PAVEWAY's accuracy made it highly suitable for use against very small targets. The first successful attack was made by PHANTOM fighter bombers on 13 May 1972 against a road/rail bridge near Hanoi without loss to any aircraft. The effectiveness of laser-guided bombs now became public knowledge and they provided the USAF with a precision bombing capability to strike and destroy virtually any target that could be seen by the pilot and acquired by the seeker.

---

* CEP is the radius of a circle centred on the target within which 50 per cent of the missiles can be expected to fall.

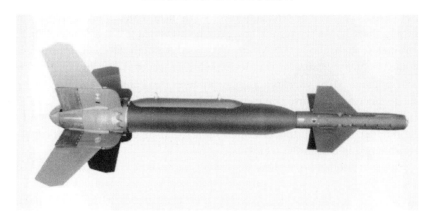

Plate 6a PAVEWAY, the first US laser-guided bomb. As shown in Plate 6b, used in Vietnam by the USAF against precision targets. It could destroy any target that could be seen by the pilot and acquired by the seeker. (*Texas Instruments*)

Plate 6b Five PAVEWAY bombs mounted on a US F-5 fighter bomber. (*Texas Instruments*)

Plate 6c. Destruction of the Thanh Hoa rail and road bridge by US PHANTOM fighter-bombers using laser-guided bombs, 13 May 1972. (*Texas Instruments*)

Inertial Guidance

So far we have been discussing relatively short-range weapons. But there are also surface-to-surface missiles (SSMs) used by ground forces against long-range targets (75–100 miles). Instead of radar direction, they depend on inertial guidance.[44] This system is contained within the missile and, once programmed, depends on gyroscopes and accelerometers to keep it on course until it reaches the target. It is less likely to be affected by ECM than radar-guided missiles.

Gyroscopic instruments to direct aircraft without signals from the ground were being developed long before the Second World War. The centre of research was the Instrumentation Laboratory at the Massachusetts Institute of Technology (MIT) under Charles Stark Draper. The scientists at Peenemunde had also considered inertial guidance for rockets and when the German team arrived in the States after the war they were asked to develop a gyro-stabilised system for the new US Army ballistic missiles. Draper, who had been working on inertial guidance systems for long range bombers, now devoted himself to missile guidance. The first US surface-to-surface tactical missile to be equipped with inertial guidance was SERGEANT which, after a long period of delay, came into service in the early 1960s. At that time it promised to be 'a fine tactical weapon.'[45]

During these years, the British had to concede that they were not yet able to produce inertial guidance systems to the 'standard of gyroscopic accuracy obtained by the Americans.'[46] As we shall see, they had to resort, for reasons

49

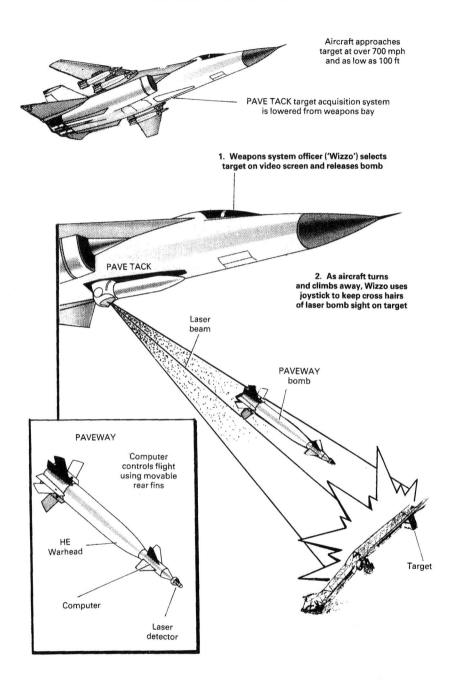

Figure 4 PAVE TACK laser-guided bombing system.

of economy, to using an American surface-to-surface missile. They were able, however, to develop an inertial guidance system for BLACK KNIGHT, a research rocket, and for the SSM (RED ROSE), though the latter had to be cancelled. Eventually inertial guidance systems for military purposes were produced by British firms.*

The Soviet Union, on the other hand, was in a better position to investigate inertial guidance. Like the Americans, they had profited from German work in the field after the war, in particular navigational and fire control systems developed for the German Navy. There was also a not inconsiderable fund of indigenous experience in the person of A Yo Ishlinsky who had been in touch with Draper for a number of years.[47] At the outset of their long-range guided missile research and development, the Russians, like the Americans, depended on radio guidance. Before long, inertial guidance took over, though without the benefit of the degree of miniaturisation enjoyed by the Americans.

Missile Propulsion

Although out of context with the main theme of this chapter, a brief glance should be taken at methods of missile propulsion. The Germans had used liquid propellants for the V-2s and the Americans followed this precedent in their early SSMs. But, as noted earlier, the Americans had already investigated solid propellants, which they found were generally superior to liquid propellants, particularly for SAMs, where rapid acceleration from the launcher to supersonic speed was essential. On the whole, the services preferred solid propellants because they lasted longer, were easy to maintain, could be stored for long periods inside the missile, were very much safer that liquid propellants and were instantly ready for action. SERGEANT was one of the first missiles to use a solid propellant.[48]

Ramjet engines, capable of operating at supersonic speeds and at altitudes over 60,000 feet were another form of propulsion and were used by the Americans and the British in several long range SAMs.

Conclusion

Perhaps the most important outcome of the technological developments just described for conventional warfare was the improvement of sensors such as radar, infra-red and lasers. In the 1970s, when they became more widely

---

* The British also investigated inertial guidance for aircraft and Siegfried Reisel, who had worked for Siemens in Germany during the war, was employed by RAE for some time, but no specific project emerged.

known, weapons using these sensors were described as 'smart' or precision-guided munitions (PGMs). Compared with other weapons, they were seen to be increasingly cost-effective. Some military analysts even predicted that as small missiles became more accurate and deadly they would replace major capital pieces of equipment like tanks, strike aircraft and large warships. We shall see that such views proved to be over-optimistic, though PGMs became an indispensable element of modern weaponry in the conflicts of the 1970s and 80s.

. 3 .

COMMUNICATIONS: THE KEY TO COMMAND – AND THE THREAT

The commander of land, sea or air forces depends upon the uninterrupted flow of information upon which he bases his decisions. Success in war is, and always has been, due to reliable information. To go no further back than the two World Wars: the Royal Navy at Jutland in May 1916 would have made a better showing had its system of command been able to absorb the information at hand about German naval movements. The Allied airborne assault across the Lower Rhine in September 1944 (Operation MARKET GARDEN) could have been a success had there been a more effective command and communications system. Though great commanders like Wellington or Montgomery used liaison officers mounted on horseback or riding in jeeps to obtain first hand intelligence and to transmit instructions to subordinate commanders, technology has provided high command with speedier, though vulnerable, means of doing both.

Optical transmission of messages began in the 18th century with the relay semaphore system invented by the Frenchman, Claude Chappe, who coined the term 'telegraph'. At the end of the 19th century, exploitation of electromagnetic waves had begun with the invention of wireless. Electrical transmission of signals involves some form of coding. In 1844, Morse became the first electrical system whereby information was translated into code and transplanted over the telegraph from its source to its point of reception. Manual morse is still used in certain situations in military operations to this day. Telecommunications,* used sparingly but effectively in the First World War and to a much more significant extent in the Second World War, have now

---

* Telecommunications are any transmission, emission or reception of signs, signals, written images and sounds or intelligence of any nature by wire, radio, visual or any other electromagnetic systems including any intervening processing and storage.

been transformed by the digital computer using solid state devices like the transistor and the integrated circuit (described in Chapter 2) enabling quantities of information to be despatched, encrypted, received, decrypted, processed and classified at speeds unthinkable before 1945.

Computerised Communications

Four innovations have revolutionised communications (a rather less clumsy term than telecommunications) in the three decades since the end of the Second World War.

1 *Geostationary communications satellites*, anticipated by the science fiction writer, Arthur Clarke,[1] in October 1945, began to be launched into orbit above the Equator at heights of about 22,000 miles some 20 years later, following the startling appearance of the Soviet *SPUTNIK*. These satellites provide long haul (strategic) transmission of single and multichannel voice and data traffic. Satellites have literally brought events on the battlefield to the desk of the commander-in-chief. The Falklands war in 1982, albeit a very small one, was commanded from the home base by satellite communications so that the commander-in-chief never set foot in the area of conflict. The same applied to the actual fighting in the Gulf eight years later. Minute by minute *political* control had become a reality. Communications satellites have advanced rapidly. The first satellite (INTELSAT I) relayed 240 telephone circuits. In the 1980s, INTELSAT VI was able to relay 30,000 circuits in addition to several TV channels. However, satellites are vulnerable both to physical attack and to electronic interference.

2 Radio techniques have been adapted to provide *multiple information channels* over a single 'carrier' system like a telephone line. Two methods, known respectively as frequency division and time division, are commonly used in both military and civil telephone and radio networks. Transmission sampling to avoid ambiguity, sorting for local delivery and receipt of data may now be performed with transistors using minute amounts of energy measured in microwatts rather than milliwatts. Combinations of time division and frequency division have also become possible. In addition, multiple signals, either frequency or time divided, can be transmitted more effectively, and hence more economically, over concentric cables (a tube with a centre conductor) or over a wave guide (an empty tube). Digital signals, in short, exploit the ability of modern radio transmission techniques to carry a wide band of frequencies and provide systems highly immune to noise and distortion.[2]

Plate 7 DSC II: US communications satellite. Satellites have literally brought events on the battlefield to the desk of the commander-in-chief. (*Jane's Information Group*)

3 *Packet switching* has been introduced to improve the flow of information over the radio. It originated in a study made by the Rand Corporation for the USAF in 1964 to find a secure tactical communications system which was also easy to operate. Rand's proposal, anticipating packet switching, was ignored by the authorities, but was rediscovered some three years later by Lawrence Roberts, Director of Information Processing at the Advanced Research Projects Agency sponsored by the US Department of Defense and, quite independently across the Atlantic, by Donald Davies in charge of a small team at the NPL which in 1973, after eight years work, built a local network with a single packet switch. A 'packet' in the jargon of communications technology is a collection of 'data bits' (or binary digits) of variable length plus the necessary addressing and control information to permit a message to pass over radio, cable or wire networks. Its complement, 'packet radio', extends the concept of packet switching to the domain of multiple access radio channels. It satisfies the needs of a large number of mobile subscribers in, for example, an army division dispersed over a wide geographical area. Packet radio is especially useful when the information is, in American parlance, 'bursty', as in computerised communications.[3] Each packet radio contains a microprocessor which breaks up messages for transmission and then dynamically schedules and controls access to the channel to prevent overlapping transmissions between several stations taking place.[4]

The concept for packet switching, suitable for civil as well as for military communications, was discussed openly by American, British and, later, French radio engineers, and the first public demonstration was given at a conference held in Washington DC in October 1972. This satisfactorily proved to a number of sceptical scientists that a 'collection of computers, wide band circuits and minor computer switching nodes – pieces of equipment totalling well over 100 – could all function reliably.'[5]

4 The *multiplexer* introduced in the 1960s was another important device for increasing radio traffic. It was capable of taking the input from six speech channels either in the form of telegraph, data or speech, enciphering the channels and impressing the result on a relay circuit, performing the reverse process at the receiving end. Where necessary at higher levels of command, the six channel system could be multiplied to provide 12 channels.[6]

Glass Fibres

Signals security will be discussed later in this chapter, but a far reaching innovation, which came in at the close of our period, was the use of glass fibres instead of copper for land-based line systems.[7] Low loss glass fibres can transmit light originating from a laser. This is particularly useful when the information is binary in form. Extremely short pulses may also be transmitted corresponding to very wide band widths (for example, as many as 10 TV channels can be handled on one fibre). The fibres are, moreover, made of silica which is a relatively inexpensive substance compared with copper; glass fibres are lighter and therefore transported and stored more easily. But from a military point of view, their non-radiating properties make them especially suitable as a transmission system. Glass, or optical, fibres are now used for underwater communications and enclosed in the interiors of ships and aircraft.

Repercussions on Systems of Command

The immense volume of information that may now be transmitted through digital communication systems, not to mention improved methods in *acquiring* intelligence through novel reconnaissance and surveillance methods (described in Chapter 6), has revolutionised the structure of command.[8] Traditionally, the commander's orders emanated from headquarters behind the front line or from the bridge of a warship by word of mouth, later supplemented by instructions sent by land line or through the air by radio.

A foretaste of what was to become known as Communications, Command and Control (C^3) was provided by the British reporting and control system for the air defence of the United Kingdom. Already operating before 1939, hostile aircraft approaching the British coastline were identified by radar and the information passed over land line to operations and filter rooms. The display of information placed simultaneously before the air commander-in-chief and the sector controllers enabled the former to put squadrons in the air as and when they were needed, while reserves could be transferred from one group to another. Thus in the critical summer of 1940, RAF Fighter Command was able to offset the numerical superiority of the German Air Force – an historic example of a 'force multiplier'.

In 1978, the US Joint Chiefs of Staff concisely defined the new concept of C^3 as follows:

> *Command and Control*: the exercise of authority and direction by a properly designated commander over assigned forces in the accomplishment of his mission. Command and control functions are performed through an arrangement of personnel, equipment, communications, facilities and procedures which are employed by a commander in planning, directing, coordinating and controlling forces and operations in the accomplishment of his mission.
> *Communications*: A method or means of conveying information of any kind from one person or place to another, except by direct unassisted conversation or correspondence through non-military postal agencies.

C^3 which, it is worth noting, is exclusively dependent on software connects the decision-makers with their information sources as well as with the forces that execute the orders and fight. In turn, results and assessments are fed back. These functions are largely hidden and unappreciated. Everyone knows that men, tanks, guns and aeroplanes matter. These are counted, their numbers are debated, their cost analysed. But none of them can be effective without C^3.[9]

The establishment of C^3 was a lengthy business as it was dependent on the application of computer technology. As already described, the US services lost no time in adapting transistors to their needs. Between 1958 and 1964 the US Army Signal Corps embarked on a major programme involving the development and manufacture of micromodule assemblies which would provide alternative functions for communication centres or networks in the event of physical destruction or jamming. In the early 1970s, integrated circuits with several hundred transistors on one chip of substrate provided opportunities to automate battlefield functions such as fire control, air defence, target identification and assessment, intelligence collection and evaluation, while digital transmissions over long distances could be handled efficiently with a minimum of signals distortion. Integrated circuits were also being used in observation satellites like SAMOS (Satellite and Missile Observation System), teletypewriter radio transmission systems, facsimile equipment and secure communications. Outside the States other NATO powers and their potential opponents in the Warsaw Pact also began to miniaturise their communications equipment.

Technological change, however, rarely fits neatly into a chronological pattern. A certain type of equipment is needed urgently to meet a defined threat or to remedy a deficiency. Command and control had already become intermeshed with sensors like radar as well as with radio or telegraphic communications. The following sections will attempt to show how the C^3 concept evolved in response to the needs of naval and land operations.

Inter-aircraft and Air-to-Ground Communications Systems

Very high frequency (VHF) radio for air crews had hardly been introduced at the outset of the Second World War (the Battle of Britain was, in fact, fought with High Frequency (HF) sets). Yet a demand to change over to Ultra High Frequency (UHF) was made as early as 1943 to cope with the increasing volume of traffic on air/ground radio telephone channels. But in war time this was clearly impossible. In the late 1940s, leading American scientists were the first to make a determined effort to produce a satisfactory UHF set which would not be subject to anomalous propagation. Progress was slow but before the end of the 1950s, the changeover had taken place.

Twenty years later, the latest UHF radios being used by the USAF were being changed over to solid state equipments. All aircraft carried a UHF/Amplitude Modulated (AM) radio and close support aircraft carried VHF/ Frequency Modulated (FM) sets. The latter type (AN/ARC-164) operated in the 225-400MHz-band and had a power output of 10W with a 30W option. It had access to 7000 channels at a channel spacing of 25 KHz. Non-secure communication could be changed over to secure. Airborne Warning and Control (AWACS) aircraft were provided with the AN/ARC-171 radio which had a power output up to 30W for AM voice and up to 100W for FM voice. It could be linked to a communications satellite and was proof against the effects of a nuclear explosion.

The first British service to adopt UHF was the Royal Navy in 1953, after an agreement made with the Americans at the Atlantic City conference in 1947 that military communications between the two countries should be interoperable.[10] But on account of the limited capacity of the British radio industry, the RAF appreciated that it would initially have to buy American sets and postponed the changeover for as long as possible on the grounds that the Americans were experiencing difficulties in operating their new sets at high altitudes while certain of the American models would not fit into British aircraft. However, by 1953, with American and Canadian aircraft operating under the aegis of NATO, the RAF found itself in the embarrassing position of being unable to communicate with its Western allies; it was further handicapped by having an insufficient number of frequencies for operational requirements.

Even more dangerous was the fact that in order to intercept the latest Soviet high altitude bomber, close, as opposed to broad, radio control was needed, 'thus greatly aggravating the difficulties due to . . . shortage of frequencies.'[11] Even so, there were those who argued that if Fighter Command waited a little longer, interceptor aircraft would be replaced by missiles. At last, in the summer of 1955, after chopping and changing, it was agreed that the American AN/ARC-52 set should be manufactured in Britain pending the production of a British set around 1959. By that time, naval conversion to UHF (including naval aircraft) had already been completed. (Further developments in naval signals will be covered in the following section.)

The startling progress made in the development of digital communications in the 1960s was naturally of great importance to air operations in which events occur very quickly and the need for continuous real time communication is paramount. More often than not, several headquarters on the ground are involved and need to have immediate access to communication channels either in plain speech or, alternatively, radio teletype or telephony. The whole system must be properly coordinated.

Two examples of digitalised communication systems in our period must suffice. The first, developed in the early 1970s, was called MATELO whereby the

RAF NIMRODS (long range maritime patrol aircraft) were controlled.[12] It was essential to be able to communicate over distances beyond 1000 miles from base and instant availability was vital. The nerve centres of MATELO were two main control centres with transmitting and receiving equipment at opposite ends of the British Isles. These stations were capable of automatically changing frequency very often. Furthermore, transmitting and receiving stations were operated remotely and, due to the employment of solid state components, the sites needed to be visited only occasionally for maintenance. Overall control of the system was exercised from one of the Main Control Centres, the other acting as a back-up. They depended on a complex network of line communications providing inter-connections between them and the various operational headquarters concerned.

The second example is an American system called the Joint Tactical Information Distribution System (JTIDS) and was intended for all US services.[13] The purpose was to develop a high capacity, reliable, secure and jam-resistant communication system. It was based on the time division multiple access technique, already described, and was designed to overlay an existing frequency allocation for operation of conventional and spread spectrum systems without mutual interference. It was secure, jam-proof and had facilities for converting verbal conversation into synthetic speech without loss of clarity. Three classes of terminal were considered for the JTIDS programme. Class I was for large airborne warning and control aircraft, surface ships and interface facilities linking JTIDS to ground-based networks. Class II terminals were for fighter aircraft and ships with volume constraints. Class III terminals were intended for use by controllers of strike aircraft, small RPVs, some tactical missiles, and selected army units. An upgraded JTIDS was prepared for the US Navy based on distributed time division multiple access techniques.

Naval Communications

In modern warfare naval surface forces rely heavily on communications and early warning because of their vulnerability to attack from the air, seaborne and underwater forces. Ships are slow-moving, easily detected and noisey. They must maintain a very high defence capability because the penetration of a vessel, even by a single weapon, may be fatal. Since they need a multitude of sensors like radar and sonar, they must have electronic countermeasures and electronic counter countermeasures in abundance. In addition, their fire power, mainly used for self-defence, must be based on good organisation, comprising

highly sophisticated ship-based command and control systems; more important, the sharing of duties and mutual support of ships and aircraft within a task group; and a variety of early warning installations, world wide navigation and telecommunications systems. Surface craft must be integrated into an overall structure, the 'non-floating' components of which may turn out to be decisive in maintaining the combat effectiveness of warships.[14]

Since the Korean War, the dominant naval powers have been the United States and the Soviet Union; the former has maintained powerful carrier forces in the Mediterranean and the Western Pacific. By 1981, there were 12 American carriers, four of which were nuclear-powered, operating across the world. They carried a complement of around 1,100 aircraft (fixed wing and heli-copter) for defence, ground and surface strikes, and anti-submarine warfare. The effectiveness of these forces is dependent on tactical data link communications. For this reason the emphasis in the following section is mainly on current American developments, though they are inter-related with progress made in the Royal Navy.

Naval communications may conveniently be divided into three functional areas:

1 strategic,
2 long haul communications to and from units at sea, and
3 tactical communications among operating units at sea.[15]

Strategic communications are especially relevant to nuclear-powered sub-marines carrying submarine launched ballistic missiles (SLBM). These long range submarines must maintain continuous communication with their land-based headquarters. Very low frequency (VLF) sets were already being developed in the latter stages of the war and research continued after 1945. In order to receive VLF broadcasts while submerged, the submarine must trail an antenna line on or near the surface of the water, or tow a communications buoy slightly below the surface.[16] When using normal VHF wave bands, submarines must raise an antenna above the sea surface thus incurring risk of detection. Western navies are currently developing Extremely Low Frequency (ELF) as well as laser communications in order to overcome the need for submarines to operate near the surface of the ocean. ELF transmissions penetrate water almost 20 times deeper than VLF transmissions and allow submarines to receive sig-nals at greater operating depths. Like VLF, ELF transmissions are usually immune to atmospheric disturbances, either natural or caused by a nuclear explosion. A major disadvantage of ELF is the very low data rate it can support.

Long haul communication may be characterised by beyond line of sight dis-tances, interconnection between fleet units and shore commands or between independent fleet units. Typical functions include intelligence and logistical information, force direction, and, in a battle situation detailed exchange of information by the commanders on the spot. In the 1970s, naval opinion held that new satellite technology would make HF communication obsolete and unnecessary. But it soon became obvious that, while satellites significantly increased the capability of communications, they were vulnerable to ECM.[17] The Americans therefore appreciated that satellite communications would have to be augmented by an up-to-date HF capability, not only to overcome hostile interference but because of the need to inter-operate with Allied navies and to support tactical operations.

Tactical communications provide the means whereby naval units are able to coordinate their actions, support distribution of local surveillance data and exercise control over their weapon systems. The area of these activities is varied but is usually contained within a circular area whose radius is about 280 miles. HF or VHF radio links capable of supporting both analogue and digital communications are usually used by American and British naval forces, though the ability to use manual morse and voice still exists in a form similar to that of the Second World War. As in air and ground operations, existing communications are vulnerable to determined attempts at electronic jamming.

Digital radio systems were introduced into the Western navies in the 1960s, the first being the US Naval Tactical Data System. It began with two links; one (LINK 4A) was designed to support an automatic landing system for carriers, later evolving into a means to coordinate an airborne early warning aircraft and carrier-based fighter aircraft equipped with LINK 4A by exchanging status and target data. LINK 11 is a data link which supports the exchange of tactical data used to coordinate ships' operation rooms in the combat area. HF is mainly used but the link is also supported by UHF where the units are within line of sight. LINK 4A and LINK 11 both use a time division multiple access technique to communicate with the various units and to exchange target information.[18]

In view of the importance attached to it, particular attention was given to the development of HF equipment by British naval scientists in the 1960s. The outcome was the Royal Navy's Integrated Communications System Phase 3 (ICS3) which set out to improve transmission and reception, automatic handling, telegraph signals, control and monitoring.[19] One obstacle which had to be overcome was to find suitable sites for aerials which were not obstructed by the superstructure. An ingenious suggestion led to the use of the superstructure itself as an aerial and this successfully overcame the difficulty. Masts and funnels have been used to provide an efficient wide band aerial system.

This improvement has been further exploited by the introduction of a novel system called the 'power bank' from which can be obtained instant frequency changes within the HF range; it also allows frequency separation between transmitter and receiver to be reduced to 100KHz and has substituted two short active aerials for a collection of whip aerial receivers.

An important advance in processing information may also be credited to

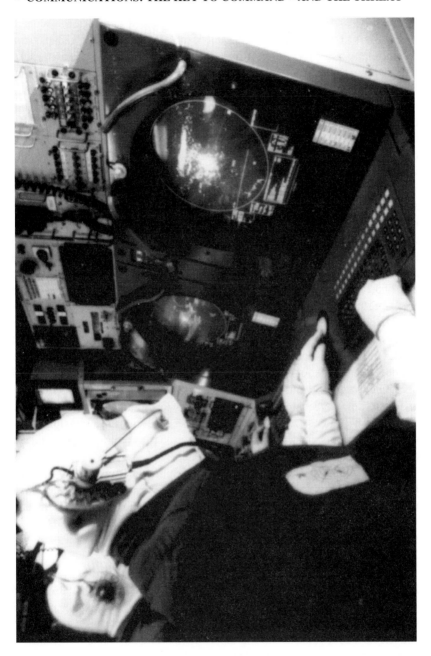

Plate 8 NAUTIS: Royal Navy command and control system used for tactical communications within a radius of about 280 miles. (*Marconi Underwater Systems Ltd*)

naval science. A Control Centre in Royal Navy ships has been introduced in recent years to monitor the vast amount of telegraphy signals sorted and stored by automatic data processing. A user of the Control Centre has now merely to press a button for him to be switched on to HF, UHF or Satcom equipment.

Royal Naval scientists have also emulated their American colleagues in the development of satellite communications. In the early 1970s, two aircraft carriers (*Ark Royal* and *Hermes*) were fitted with mobile terminals operating through the British SKYNET* and American and NATO terminals.[20] The success of these experiments with satellites stimulated the Navy into developing a small light weight system called SCOT. There are two kinds of this equipment, one handling telegraph traffic and the other can be adapted to carry speech as well if the power in the satellite is available. A number of ships were equipped with the facilities to take SCOT on board if the need arose. What does not appear to have been foreseen was the lack of compatability between satellite communications and radar/ECM. When HMS *Sheffield* was struck by an EXOCET missile in the Falklands war the electronic system for releasing chaff had been switched off to allow radio transmissions from a communications satellite to take place.

UHF techniques have not been neglected by the British. For many years voice communication between ships, the shore and ships, and especially between ships and aircraft was handicapped by lack of a wide band. Provision has now been made for equipment accommodating wide band analogue or digital voice telegraphy and high speed data with a multicoupler of special filters and matching circuits to enable 12 channels to be radiated through a single antenna. The latter is itself a notable British invention; the transmitting and receiving sections are wrapped around the pole mast with physical and electrical separation.

The importance of mechanical design in communications is well illustrated by the Royal Navy aerial for submarines incorporating a compounded periscope and telescopic system enabling the captain to communicate at HF, VHF, UHF and to navigate by satellite.

Communications and Command in the Land Battle

For about 20 years after the Second World War army communications in the Western world were still relying on equipment proved in the latter part of the war. The British continued to use the No 19 set, hastily manufactured by Pye and first issued to units of the Eighth Army in North Africa, although they had begun to be replaced by the Canadian 52 set. The Americans were being

---

* SKYNET was built in the USA embodying British features and was put into orbit by the USA in 1969.

issued with the AN/TRC series first used to good effect in North-West Europe and the Pacific. These FM sets with a range of about a mile (and up to five miles in good atmospheric conditions) were a prime factor in the success of Patton's rapid armoured thrusts towards the German frontier in 1944 because they were not subject to the interference experienced by the AM sets being used by other Allied troops and by the Germans. It was not unknown for a radio operator using an AM set to hear at least 20 stations 'English, French, German, Russian. We never did establish contact with the station we were trying to reach.'[21]

The AN/TRC series, or 'Antracs' as they were called by the troops, were also used by the British after the war and known as Radio Relay. Originally, they were developed by US Signal Corps engineers in 1943 at their laboratory at Camp Coles in New Jersey. The sets had the advantage of range and compactness. A 100 mile system of two terminals and three relay stations in between could be installed by 44 men in two days compared with a land line which took ten days to be laid by nearly 2000 men. The transport needed to carry Antrac equipment for relay was about 30 per cent less in volume than a comparable wire system. The early models were four channel VHF radio relay systems operating between 70 and 100 MHz. Each channel carried a voice circuit or four telex circuits. Later, microwave versions were introduced similar to the British No 10 set which enabled Montgomery to speak to any unit under his command as well as to confer with Supreme Headquarters or with the War Office in Whitehall. Long haul communications in the 1950s (up to 1,200 miles) were based upon HF Skywave FM propagation. Pre-satellite transmissions were not reflected by the ionosphere but went through outer space.[22]

However, the introduction of tactical nuclear weapons in the mid-1950s made a thorough overhaul of battlefield communication systems necessary. Hitherto, communications had followed corps and divisional headquarters. The commander was usually in close proximity to his staff where information was processed and presented. When decisions were made, they were passed down an axis that ran from the decision-making headquarters to the implementing headquarters as well as to the senior headquarters in the rear. But the possibility of a nuclear strike made the existence of small compact headquarters extremely hazardous; communications systems would in future have to be dispersed and provision made for alternative routing.

The first British attempt to provide an answer to conditions imposed by nuclear warfare was the programme called LARKSPUR which was started in 1962.[23] An important innovation was that radios were provided with crypto-protection by digitising the voice signal and encrypting the digit stream. Another valuable aid made available at that time was the provision of communication satellites by the Americans which were tested and evaluated by NATO forces from 1967–70. In 1970 the first NATO-owned satellites were

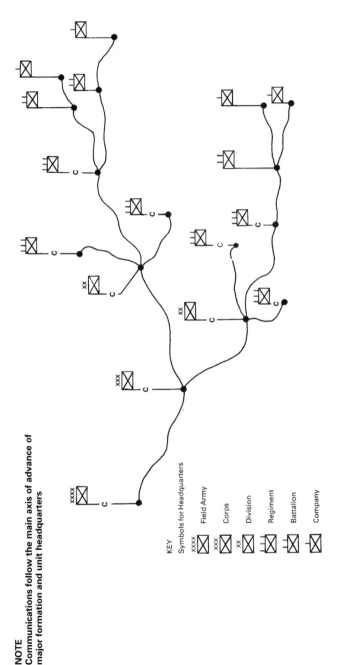

NOTE
Communications follow the main axis of advance of major formation and unit headquarters

KEY

Symbols for Headquarters

XXXX	Field Army
XXX	Corps
XX	Division
	Regiment
	Battalion
	Company

Figure 5 Axis of signal communications used by the US Army in the Second World War. Information was processed and presented to the commander situated in close proximity to his staff. Decisions were passed down this axis to implementing HQs and to higher formations in rear. Some lines of communication were electrical and provided voice and relatively crude data transmission. The latter was mainly by means of precoded texts utilising morse code. Later morse was augmented by electric teletyper. (*William M Mannel, Future Communications – concepts in support of US Army Command and Control, 1980*)

Note: *Figures 5–10 are taken from IEE Trans. on Comns, Vol. Com-28, No. 9 September 1980 © 1980 IEEE*

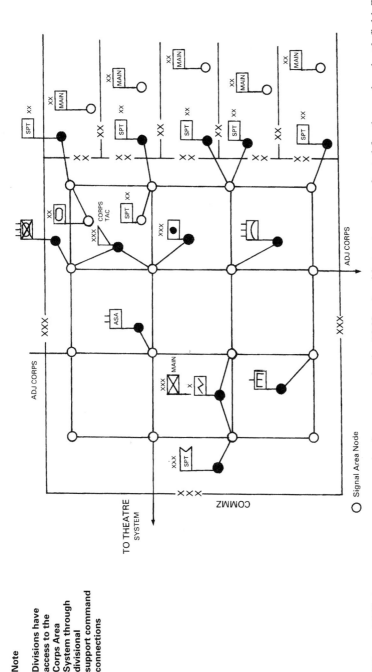

Figure 6 US Army corps area communications system in the 1960s. A grid structure was adopted for the nuclear battlefield. The grid provided alternate routeing of information in the event of one or more nodes within the grid being destroyed. But switching was required when major command centres wanted to exchange information with one another directly. Terrain features and the flow of battle could easily distort this layout. (*Mannel, op. cit.*)

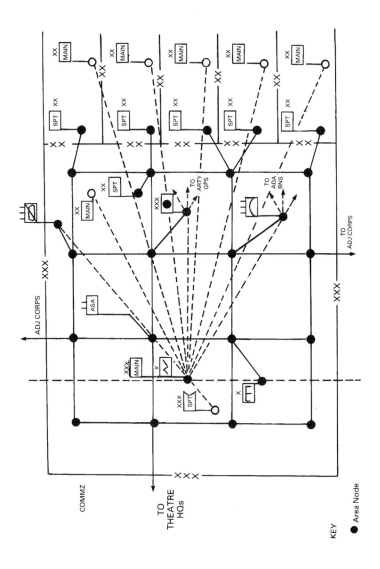

Figure 7 US Army corps composite area and command communications system (1980s). In order to increase the speed and directness of the flow of information for command traffic between major HQs, a command communications system was created for use in the field. (*Mannel, op. cit*)

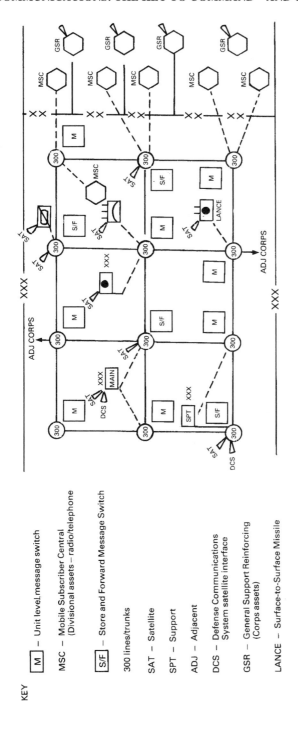

KEY

M – Unit level message switch

MSC – Mobile Subscriber Central
(Divisional assets – radio/telephone)

S/F – Store and Forward Message Switch

300 lines/trunks

SAT – Satellite

SPT – Support

ADJ – Adjacent

DCS – Defense Communications
System satellite interface

GSR – General Support Reinforcing
(Corps assets)

LANCE – Surface-to-Surface Missile

Figure 8 US Army corps communications planned for the late 1980s. The diagram shows a major digital trunk network with mobile radio interfaces. (*Mannel, op. cit*)

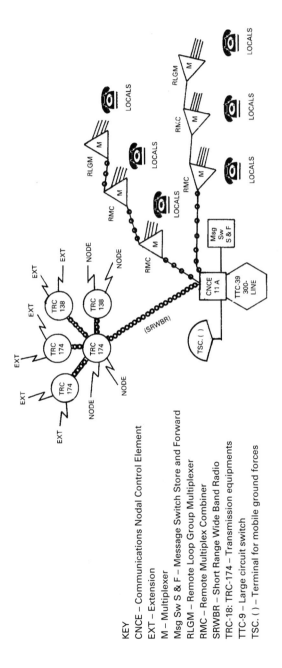

KEY
CNCE – Communications Nodal Control Element
EXT – Extension
M – Multiplexer
Msg Sw S & F – Message Switch Store and Forward
RLGM – Remote Loop Group Multiplexer
RMC – Remote Multiplex Combiner
SRWBR – Short Range Wide Band Radio
TRC-18; TRC-174 – Transmission equipments
TTC-9 – Large circuit switch
TSC. ( ) – Terminal for mobile ground forces

Figure 9 US Army corps communications in the 1980s. The diagram shows:

1   the basic node configuration

2   the local demoting capability with extensions to remote transmission facilities

A time domain multiple addressing system overlaid this network for rapid dissemination of highly perishable reactive type data. (*Mannel, op. cit*)

70

launched with an operational life of five years. They now superseded the HF Skywave techniques (kept in reserve) and were responsible for a dramatic improvement in the quality and reliability of field radio communications, and also enabled new signals methods to be introduced.

Three years earlier the policy of 'massive retaliation' was superseded by 'flexible response'. The new policy adopted by NATO in 1967 (see page 110) had implications for communications. Previously, they had consisted of a series of point-to-point links designed to convey instructions to commanders responsible for launching a retaliatory nuclear strike. Now flexibility involved responses to situations which ranged from peace to semi-war and, only in the last resort, full scale conventional or nuclear war.

In 1971, the NATO Integrated Communications System (NICS) Management Agency was formed to engineer and implement the NICS structure. Further developments at this time included the NATO-wide communications system (NWCS) – a combined manual/automatic message relay net providing low speed, secure teletype communications between NATO headquarters in Brussels and the principal NATO commanders.

Point to point systems for forward and lateral communications were created for Allied Command Europe (ACE) and called ACE HIGH. This is a chain of static communications stations, with multi-channel links providing dedicated voice and telegraph circuits between users, running from Norway, through Britain, across Europe to Turkey. It has also provided a link between a number of NATO headquarters. ACE HIGH is based on forward scatter, the technique of using the troposphere as the reflective element for high power radio communication at super high frequency (SHF).[24]

Plans for radical changes in tactical area communications had already been set in motion by the British in 1961 and similar planning was begun at the same time by the Americans and the French. The principal requirements were mobility to meet a rapidly changing front, dispersal to avoid presenting a nuclear target, a flexible but reliable command and control system, and interoperability between one national army and another. Cable and line systems had become too vulnerable and inflexible. HF also had a number of deficiencies and was, of course, vulnerable to Soviet jamming, now yearly increasing in sophistication. Fortunately, computers and integrated circuits were available to provide answers to these problems.

The plan for the British Army approved by the Army Council in June 1961 was known as HOBART. After three years initial study, it was split into three sub-projects to facilitate the management of feasibility studies then taking place.[25] They were called ALLERTON, a switched trunk network, BOXFORD, the radio trunk extension (later called the Single Channel Radio Access), and CLANSMAN, a new range of net radios. As it was anticipated that the full development of an area communication system would take a num-

71

ber of years to bring to fruition, while the British Army of the Rhine (BAOR) had always to be ready to meet a threat, an interim plan called BRUIN was put into motion in the 1960s during exercises taking place in Germany.

The exercises were intended to overcome teething problems and to develop user drills with the new equipment. The way it was done was as follows. A major part of each signals unit serving a formation in the field would be separated from headquarters, handling the trunk communications from sites chosen for their signalling advantage. Tributaries, originally using cables and later radio relay, could move within this radius allowing the majority of signals vehicles to remain where they were until it was time for them to carry out their own separate movement plan.

BRUIN was primarily intended to provide the means for command and control of the fighting units, but it was appreciated that communications with the rear combat and communications zones were equally important.[26] Vital decisions, on which the prevention of hostilities from breaking out might depend, would have to be circulated to both forward and rear areas. In addition, a number of interesting new developments were associated with BRUIN. One was the introduction of the multiplexer already described. Second, the introduction of HARRIER aircraft which would not be tied to concrete runways produced a new requirement for flexible communications. As BRUIN appeared in rear areas, other innovations were brought about. One was the introduction of secure facsimile between the rear headquarters of 1st British Corps, HQ BAOR and the HQ Forward Maintenance Area for arranging daily resupply in the field. Interfacing problems also arose between the new technologies and those of other existing systems. A resourceful technician in BAOR designed and built an interface unit to link BRUIN with the Ministry of Defence secure speech system, showing that scope still existed for inventiveness in the field army.

Difficulties were also encountered with the novel satellite communications. At first the main problem was to keep the satellite on station, so that it served the required land area, and to provide the power source to make its radio equipment operate. Before the advent of geostationary satellites, power outputs were minimal and immense steerable dish antennae were used to collect a signal strong enough to be of value. By the end of the 1960s, geostationary satellites were being launched. By 1971, a British mobile satcom station had been connected with BRUIN in Germany. Six years later, two experimental mobile stations mounted on Land Rovers had been built by the Signals Research and Development Establishment (SRDE) which took part in exercises with HQ 1st (British) Corps. Further development was spurred on by the Mogadishu air hijacking, which alerted the British Government to the urgent need for secure, reliable high quality rear link communications from the location of such incidents wherever they happened to be.

Meanwhile, the HOBART planners had been busy. The theoretical side was the responsibility of the Planning Wing, School of Signals at Blandford in Dorset, their conclusions being summarised in Study No 27, while technical development took place at SRDE, first at Christchurch and later at Malvern, In essence, the planners had to design a digital trunk communications system, as summarised above, using speech, facsimile pictures or messages capable of being conveyed with the maximum security across the battlefield wherever required. But progress became bogged down, not so much on account of technical problems but because of the escalating cost of equipment, relations with other NATO states in which similar developments were taking place at different rates of progress, and perhaps inevitably, reservations about some aspects of the scheme, both at General Staff level and from critics like the Post Office experts, who then believed that it was 'absurd to think in terms of computers as the heart of telephone switches.'

Nevertheless, the Americans and the Canadians were impressed. In 1962, a British Army lecture team in North America created the impression that HOBART was 'the most advanced concept in the Western World at the time.'[27] It was, in fact, only when the Americans had been drawn into the programme, as a result of discussions between Zuckerman, then Chief Scientific Adviser in the Ministry of Defence, and Harold Brown, Director of Defense Research and Engineering in the States, that a British team seeking cooperation in Washington was able to send home the signal 'HOBART rides again.' Not long after, the Australians and Canadians were enticed into the project and a decision was made in Australia to set up a Quadripartite Standing Working Group (QSWG) on secure tactical trunk communications systems (the scheme now being known as MALLARD). The task of this group was to define operational concepts and requirements, and technical options of procurement on a shared international basis

Unfortunately this promising start made by Commonwealth and United States officers working together foundered over the procurement issue and the allocation of contracts to radio firms. Then, in October 1970, the Americans withdrew from the venture because of restraints on the military budget. Australia and Canada then decided to withdraw leaving the British to go it alone.[28] A fresh beginning had to be made, the scheme now being known as PTARMIGAN. Plessey won the contract for initiating the programme in September 1973, just when the Post Office was embarking on a digital switching programme. Even so, it took another two years before the operational requirements were worked out. The Defence Equipment Policy Committee, then under the Chief Scientific Adviser, Sir Herman Bondi, had reservations about the feasibility of the software programme and it did not give full approval until after a thorough review had been made by SRDE.

PTARMIGAN was still not assured of a safe passage and again it might

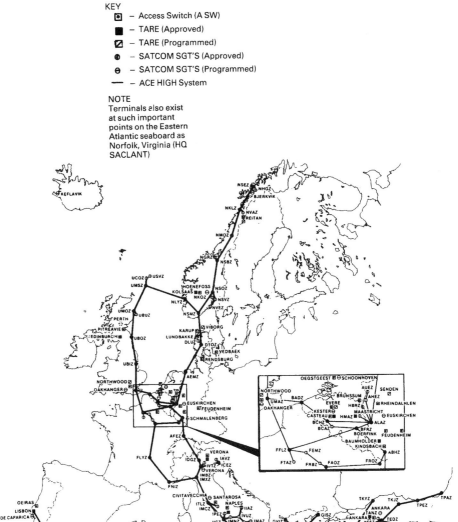

Figure 10 NATO Integrated Communications System, 1980, providing a flexible response to both 'semi-war' and 'hot war' situations. A combined manual/automatic message relay net provided secure teletype communications between NATO Headquarters in Brussels and the principal NATO commanders. (*Larry K Wentz and Gope D Hingorani 'NATO Communications in Transition' 1980*)

have died a natural death had it not been for the British decision to support Eurogroup (a NATO group minus the US and Canada), the purpose of which was to improve technical relations between each country making Europe less dependent on North America. The British, with the support of leading radio manufacturers and fortified by their experience in developing the earlier scheme MALLARD were clearly in the ascendancy. There was some opposition from the French and the Germans over a single channel radio access. But, by the end of 1971, the other NATO states were sufficiently in agreement for Lord Carrington, Minister of Defence, to state that Britain would continue to develop PTARMIGAN which would, in effect, be the first 'Eurocom' system.

PTARMIGAN began to come into service in 1984. It was claimed as being a 'quantum jump' forward in tactical communications technology and in simplicity of use by non-technical users'.[29] A divisional commander could have an instant telephone conference with his brigade commanders and could even send them a marked map at the same time. Above all it could not be tapped by enemy eavesdroppers. In the event of serious damage to the network, it could function (admittedly with limited range) with as little as one trunk node still in operation. The Americans were quick to recognise the value of 'Eurocom' and, despite being non-members, kept in touch to ensure that the standard of their equipment was in line with that of the forces in Europe.

In due course, PTARMIGAN was linked with WAVELL, the first British computerised mobile communications and control system for army tactical applications. The computer installation for WAVELL was carried either in a four ton air-conditioned truck or in a tracked armoured vehicle.[30] It was able to store and distribute automatically data inputs via PTARMIGAN from individual subscribers to others on the same trunk system. As early as its trial period, it could provide more accurate information and greater success than manual operation over poor radio circuits. Moreover, the automatic despatch of reports and returns eliminated the chores of watch and log keeping. More importantly, staffs were able to spend more time on evaluating and analysing information which is, after all, the basis of decision making. WAVELL was not, however, able to integrate automatically any surveillance information. Nor was it capable of making decisions. Another automated system relaying information through PTARMIGAN was the Battlefield Artillery Target Engagement System (BATES) sifting target information and providing fire control on a corps area (see page 141).

CLANSMAN, the combat net radio system either carried by the soldier or in a vehicle, was for general use in the British Army.[31] It was designed to be as simple as possible with the minimum number of types combined with the greatest possible commonality of parts and accessories in order to simplify maintenance and supply of spare parts and to reduce costs. The controls were

Plate 9 PTARMIGAN: the British Army tactical communications system. It is not completely secure but if a node is knocked out, another automatically takes over its work. (*Royal Signals Museum*)

made so that troops trained on one set could easily transfer to another. Sets were to be as small and as light in weight as possible and reliable and easy to repair.

Operationally, CLANSMAN had three main requirements: it had to find a desired frequency without long netting calls; sets must be able to operate in close proximity to one another; command voice and telegraph nets had to be secure. All these were achieved; the first by Plessey which made a technical breakthrough by providing frequency synthesizer modules (using integrated circuits) for both HF and VHF sets and supplied to all the set manufacturers as a common item. For the first time, transmissions could be made exactly on frequency. Cosite performance was obtained by setting very high performance specifications for the 'front end' of transmitters and receivers, which the manufacturers had managed with some effort to meet. Security for speech with standard VHF vehicle radio was achieved by using 'delta modulation' to convert voice signals to a 16k bits per second data stream and then encrypting it. On the equivalent HF vehicle set, security was applied to the telegraph signals but not to voice, where there were still some problems to be solved.

All the fundamental research on the project was carried out at the Royal Signals and Radar Establishment, as SRDE had now become, while production was spread across the radio industry including Plessey, Marconi and Racal; sets began to come into service around 1986. One unusual aspect of the CLANSMAN programme was that most of the sets turned out to be cheaper than first estimates suggested.

The French and Belgians developed their own tactical communications system known as Réseau Intégré de Transmission Automatique (*RITA*) more or less concurrently with the British scheme but 15 years elapsed before it took to the field.[32] From the mid-1960s, the US Army had been developing modern tactical circuit and message switches which were to be part of the tri-service system called TRI-TAC.[33] But this programme, which was intended to embrace battlefield *and* theatre command and control of the three Services proved to be too ambitious for immediate application and instead the US Army concentrated on its own scheme for battlefield communications known as the Integrated Tactical Communications Study (INTACS). It was developed at the Army Signals Centre, Fort Gordon, Georgia. The basis of the proposal was a grid system consisting of 16 nodes each of which had similar equipment configurations; the object was to link up widely scattered units and to provide alternative routing of information in the event of the total destruction of one or more nodes within the grid structure. The scheme complemented the 1982 'AirLand Battle' strategy which will be discussed in Chapter 5.

INTACS was to provide the basis of tactical radio communications for the US Army for the next 20 years. Like PTARMIGAN, the study contained a

Plate 10a WAVELL: the first mobile command and control system for a British Army corps . It is able to store and distribute data inputs automatically via trunk communications from individual subscribers to all others on the trunk system. (*Siemens Plessey Defence Systems*)

Plate 10b WAVELL: the vehicle. (*Siemens Plessey Defence Systems*)

78

provisional plan 'permitting the use of existing equipment . . . and providing during the transition new equipment . . . to effectively operate with both the new projected equipments and existing inventory equipments.'[34] The heart of INTACS was to be a terrestial long haul, digital tandem-trunked area system providing interconnections to the major command headquarters echeloned throughout the main battle area. Instead of information being channelled directly to these centres, probably causing confusion, decision-making uncertainty, or attracting enemy jamming, command centres would be connected to a number of signal nodes using either coaxial cable, highly directive laser systems, or fibre optic or microwave systems operating at extremely high frequencies (EHF) and employing adaptive antennae (described in the section on electronic warfare below) to prevent enemy interception and jamming.

Complementary to these systems would be a family of satellite ground terminals providing access to a multi-channel tactical satellite system. Such satellite communications would augment the terrestial long haul microwave system at selected nodes to provide a special communications service and skip node capability – an essential feature for the effective distribution of intelligence data. The satellite systems would operate at UHF, super high frequency (SHF), or EHF.

All this highly complicated technology, while substantially increasing information processing did, however, require 'a new type of soldier with levels of training and expertise quite different from that currently required.'[35]

Control and Command in the Soviet Union

As we have already seen (page 32), the Soviet armed forces had eagerly absorbed the doctrine of cybernetics as enunciated by Wiener in the late 1940s, and by 1959 this new theory had already become sufficiently acceptable to warrant the formation of a Scientific Council of Cybernetics in the USSR Academy of Sciences. Although not specifically concerned with the military aspects of the subject, it is significant that the Council was headed by an ex-naval radar officer. Ten years later, a senior army engineer officer wrote that 'the means of automatic control of troops and weapons – computing, data processing, logic control and analogue devices – have become a most important form of military equipment.'[36]

In the event, the actual issue of hardware in the form of the third generation of the RYAD computer was slow, but troops probably became familiar with automatic data processing from the mid-1970s onwards. The computers were deployed at tactical levels down to divisional headquarters, enabling the commander to make decisions based on a data retrieval system integrated at Front or even Theatre level. Although Soviet computer technology was much less sophisticated than anything comparable in the West, RYAD-2 models with greater memory, storage capacity, and block multiplexer channels were entering service in the mid-1980s They were used for digesting information for tactical applications though some time elapsed before they could assist in operations control and intelligence. In effect, therefore, the Russians were not so far behind the introduction of automated communications and control equipment like WAVELL or *RITA* to forces in NATO.[37]

No less than electronic warfare experts in the West, the Russians were, from the start, acutely concerned about the necessity to preserve communications security. They were also just as conscious of the vulnerability of a potential enemy's communications and control system, not to mention the tactical advantages to be gained when these were dislocated. ECM have thus always been accorded an important role in Soviet military doctrine, Especially significant was the doctrine of *Razvedka* embracing both reconnaissance and intelligence (electronic reconnaissance will be discussed in Chapter 4) and led to the formation of special signals intelligence units to support all levels of command above regimental level. A similar process called Radio Electronic Combat was specifically developed for the purpose of neutralising enemy communications and control systems. The high priority given by the Russians to electronic warfare became manifest in their occupation of Czechoslovakia in 1968 and the Soviet-made equipment used by the North Vietnamese against the Americans and by the Egyptians against the Israeli forces in the Yom Kippur war.

The Achilles Heel of Communications: Electronic Warfare

So far we have seen that the effective use of C^3 is a powerful type of force *multiplier*. By the same token the neutralisation of C^3 systems is a powerful force *divider*.[38] The interception and jamming of radio (and later radar) signals began in the First World War and was especially valuable in the anti-U boat campaigns, both then and in the Second World War But the increasing use of the electromagnetic spectrum which began in the 1940s led to the 'unseen' struggle of measure and countermeasure which became known as Electronic Warfare (EW). EW became a crucial factor in battle. At one point in the Yom Kippur war, for example, the Israeli Air Force had to use runners to take messages from an airfield control tower to pilots in their aircraft awaiting take-off, so effective were the Egyptians' ECM.

EW is common to air, land and sea warfare and is waged to protect or to disrupt radio communications or radar transmissions. It has three basic functions common to both (here we are only concerned with communications). These functions are defined as follows.[39]

1 *Electronic Support Measures (ESM)* cover the interception, location and analysis of radiated electromagnetic energy. They are based on the intercept or warning receivers and rely on a compilation of tactical and strategic electronic intelligence (ELINT). In a communications system they identify the operating frequency of active emitters, measure their bearing or location and analyse radio traffic to assess its threat significance and update a current data base.

2 *Electronic Countermeasures (ECM)* consist of actions taken to prevent or reduce the enemy's use of the electromagnetic spectrum, In communications the object is:

a to deny the enemy the use of his C^3 structure and associated radar nets;

b to prevent the gathering of ELINT (described on page 92);

c to overload or saturate the data processing and operator capability of the enemy's systems and to deny accurate detection of radar targets; and

d to introduce false deception data into the enemy's electronic systems to generate ineffective responses and to confuse his personnel or C^3 systems.

3 *Electronic Counter Countermeasures (ECCM)* are actions taken to retain the use of the electromagnetic spectrum despite the enemy's use of ECM techniques. They include coding techniques which spread the signal energy over a wide bandwidth and they employ various techniques which reduce the effect of jamming and interference.

Such is the importance of safeguarding communications, whether in the battle area or over long distances and in difficult environments (eg land-based headquarters to submarines), that four of these techniques will be described: null steering, frequency hopping (FH), spread spectrum (SS) and burst transmissions.

The term *null steering*, or antenna nulling, was given to radio (or radar) antennae which have the capability of adaptively changing their antennae pattern where jammers or other interfering sources exist. An area of no-response, or null, is created by narrowing the beam when directed towards the hostile jammer. At the same time communication can still be maintained with friendly radio stations by widening instead of narrowing the beam. Adaptive antennae were used by the Services from the mid-1970s onwards.

In *FH*, sequence generators change frequency in random fashion as determined by an electronically-generated, unpredictable (to the enemy) or 'pseudorandom'* code.[40] FH has a long history as the inevitability of interference with radio transmissions was anticipated as early as 1899. But technology was not seriously applied to countermeasures until the early 1930s and then more intensively in the Second World War when both sides became acutely aware of the need to safeguard radio communications. Progress to this end was first made by engineers and service officers in Germany and the United States, though there were occasional contributions from the non-military world.

Two of the more bizarre inventors were the film star Hedy Lamarr (a refugee from Austria and a passionate anti-Nazi) and the avant-garde composer George Antheil, both then living in California. Antheil's proposal, made in 1941 before Pearl Harbour, was to synchronise radio transmission and reception frequencies by means of twin, identically crypto-code slotted, paper music rolls like those used in player piano mechanisms. This device proved that an FH repertoire of 88 radio frequencies could easily be accommodated. Although well within the manufacturing capabilities of the 1940s, the FH features of the invention, despite being scrutinised with approval by the National Inventors Council, failed to interest the services.

At that time priority was given to interception of or listening in to radio transmissions rather than to jamming them. But when radio-guided missiles made their appearance the electromagnetic frequencies used to guide these weapons suddenly became too dangerous to neglect. The study of FH became a priority, much of the fundamental research taking place at the Lincoln Laboratory. In due course, FH was applied to HF, VHF and UHF transmissions. FH is also able to operate in a fixed frequency mode. But it can now be countered by monitoring the spectrum for transmissions and then quickly tuning the jamming transmitter into that frequency.

SS techniques involve spreading signal energy over a very wide band width before modulating it to a radio frequency, thus making it difficult to intercept, as the whole, very wide, band width must be covered. SS, like FH, was a natural result of the battle for electronic superiority in the Second World War, and every possible means of preventing jamming of radio communications had, by the end of the war, been investigated by both the Allied and the Axis powers.[41] It is believed that at one time nearly 90 per cent of all German electronic engineers were engaged in a vast, though unsuccessful, anti-jamming programme. Two projects, drawing on pre-war attempts to mask radio telephone communications, were however successful. One was a system for encoding speech emanating from Telefunken and used on the wire line connecting Berlin with Rommel's headquarters in North Africa. The

---

* Pseudonoise codes are used to control modulation techniques like FH.

other was the X system (nicknamed GREEN HORNET) and also called the SIGSALY digital voice system, evolved from research at BTL, which safeguarded radio telephone consultations across the Atlantic between Churchill and Roosevelt.

After the war, the SS idea easily chimed in with the theory of communication within a statistical framework then being pioneered by Norbert Wiener and Claude Shannon (the latter mentioned earlier in connection with automated air defence systems). SS development seriously got underway in 1953 after the US Institute of Radio Engineers formed a Professional Group on Information Theory to investigate the problem. Another important figure to promote SS research was Jerome Wiesner (later scientific adviser to President Kennedy) who was working on high performance correlators at MIT. His interest engaged, Wiesner played a major part in the invention of a wide band unpredictable carrier, called a Transmitted Reference System, designed to provide more secure communications. This originally stemmed from a study carried out at MIT in August 1950 (Project Hartwell) to investigate, among other matters, a means of hiding fleet communications transmissions so that enemy submarines could not utilise them for direction-finding. A similar need recurred for making communications within the SAGE air defence system secure. In due course, requirements were made by the US Navy and USAF for increasing the security of signals traffic. They led to research contracts with commercial laboratories, notably Sylvania, which coined the term 'spread spectrum' to describe a noise-like communications carrier system called HUSH-UP. Even so, the first operational use of an SS system did not occur until 1963 when the US Navy experimented with BLADES (Buffalo Laboratories Application of Digital Spectra) originally intended for submarine communications, Actually, a prototype of BLADES had been taken into the blockade during the Cuban missile crisis but was never used, due to a radio silence order. At the same time, the British and the Canadians were investigating SS techniques; the former had studied pseudo noise-sequences in depth several years before the Americans developed the idea. There was, of course, much curiosity about the extent of Russian knowledge of the subject. In the event, their first unclassified paper on the transmission of signals by modulated noise was published in 1957. By the following year, unclassified American papers dealing with aspects of SS were being translated regularly into Russian.

Finally, a brief reference to *'burst' transmissions*. These are a device by which keyed messages are passed very rapidly in order to reduce transmission time to an absolute minimum and so to defeat the enemy's ECM. They are unsuitable for voice transmission; they either use a very narrow band for a long time or a wide band for a short time to transmit a very short signal (usually in morse).

Plate 11 Jerome B Wiesner, pioneer of the spread spectrum technique and Scientific Adviser to President Kennedy. (*Karsh/Ottawa*)

All the devices and techniques described above required specialist units to operate them. Such units had already existed in embryo during and after the Second World War, but acquired additional significance as the electronic revolution transformed the communications scene. We have already noted the Soviet interest. At around the same time, NATO agreed that each national army should form its own electronic warfare units. In 1977, the British 14th Signal Regiment (EW) was formed, another unit being added after the Falklands War to provide EW support outside the Central European Front.[42] The Americans formed Combat EW and Intelligence Units as a result of the Vietnam war. At the same time, the Russians expanded their number of specialist units which, in the event of war, would be responsible for jamming and deception operations against the electronic systems of NATO.

Conclusion

The reader will by now have some idea of how much communications on land, sea, and in the air have been, and are still being, transformed by modern technology, especially the computer. In every sphere of activity they have become more flexible, more secure, and more adaptable to the extreme (and hopefully unlikely) case of nuclear war. But, as ever, technological change breeds its own problems. The ability of a Prime Minister or a President to speak directly to a commander on the ground, in the air, or at sea would hardly suit the temperament of commanders like Nelson or Wingate, Again, tactical communication systems now permit a commander-in-chief at GHQ to talk to a private in the forward battle area, or vice-versa, but as a signals historian has laconically observed, 'The Army felt that neither C-in-C's nor privates would be likely to over-use this facility.'[43] Furthermore, the sharp increase in the variety and volume of radio traffic has created a new set of highly technical problems. Their solution depends on the ability and imagination of human operators, especially junior officers, who more than ever before, must display the traditional qualities of leadership. One solution to the time-consuming chore of maintaining sets and batteries in the field may well be Systems Management, currently receiving attention in the British Army.

Overcoming the Achilles heel of communications is likely to prove a permanent problem. As we have seen, there are no bounds to human ingenuity. Obviously, the best countermeasures are silence and deception of which no better example exists than the deception plan which ensured the success of the Normandy landings in 1944. But silence in operations sooner or later has to be broken; and despite all the wizardry of electronic coding, orders and co-ordination, instructions must frequently be given in plain language. The intercept operator and analyst will continue to depend upon the traditional skills of translating foreign languages.

Advance information of enemy movements will continue to be the winning card in the commander's hand; and it is the new forms of intelligence gathering under the heading of reconnaissance and surveillance that must now be considered.

. 4 .

TO SEEK, TO FIND

The collection of intelligence about a potential or actual enemy is essential for the formulation of strategy in the long term or for planning immediate operations in the battle area or reacting to a sudden, unexpected move by the enemy. Clausewitz in his classic study 'On War' emphasised the difficulty of *accurate recognition*' as being one of the 'most serious sources of friction in war, by making things appear entirely different from what one had expected.'[1] Modern technology, though by no means eliminating the element of doubt in intelligence obtained under warlike conditions, has at least multiplied the means of acquisition and of speeding up the arduous process of interpretation and analysis.

While aircraft were, from the start, recognised as primary intelligence gatherers in land and sea warfare, it was only on the eve of the Second World War that specialised reconnaissance aircraft and cameras were introduced for this purpose. Especially noteworthy were the exploits of the Australian pilot Sydney Cotton who, in a specially-fitted LOCKHEED aircraft, painted duck egg blue, flew a number of photographic reconnaissances on behalf of the British Secret Intelligence Service over Germany and Italian possessions in the Mediterranean in the summer of 1939.[2] Cotton and his co-pilot flew at ranges of up to 1,600 miles at altitudes of 20,000 feet. He appreciated the importance of taking vertical photographs as opposed to the conventional oblique photographs taken by RAF machines outside the six mile territorial limit of foreign countries. These overlapping photographs covered strips of territory 111 miles long. The success of Cotton's flights persuaded the RAF (inherently opposed to specialised units) to form special photographic reconnaissance (PR) units and, equally important, a central photographic interpretation unit able to assess the information portrayed and to pass it rapidly to the appropriate quarters. When the Americans came into the war, they quickly appreciated the importance of these techniques. They were well in advance in new techniques of photography including infra-red. Another aspect of wartime photography was the need to take post-raid photographs of the RAF's night bomber offensive, the results of which had been so badly over-estimated in its early stages.

After the war, high resolution cameras and high sensitivity film, new optical systems and television equipment, as well as reliable recorders and telemetry devices, were adopted for military reconnaissance and surveillance. Sideways-looking radars, able to create high resolution strip maps of vast tracts of territory were introduced, while the growth of electronic warfare led to electronic reconnaissance – the vitally important collection and processing of information about electromagnetic emanations from ground radars.[3]

The importance of electronic intelligence justifies a section to itself. Otherwise this chapter is broadly divided into strategic and tactical reconnaissance and surveillance, and the execution of these tasks by manned and unmanned airborne vehicles. In the former case, strategic reconnaissance by modified bomber aircraft is followed by the specialised high altitude reconnaissance aircraft developed by the Americans for cross-continental flights. They were followed by unmanned observation satellites, which evolved surprisingly quickly when powerful rocket boosters became available to launch them into space. In the case of tactical reconnaissance, strike aircraft were equipped with the latest cameras and forward looking infra-red equipment; they were then supplemented by unmanned aircraft – drones and remotely-piloted vehicles (RPVs) which had existed for many years but were now revived to exploit new guidance and sensor systems.

Strategic Reconnaissance: Manned Aircraft

The Soviet blockade of Berlin in the summer of 1948 signalled the outbreak of the 'Cold War' and the Western air forces were now required to provide long range PR for the strategic bomber force and tactical PR for the armies in West Germany. The RAF had already ordered the CANBERRA for this purpose but the first aircraft were not due to arrive until the early 1950s. On 20 August 1949, the Assistant Chief of Air Staff (Policy) was informed 'that our total resources in long range PR aircraft on the outbreak of war would consist of eight MOSQUITOS and it is for consideration whether we should not find ways and means of improving the position.'[4] Although the MOSQUITOS had performed splendidly in the Second World War, they were no match for the Soviet MiG-15 fighter; they would either be forced to operate above cloud and so be unable to take good photographs or risk being shot down in the first few days of war with little hope of replacement.

The immediate solution was to order some specially-modified PR MOSQUITOS Mark 35 for use both for long range reconnaissance and for the critically important night PR needs of the Army. They still did not have modern high altitude cameras for use at altitudes over 50,000 feet by day or by night. Like the CANBERRAS, these equipments were unlikely to be available before 1952. The PR aircraft crisis was at last resolved when three CANBERRA squadrons entered service in the United Kingdom and the Middle East in 1953. Three more squadrons, with improved equipment, were formed in 1954. These had a range of 3050 miles.

The Korean war created urgent demands for large scale photographs taken from the air at high speeds and at low levels. An organisation was needed to process and assess photographs. In the RAF there was a 'sad shortage of skilled photographic interpreters' and in the USAF the situation was little better. Eventually, an Allied directorate was formed to coordinate all reconnaissance requirements for the whole theatre. The Americans would have liked the RAF to supply a PR CANBERRA squadron for service in Korea, but the Air Staff felt it would be unwise to send it before the crews had been thoroughly trained.[5]

In the meantime, the Air Staff was exercising itself on how to provide target intelligence for the nascent V bomber force, how to ensure that the targets were found, and, finally, how to make an assessment of the damage inflicted. The principal targets lay deep in the Soviet Union at ranges of over 1000 miles from the bombers' bases. Current maps were largely unreliable and to penetrate the Soviet air defences would be a severe test of RAF Bomber Command's capabilities. Cameras or radar providing detailed ground resolution would at least provide some kind of answer to the target identification problem.[6] Unlike the Americans, who were equipping their PR aircraft with cameras of very long focal length (100–120 inches) requiring aircraft to be built specially for the purpose, the British settled for the F96 high altitude camera with a focal length of 48 inches. Again, unlike its American counterpart, the shorter length provided a much wider area of coverage. Wide horizon to horizon cover was obtained by installing fans of eight F96 and F49 cameras in VALIANT and later in VICTOR bombers which were converted into long range PR aircraft. This compromise was unfortunate as the photographic equipment became subject to vibration, aerodynamic buffeting and heating problems. In spite of this, useful PR cover was provided for operations in Kenya and Borneo in the 1950s and 1960s.

The introduction of sideways-looking radar in the late 1950s, which could provide cover at 100 miles distance from the aircraft, was an important advance. The first RAF bomber to be so equipped was the CANBERRA which also carried the latest mark of H2S scanner to provide a forward view. CANBERRAS were able to survey an area of 20,000 square miles for every hour that they were in the air. In the late 1950s, a new airborne radar reconnaissance system called YELLOW ASTER began to be developed. YELLOW

ASTER comprised two equipments. One called BLUE SHADOW was a 3 centimetre navigational radar which gave a presentation of the ground over which the aircraft had just flown on electro-sensitive recording paper.[7] To complement this, two auto observer units amplified signals from BLUE SHADOW on the cathode ray tube. These were automatically photographed by an F73 camera. One auto observer was set at a 20 mile time base to provide detailed information and the second auto-observer at 60 miles to provide wide area coverage. In time, YELLOW ASTER was superseded by a new high resolution airborne reconnaissance radar fitted into the VICTOR B (PR) Mark 2. As we shall see, improved sideways-looking radar was designed for the TSR 2 and later installed in the PHANTOM jets.

The accumulation of such prodigious amounts of photographic material demanded the modernisation of interpreting techniques and the rapid transmission of data. Unfortunately, by the end of the 1950s, the RAF, forgetting the lessons of the Second World War, had allowed photographic interpretation to pass back to the Intelligence Department of the Air Staff and the responsibility for PR to be taken over by Bomber Command. The Suez operation in October 1956 showed how unwise this decision had been and how important it was to pass information 'extracted from the right photographs to the right people in time,' rather than passing over a mass of prints. Consequently, in April 1957 (coinciding with the Sandys Defence White Paper), a Central Reconnaissance Establishment was formed at Brampton to control the Joint Air Reconnaissance Intelligence Centre (JARIC).

Yet no more than two months later, the Air Staff admitted that the camera capacity of the V bombers 'if used to the fullest extent, would swamp either or both the ground photographic and intelligence agencies.' Thus the ability of the V bombers to carry a large fan of cameras was actually a disadvantage. They were also easily upset by bad weather. 'In that case', it was argued, 'the present camera fit without the F95 camera can take pictures neither vertically nor obliquely.'[8] But the main difficulty was that the PR VICTOR had to revert to being a bomber should the need arise. At last, in 1959, a specialised CANBERRA 9 became available to cover 'all designated and potential targets' (refuelling on Scandinavian and NATO airfields when necessary). Carrying (unlike the VICTOR) an F95 camera, it was a much more flexible aircraft.

But by now, with the Cold War apparently continuing indefinitely, special aircraft were required for 'clandestine peacetime reconnaissance' (the VICTOR was disqualified for this role as its configuration was identical for both bomber and reconnaissance purposes). It was left for the Americans to form a special reconnaissance unit, backed up by highly trained personnel and research laboratories, working for the demands of the intelligence agencies as well as the Services. The outcome was the well-known UTILITY 2 (U-2) high altitude plane flying at heights of 70,000 feet and covering 3,500 miles.

It was developed by the so-called Skunk Works under Clarence 'Kelly' Johnson who had founded a small factory for developing highly secret aircraft in the war. With the approval of President Eisenhower and $20m in covert funds from the CIA, the Skunk Works built and flew their first high altitude aircraft in eight months.[9] Installed in the U-2 was a camera with a 48 inch focal length. Much effort had been expended by the USAF in obtaining very high ground resolutions with their strategic reconnaissance cameras since 1948; and the U-2 camera's resolution probably gave an accuracy of 1.5 feet. This, of course, did not take into account degradations due to vibrations, aircraft motion and atmospheric effects. But it was an impressive achievement. In the early 1960s, the USAF was using a camera which could identify an object only two feet long in an aircraft flying at Mach 2 at a height of 100,000 feet.

Reconnaissance flights over the Soviet Union began in 1956. It was well appreciated that it would only be a matter of time before Soviet radar and SAMs would bring these overflights to an end. The inevitable happened on 1 May 1960, when Francis Gary Powers was shot down by a Soviet missile; politically this came at an inopportune moment and abruptly ended a Four Power summit meeting in Paris. Significantly, this was the first time that an aircraft had been shot down by a SAM system at such a height, thereby giving new emphasis to the potential of modern air defence systems, in which radar now played such a key role.

Although U-2 flights over the Soviet Union had to cease, they did continue surreptitiously over China and along the border of the Soviet Union using slant photography and electronic reconnaissance techniques. Across the Atlantic, these spy planes provided valuable information about Soviet missile sites in the Cuba crisis of 1962. Meanwhile, the CIA approved construction of a Mach 3 reconnaissance aircraft able to fly at 80,000 feet and possessing a very low radar cross section to avoid detection*, From it evolved the SR-71 later to be used by NATO as a strategic reconnaissance aircraft; it was also equipped to carry out electronic warfare. Unmanned aircraft fitted with cameras, radar or television were another solution to the need for overflights and their evolution will be described on page 103.

Electronic Reconnaissance

Powers's U-2 carried equipment to record radio and radar signals detected by the aircraft's sensors, though he could not protect himself against electronic

---

* The radar cross section is measured by calculating the amount of energy reflected by a target back to the observer and then calculating the size of a sphere that would reflect the same amount of radar energy. The area of a disc of the same diameter is then called the radar cross section (RCS).

countermeasures. However, long before the U-2 flights, British and United States aircraft were being used to monitor radio and radar transmissions. The main purpose of electronic intelligence is to discover:

1 the accuracy of a hostile radar's frequency, how accurately it can plot targets, the extent it can see through cloud, and its performance against low-flying aircraft.

2 The purpose of the radar (ie. whether it was designed for all-round search, height-finding, and so forth) and its performance by determining the rate at which the beam is made to scan through the aircraft.

In addition:

3 The rate of transmission of radar pulses make it possible to estimate the approximate range of the radar.

4 The ability of the radar to discriminate between one aircraft and another (or to discriminate between an aircraft and chaff) can be learned from the time width of the radar pulses.

5 It is possible to obtain from the location of the reconnaissance aircraft some idea of where the radar is located and also to determine those areas of high radar density where the defences are strong as well as those of low density, where the defences are weak.[10]

ELINT goes back to the summer of 1939, when officers of the German signals corps loaded the last surviving Zeppelin rigid airship with high frequency receivers and flew off the British East coast to discover whether the high aerial masts then being erected at certain points were, in fact, radar transmitters. The wrong deductions made as a result of these flights had a profound effect on the Battle of Britain a year later, for if the Germans had appreciated that the British already had an early warning system, they would have taken steps to eliminate the radar stations. Instead the *Luftwaffe* concentrated its attacks on airfields, As the war continued, ELINT gathering became more and more important. One successful example was when the RAF flew a vulnerable aircraft over Germany in order to obtain information from the latest aircraft interception equipment being used by German night fighters. After weeks of frustration, the aircraft was intercepted with the aid of the new device and, despite being wounded, the crew were able to measure the radar frequency and record other details before returning to base.

ELINT gathering was resumed with the opening of the Cold War.[11] From the early 1950s specially-adapted aircraft were flying combined photo and electronic reconnaissance missions over eastern Europe and sometimes over the Soviet Union. An RB-66 was shot down over East Germany on one of these missions although it may have crossed the frontier intentionally. Information was badly needed at that time as to whether or not the Soviet Air Force possessed airborne interception (AI) radar. It was vital to know this should a 'hot' war break out and air attacks have to be made on Soviet targets. The matter was debated at length by service chiefs in Washington, but eventually the RAF made a 20 second recording of an airborne radar in a Soviet interception. Not long after this incident Western intelligence was startled by the discovery of a Soviet early warning radar which was comparable to the latest equipment being used by NATO. Until then, it had been assumed that the Soviets had nothing more advanced than the war time lend-lease radar. However, sceptics had to be convinced that the equipment was not a dummy. After one of the new radars had been spotted on the Polish Baltic coast, it was interrogated by American and British radar engineers. They established that the frequencies from the set were similar to those emitted from a Western set, so that each beam had a common pulse repetition frequency, that rotation rates were being synchronised, and that peak power was obviously high and determined the basic equipment parameters. This information was obtained only four months after the first prototype (later named TOKEN) was seen on an airfield near Moscow. By June 1952, just over six months after the initial discovery, electronic reconnaissance had confirmed that TOKEN radars had ringed the Soviet Union.

ELINT was invaluable in the Korean war. The discovery by the Americans that the Chinese had transferred an early warning radar from Shanghai to the Yalu River in the autumn of 1952 gave them about a month's warning of Chinese intervention in the war.

As the Cold War continued, the most effective ELINT was derived from limited operations against a specific radar or technical target. The existence of an important Soviet search receiver located in Austria was discovered after much patient work by a British technical reconnaissance team employing centimetre and millimetre wave lengths coordinated with studies made by ground observers. The activity of the device against Allied radar emanations was verified and even the interception range of the equipment was determined. At the time, its performance was one of the few facts available on Soviet electronic countermeasures capability.

Electronic reconnaissance was also conducted from land and seabased installations around the borders of the Soviet Union. Their main function was to monitor radio traffic. The US Navy loaded a number of small 'ferret' vessels with electronic gear to carry out coastal reconnaissances. One of them, the *Pueblo*, was seized off the north Korean coast in the course of 'electronic snooping'. After this incident, the 'ferret' fleet was armed with scuttle and destruction mechanisms. The capture of the *Pueblo* received much publicity at the time and to the initiated it demonstrated the importance of electronic warfare and C³. What perhaps was less obvious was the way in which new data processing techniques were transforming the traditional methods of intelligence gathering. The Soviets were similarly engaged in ELINT-gathering and maintained a fleet of trawlers cruising in every ocean for this purpose.

In sum, manned strategic reconnaissance and ELINT missions provided the Western powers (especially the United States) with a great deal of information with regard to the size, location and character not only of the Soviet air defences but also of their long range strategic nuclear forces, while many of the military areas of importance had been mapped. By 1957, it was possible to formulate purely military targets, such as airfields and industrial complexes, which could be attacked by a strategic counterforce in retaliation for a Soviet nuclear strike.

Unmanned Reconnaissance Vehicles: Satellites

Nevertheless, the U-2 force could not provide *continuous* surveillance over the Soviet Union and China. Their range, though extensive, was restricted, as was the endurance of their aircrew; the shooting down of Powers's aircraft had demonstrated that highflying aircraft could no longer penetrate Soviet air space with impunity. The moment was ripe for the *entrée* of the unmanned reconnaissance satellite orbiting the earth at distances of 200 miles and over, equipped with very high resolution optics and film with which it would be possible to monitor ground-based military activities all over the world. Moreover, as opposed to manned aircraft, observation from space did not violate international law and did not infringe any territorial boundaries.[12]

The possibilities of artificial earth satellites and their potential, not only for photographic reconnaissance but also for weather forcasting, providing navigational data and ELINT, were appreciated by the Americans as soon as the Second World War was over. Perhaps the first operational requirement for an observation satellite came from the US Navy in May 1946 for the purpose of improving the performance of guided missiles, communications, meteorology and other technical fields with military applications. A series of Rand studies made for the USAF subsequently examined many of the strategic and technical aspects of reconnaissance satellites.

Possibly the first was written in 1946 and entitled 'Preliminary Design of Experimental World-Orbiting Spaceship'. But development had to wait until the mid-1950s when reliable rocket boosters became available and transistors, solid state circuitry and digital computers could process and store the information acquired by the satellite's optical equipment. On 16 March 1955 the USAF made its first operational requirement for a strategic observation satellite system under the sponsorship of the CIA. During the following year, after a competition had been held between a selected number of aircraft companies, Lockheed was chosen to develop a self-powered satellite vehicle later called AGENA.

At the same time, the British were investigating the possibilities of orbiting observation vehicles and a detailed study was made by Desmond King-Hele of RAE at the request of the DRPC.[13] Opinion was that infra-red photography was probably the best method of obtaining pictures of the earth, the photographs being scanned for transmission to the ground while over friendly territory. It was reckoned that ground detail of the order of 100 feet would be seen 'on a small percentage of occasions and 200 feet on most occasions.' King-Hele, however, thought that a 'direct TV system with instantaneous transmission was technically possible' and that 'intermediate storage on magnetic tape with later transmission' required further research. With regard to general policy, he complained that 'the whole subject of reconnaissance requirements is in a very vague state as regards both the RAF and Army requirements. It would be encouraging to have some more definite Service requirements.'[14] The restricted military research and development budget of the time could not support the extensive development of light cameras with long focal length and methods of data recovery, quite apart from the development and construction of rocket boosters.

Inevitably, therefore, the Americans were in the vanguard of reconnaissance satellite development. A distinct jolt was given to their programme by the appearance of the Soviet *SPUTNIK* in October 1958, though it was generally considered that space vehicles of that size would be incapable of carrying cameras. Of primary importance was the stabilisation and orientation of the spacecraft. Then came the question of transmission. The favoured method of transmitting data from the satellites, developed by Eastman Kodak, Philco and the Columbia Broadcasting System Laboratories, was to scan film electronically and transmit it to ground stations. A recoverable film capsule was also to be introduced as advances in associated technologies permitted. At that time, the possibility of using TV cameras was rejected because of insufficient technical progress. The test vehicles for the development of the recoverable capsule were the DISCOVERER satellites. In August 1960, after a long string of failures, the capsules from DISCOVERERS 13 and 14 were successfully recovered, the latter by mid-air capture. They probably contained a small camera and may have produced the first satellite pictures of the Soviet Union, If so, the timing was propitious, as Powers's U-2 had been shot down only three months before.

After the end of the U-2 flights, greater impetus was given to observation satellites.[15] The Satellite and Missile Observation System (SAMOS) was placed under the direct authority of the Secretary of the USAF. Tracking and command stations were built round the world to maintain contact with the

SAMOS satellites. A command centre was established at Sunnyvale, California jointly manned by Air Force and Lockheed personnel. The highlight of these early flights was achieved by SAMOS II carrying 300–400lb of instruments which entered a polar orbit between 300 and 350 miles from the Earth on 31 January 1961. Six days after its launching, it had provided photographic coverage which overturned the current opinion that the Soviets had built and deployed more long range missiles than the Americans. On 6 February 1961, McNamara, the US Secretary of Defense, announced that there was no evidence of a 'missile gap'. By September 1961, after more capsules from DISCOVERER satellites orbiting at lower altitudes, and thus providing pictures with much higher resolution, had been recovered, it was estimated that the Soviet Union had less than 10 ICBMs operational.

The DISCOVERER programme ended officially in 1962 but recoverable satellites continued to orbit under a different designation. The descendants of the early SAMOS satellites were relatively small radio transmission satellites whose sensors and orbital parameters were chosen to maximise their degree of coverage. Remaining in orbit for about a month, they were able to provide virtually full coverage of the Soviet Union and complete coverage of China.

In May 1963, the first area surveillance satellites known as THRUST AUGMENTED THOR/AGENA-D were launched, They were able to carry a larger camera, more film and other consumables resulting in an increase in useful life time. An even heavier third generation satellite called the LONG TANK THRUST-AUGMENTED THOR/AGENA was test-launched in August 1966 and this booster was introduced into regular service in May 1967. It was probably equipped with a longer focal length camera, a larger film supply, and an infra-red optical system for night photography, plus a new transmission system with an increased data rate. Later sideways-looking radar may well have been included in the sensor package. In due course a communications relay satellite provided immediate transmission of data from the observation satellite to the Intelligence Headquarters in the United States. The purpose of surveillance satellites was to survey wide areas with sensors of moderate resolution and to reveal targets which might merit a closer look with higher resolution cameras to provide greater detail. For the latter purpose close-look satellites were used.

Close-look satellites were heavier than area satellites as they carried a camera with longer focal length and wider aperture. They operated in a lower orbit with a perigee of about 80 miles in order to maximise resolution. Interesting targets identified by a previous area satellite could then be rephotographed and examined more closely. To minimise information loss due to electronic data storage and transmission, satellites sent their film packs back to earth in a re-entry capsule, using mid-air recovery by a specially-equipped aircraft. The first launch of a close-look satellite took place on 26 April 1962 when a THOR/AGENA booster put into orbit a satellite carrying a recovery capsule designated E-6. Three days later, the capsule and its film were recovered. Operational status was achieved in mid-1963. As they had a shorter lifetime, close-look satellites were subjected to less stringent reliability requirements than area surveillance models. These high resolution satellites were launched about once a month and remained in orbit for from three to five days before sending their film package back to earth.

In 1967, larger rocket boosters, like the TITAN 3B, extended the life time of the close-look satellites up to two weeks. This third generation of satellites had a greater film capacity and new sensors including multi-spectral photography (described below), able to detect camouflage and infra-red photography able to measure the thermal output of warm bodies in underground silos or buildings.

In the 1970s, a new generation of satellites known collectively as BIG BIRD came into service.[16] They weighed about 25,000 pounds allowing them to carry a large camera whose high resolution film was periodically ejected in large re-entry cannisters landing near Hawaii. They were able to combine both area surveillance and close look roles. They had on-board film processing, scanning and transmission, enabling them to carry out real time reconnaissance for the first time. By the close of our period, they could stay aloft for 160 days. For this purpose, they were placed in a higher and more elliptical orbit. At their lowest orbit, they came within about 100 miles of the earth and at their farthest, about 180 miles. By this time, improvements in optics and film quality had facilitated ground resolution of anything between two and six inches from a relatively low orbit, depending on the weather, pollution, and such factors as the alignment, stability and vibration of the sensor as well as the movement of the target. This technical advance enabled photographs to be taken of objects a foot long and, after magnification, even to show details as small as bolts on the decks of warships and, in one well known instance, to distinguish the name of a newspaper (*Pravda*) being read by a man on the street of a north Russian town.

The revelation of such minute detail could only be done through digital image processing (DIP) techniques which were even able to disclose detail hidden in cloud or mist.[17] Since digital computers can only deal with numbers, it is necessary to use either electronic devices that automatically give numbers or to read and convert the film darkness (density) in small regions (pixels) into numbers. DIP methods can rectify the blurred areas of photographs, restoring lines and edges by 'searching for the shortest distance through the grey transition region in the same way that [humans] can search out the steepest and shortest path down a mountain.'

A number of defects in photographic film used in satellites have also been overcome by new technology. In particular the quality of film has been greatly improved by the development of charge-coupled devices (CCD) which are semi-conductors sensitive to light. They can be read directly by computers, eliminating the awkward process of dropping film cannisters from satellites and converting the images to digital data. CCDs are more efficient than film in that they are linear; the charge stored is proportional to the time of exposure; they are sensitive to a broader range of frequencies into the infra-red and they have a much more dynamic range between white and black.[18]

Electronic Reconnaissance Satellites

With the rapidly-growing developments in electronic warfare, satellites were soon given an electronic reconnaissance role. They were, in fact, highly suitable for collecting ELINT. Nearly all radars, data links and field communications use VHF, UHF, or microwaves, all of which take a straight path and do not bend over the horizon. Receivers in satellites at heights of 100 miles are able to intercept transmissions at great distances. Satellites are also valuable for collecting telemetric information about the flights of long range missiles. They are known by the names of RHYOLITE and CHALET and operate at geosynchronous orbits of 22,000 miles from the Earth. A FERRET satellite operating in an orbit of 372 miles above the Earth collects information about missile launches and the operation of early warning radars.

Soviet Observation Satellite Development

In the early stages of observation satellite development, some experts in the West believed that the Soviet Union had less to gain from this new method of obtaining intelligence than the Western powers and that they would continue to rely on well-proven sources of gaining information. If so, this did not hold for long. By the 1970s, the Soviet Union was expending a far greater effort on launching space vehicles than the United States and probably more of the pay loads had military functions than those of the Americans.[19] Between 1975 (four years after the BIG BIRD satellite programme began) and 1982, the Soviet Union launched about 35 military observation satellites annually, as opposed to two or four launched by the United States during the same period. However, the launch rate of the Soviets was deceptive as the life times of the Soviet satellites were much shorter than those of the American – usually around 10 to 13 days after which they re-entered the atmosphere and returned their exposed film cargoes to the Soviet Union. By the early 1980s, missions had become longer in duration. The Soviets were also handicapped in two ways; one, they returned film in satellites rather than in capsules. This meant that a replacement PR satellite had to be launched every time current PR data was required. Secondly, during the period under review, PR satellites were unable to provide real time information for battle management and troop control.

It was Soviet policy to fly separate satellites for high resolution (point) versus medium and low resolution (area) PR missions. High resolution satellites were manoeuvrable, orbiting with apogees of about 217 miles and perigees as low as 102 miles. Medium and low resolution satellites travelled in orbits that were more circular with perigees above 140 miles.

Special interests for Soviet PR satellites were the United States and Western Europe, the latter more so as the Russians regarded the United States as the strategic rear area of Europe. Numerous PR missions were launched during periods of Third World crises.

The Soviets paid great attention to the collection of ELINT about radar, radio communications, data relay systems, C^3 facilities, and forces in the field. During the early 1980s, the Soviet Union maintained a six satellite constellation to support their global ELINT effort. ELINT satellites travelled in near circular orbits at 370 miles from the earth.

Reconnaissance satellites played an important part in Soviet naval operations, providing location, tracking, and other intelligence data on foreign naval forces. Two types of satellite were used in our period: the active radar-equipped ocean reconnaissance satellites (RORSAT) and the passive sensor-equipped ELINT ocean reconnaissance satellites (EORSAT). The RORSATS were equipped with small nuclear reactors to power the radars used for locating and tracking ships at sea. In the early 1980s, two of these satellites malfunctioned and re-entered the atmosphere, one crashing in Canada and creating local radioactive contamination. EORSAT had a longer life time than RORSAT, orbiting at higher altitudes and designed for missions at least 180 days in duration. Its sensors were powered by solar panels.

Despite all the effort which has gone into Soviet ocean reconnaissance satellites, they are not considered by foreign observers to be essential to naval operations; reliance continued to be placed on conventional surface and submarine surface methods to obtain intelligence. This was confirmed by the Falklands War when observation satellites were not launched by the Soviet Union until either the latter part of the operations or even after the conclusion of hostilities.

Observation satellites, like every other type of military equipment, have their drawbacks as well as their advantages. Their movement in orbit is, of course, predictable and makes them vulnerable to interception. Satellites travelling in very low orbits (180 miles from the Earth) are short-lived as air drag on the fringes of the atmosphere causes them to fall towards the Earth and burn up. Satellites orbiting at 300 miles and over have much greater endurance (as much as two years) but the spatial resolution of their sensors decreases with height. Satellites engaged in ocean surveillance have periods during their orbit when they are unable to provide full time coverage (15 hours over the Atlantic and 16.5 hours over the Pacific). This limitation can only be rectified when the number of satellites deployed increases and they are able to work in phase. Surveillance may be hampered by poor weather conditions though this has, to some extent, been eliminated by DIP techniques. Finally, it can be said that satellites represented a great political asset in that during the Cold War they proved to be a stabilising rather than a destabilising factor, correcting false assumptions about potential enemy strengths and, in the last resort of war, they could provide accurate information of purely military targets.

Tactical Reconnaissance: Manned Aircraft

Compared with the great ranges demanded in strategic reconnaissance coverage, the depth of the battle area is restricted to around 40,000 yards for an army corps and 200–300 miles for an army. The objects of interest are usually quite small, often mobile, and generally good use is made of camouflage. Reconnaissance is needed regardless of weather conditions and especially at night, when ground forces take the opportunity to make new dispositions. It is essential that the information brought back be processed and interpreted rapidly and transmitted with the utmost speed to the appropriate commander.

In the 1950s and onwards, extensive research was undertaken by the British and the Americans in developing radar, infra-red and photography for improving surveillance over the battlefield. Sideways-looking radar, which in the 1950s was expected to give cover up to 100 miles, was useful in enabling aircraft to 'see' into enemy territory from friendly air space. Infra-red sensors were invaluable in detecting heat-emitting targets like tanks and wheeled vehicles. The possibilities of television did not at that time offer the high resolution obtainable from aerial photography. It was recognised that the processing of intelligence and onward transmission would be greatly facilitated by the new data processing techniques then emerging. In 1956 the US Army was already experimenting with the Computing Machine (MIDAC) for handling information. In contrast, the British at this stage felt that insufficient attention had been given to determining operational requirements for information in the field. Consequently, in November 1955, an operational research team was instructed by the War Office to:

> study all promising methods of collecting and handling battlefield information. It should consider the relative military importance of the various methods and equipment studied and should make recommendations for future research and development in this field.[20]

Although high resolution photographs were able to provide very detailed information, particularly on military installations, they were unable to satisfy all the needs of the tactical commander in mobile warfare, in which troops or vehicle concentrations never stay in the same place for long. Real time reconnaissance was needed in this case to deny the enemy the classical force multiplier of surprise. Aerial tactical reconnaissance stretched from 100–300 miles from the forward edge of the battle area. For the whole of the period under review, the pilot's eye continued to provide much of the real time information, though he was increasingly assisted by cameras, electro-optical devices, such as laser linescan and by non-optical sensors including synthetic aperture radar, able to penetrate cloud and darkness, and infra-red-linescan.[21] The principal low level reconnaissance aircraft of the RAF in the late 1970s were the JAGUAR and the PHANTOM. The former carried a reconnaissance pod containing a fan of cameras providing optical coverage of 195 degrees. For night surveillance an infra-red linescan service operated in the passive 8–14 micrometre part of the spectrum. PHANTOMS were fitted with sideways-looking radar (the P391) which gave high resolution radar capacity in all weathers and at night.[22] The HARRIER operating under direct control of the land forces proved to be invaluable in the Falklands War in providing low level cover.

Infra-red techniques were especially useful for tactical reconnaissance because they were image-making sensors, offering the observer an indication of the geometrical and spatial distribution of the energy from the target.[23] Black and white infra-red film for aerial photographic reconnaissance was introduced early in the Second World War and exposed much of contemporary camouflage which attempted to blend an object with its surroundings by the use of overlying nets interlaced with strips of coloured fabric, by paints, or simply by natural foliage; the spectral reflectance of these materials became easy to distinguish from their immediate surroundings. (Camouflage is described in more detail on page 162). Colour film in infra-red was also used in the Second World War for photographic reconnaissance. In the film, deciduous foliage and grass appear as bright red; ordinary green paint appears blue; and high infra-red reflecting paint appears purplish. One outstanding example was the appearance of camouflaged flying bomb sites in Northern France as a large blue fan on colour infra-red film.[24] The sites had not been detected with panchromatic film, despite intensive reconnaissance for many weeks. The ability of infra-red cameras to penetrate haze, mist and fog has been exaggerated. When a haze of small particles is formed, quite good photographs can be taken, but it is usually difficult to penetrate fog, mist or cloud which is grey or neutral in colour.

After the war, the use of multi-spectral sensors was investigated. One of the earliest was a special camera taking nine simultaneous black and white photographs, in narrow spectral bands. Later, coloured techniques were used to produce a colour-positive photograph from the black and white negatives. This was achieved by making four negatives simultaneously, one each in the blue, green, red and near infra-red bands. Each negative was printed to yield a positive black and white transparency. The four positives were then placed in a special viewer that illuminated each transparency with coloured light and optically superimposed the four to yield a colour picture. It was found easier to interpret a colour rather than a black and white photograph of the same subject.

Another valuable improvement in the early 1970s was the introduction of mechanical or optical scanning mechanisms which could be combined with infra-red detectors, thus making it possible to cover a much larger search field. The time required for one complete scan of the search field is called 'the frame time'.

The operation of thermal mapping sensors was similar to that of multispectral scanners. Thermal mappers were used in Vietnam and were able to detect cooking fires and truck engines. Detection of submerged submarines by these means has been less successful.

What was lacking, however, was a sensor able to provide high resolution imagery in *real time*. Early in the 1960s forward looking infra-red (FLIR) sensors began to emerge from American technology.[25] At first they could only be used for fire control purposes. But limited war conditions, as in Vietnam, called for sensors to detect both airborne targets and the whole broad spectrum of interesting ground targets by day and night. After about 10 years, FLIR sensors could be used like television scene viewing devices and their images were as good as TV pictures. They were especially valuable in locating targets with temperatures significantly different from their surroundings, such as hot truck engines, hot gun barrels, or generators. For the first time, they could provide a real time picture at night without recourse to any external illumination and thus extended the ability of a reconnaissance aircraft to perform in total darkness as well as in daylight. However the range of FLIR is somewhat reduced in cloud, rain or humidity, all of which absorb and scatter infra-red energy. But, in contrast to the human eye or any other visual sensor, FLIR can penetrate fog and haze because the wave lengths of the energy detected by the sensor are much larger than haze or even fog particles, and hence less subject to scattering. Under such conditions, infra-red range can be three to six times that of visual range.

The expanding flow of information from the sensor described above must be skilfully interpreted, analysed, and the intelligence disseminated speedily. While the interpretation of reconnaissance results does not lend itself to automation, the actual handling of data can be automated and can dispose of much irrelevant material. Digital image processing is essential for the extraction of information from infra-red photography to pick out fine detail which it is otherwise impossible to interpret by optical means.

Strategic and Tactical Reconnaissance by Unmanned Aircraft

The employment of manned aircraft on photographic reconnaissance in 'Cold' or 'Hot' War circumstances became extremely expensive both in terms of pilots and aircraft as the latter became more sophisticated and expensive and as anti-aircraft defences became more accurate. By the 1960s, the possibility of using very small unmanned aircraft, either pre-programmed or expertly radio-controlled from the ground, began to attract attention. Unmanned aircraft were by no means novel, having either been proposed or used in one form or another since the early years of the century but only in a very limited form on account of the technical problems of control and recovery. Up to the Second World War, however, the practice of flying unmanned aircraft, known as drones, to provide targets for anti-aircraft guns was widespread. Later in the war, as we have seen, they were fitted with bombs and put to offensive uses most successfully by the Germans, though the Americans made rather limited use of guided aircraft against small ground targets.

When the U-2 aircraft could no longer be used for long distance photographic reconnaissance, the Americans looked round for a vehicle which was inexpensive to make, yet could carry photographic equipment or other sensors which could either be relayed to the ground or the vehicle itself recovered. Above all, it would eliminate the need for a pilot.[26] In 1959, production of a new generation of drones and remotely piloted vehicles (RPVs), eg: radio-controlled from an airborne or ground station, was put in hand, mainly by the Teledyne Ryan Aeronautical Company.

British defence scientists had by then already considered the possibility of installing cameras into small drones, such as the JINDIVIC evolved by the Australians, which could be used for battle field reconnaissance.[27] The principal objections at the time to the proposal appeared to be the vulnerability of the aircraft and the slowness of recovery of information. As Tizard observed, speed was essential in 'getting the photographs, interpreting them and issuing orders.' It was decided that until these technical difficulties had been solved, it was better to continue to rely on manned aircraft for information. It was left for the Americans to work out whether the drone or the RPV was the better aircraft for the purpose.[28] Drones had a number of advantages as they could be adapted for other roles and could be powered by light engines, either piston-driven or turbo-propelled; their electronic components could be miniaturised and they presented a very small radar target (special attention being paid to reducing radar reflectivity). On the other hand, their pre-arranged flight control system could easily be upset by an enemy. RPVs, apart from having reliable sensors, needed a trustworthy communications system relaying information back to a distant ground operating team, and conversely transmitting commands from the ground to the aircraft; skilled ground operators were necessary

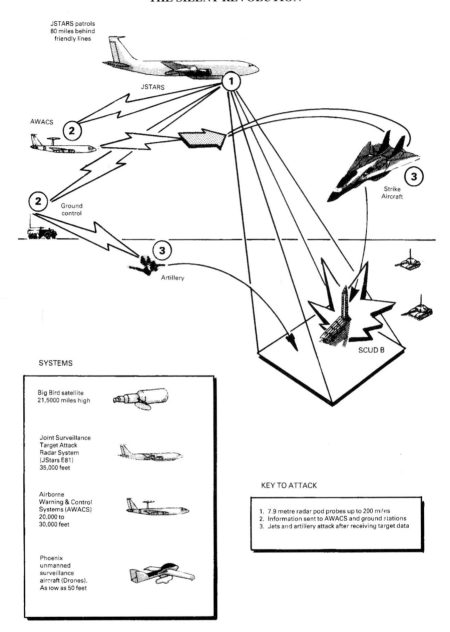

Figure 11 Surveillance systems in operation in the Gulf War (January 1991).

who understood the capabilities of the machine they were controlling and its aerodynamic characteristics.

The Cuban crisis was the first major test of this new generation of drones and RPVs. Typical of the first was the RYAN 147B (also known as AQM – air-launched, drones, guided missile). It had a maximum ceiling of 62,500 feet and a range of 1,930 miles. It was possible to recover it by parachute. In a short while, these drones were re-equipped with an improved navigational system, an on-board programmer and Doppler radar. Such was their success that in mid-1963, the first strategic reconnaissance squadron was formed.

By then, with trouble brewing in South-East Asia and possible intervention in Vietnam by China (which exploded her first nuclear device in October 1964), unmanned aircraft based on Okinawa began to carry out strategic reconnaissance flights over China. As the Americans became increasingly embroiled in Vietnam, flights were extended to that region for PR, ELINT and ECM tasks. Drones and RPVs were air-launched and could be recovered by parachute at the end of their mission. They were fitted with horizon-to-horizon cameras which provided very high resolution pictures of objects as small as one foot in length. Following the success of the AQM146, a night reconnaissance model was produced using infra-red as a sensor. Out of a total of 3,435 sorties flown in South-East Asia only four per cent of the unmanned aircraft flown were destroyed.

Curiously enough, after Vietnam, American service interest in RPVs rather dwindled in the mid-1970s. A $120m programme to develop a very high altitude (70,000 feet) RPV for PR, ELINT and radar surveillance was abandoned by the USAF in 1977 after four years of trials on the grounds that the aircraft would not be able to carry the required payload of 1,500 pounds in the time envisaged for development.

Attention now focussed on Israeli development of miniature RPVs, driven by low-powered, two stroke engines making a conventional take-off and which were recovered into a net at the end of their mission. The Israelis had already used RYAN drones with some success in the Yom Kippur war, both for reconnaissance and for decoys. Their own RPVs, no more than 10 feet in length and with a wing span of 13 feet and carrying a pay load of 66 pounds, were to be used for photographic reconnaissance, electronic warfare, and infra-red sensors.

These MASTIFFS and SCOUTS, as they were called, were employed in what is now recognised as a classic operation which took place when the Israeli Air Force was operating against the Syrian Army in the Bekaa Valley during the Israeli invasion of the Lebanon in June 1982. The role given to the RPVs was to obtain the frequencies employed by the surface-to-air missile radars and those used for communication between the Syrian ground and air forces. This information was passed on to Israeli command and control aircraft for transmission to strike aircraft. The Israelis then used SEA STALLION helicopters to jam the enemy communications frequencies and SAMSON tactical decoy drones (air-launched unpowered gliders) to mimic Israeli fighters. The Syrians were thereby fooled into locking on to these decoys with their radars. As the sun was behind the Israeli aircraft, the Syrians were forced to rely on non-optical methods for detection. When they launched their missiles at the Israeli manned strike, as both fire control radars and missile sites had now revealed their positions, they immediately became vulnerable to attack from Israeli anti-radiation missiles (ARMs) or bombs. The Syrians lost 19 surface-to-air missile batteries in this action as well as 86 combat aircraft, while the Israelis lost only one aircraft, This was a well-thought out, well-executed operation and, allowing for exaggerated reports about the part played by the RPVs in the battle, they undoubtedly made a substantial contribution. Nevertheless, the lesson of this operation having been digested, it is unlikely that such a 'degree of surprise and its consequent success [will be] repeated in this way in any future conflict.'[29] It is worth noting that, only a year later, when American naval aircraft attacked Syrian missile sites in the same valley, three machines were lost, indicating that the greatest value of unmanned aircraft is when a mission is too dangerous for manned aircraft to go it alone.

While interest in unmanned aircraft slackened in the United States in the late

Plate 12 PHOENIX: remotely-piloted vehicle for the British Army. It provides commanders with real time information by day and night and in adverse weather conditions. It was designed to meet a requirement for a target location system in support of MLRS. (*Royal Aeronautical Society*)

1970s, active development continued in other NAT0 countries, The aim was to use RPVs for surveillance, reconnaissance and target acquisition, not to mention their possible use as offensive weapons, eg for battlefield interdiction. The first RPV to be used by the British was MIDGE – a Canadian design, but which had the drawback of being unable to provide real time intelligence.[30] It was succeeded by PHOENIX, a small RPV which could be launched from the ground and recovered by parachute; it was fully equipped for real time remote targeting and surveillance, and designed to be as inconspicuous as possible from radar, infra-red and acoustic detection.[31] Another RPV called CASTOR was similar to the US Joint Surveillance and Target Attack Radar System (JSTARS),* monitoring enemy movement behind the forward edge of the battle area and providing direct real time warning to corps headquarters through WAVELL, the corps communications computer and BATES, the British automated fire control system. Experiments were also made with helicopter RPVs, one of the most interesting being the West German *KIEBITZ* (Peewit) first demonstrated in 1979. Fitted with optical equipment or radar, it could send back a range of information on enemy activities by day or by night and in weather conditions that would ground a manned aircraft.

Conclusion

Of the various aspects of strategic and tactical reconnaissance and surveillance that have been discussed, the most far-reaching technical advances relate to observation satellites and especially close-look satellites. This was due to the superpowers' need to discover and keep record of, not only each other's military activities, but also those of countries in the Third World in which they retained an interest. These satellites have also contributed towards international stability. President Johnson once declared that satellite reconnaissance was worth 10 times the amount of money that the United States spent on space technology because he then knew 'how many missiles the enemy has', implying that this knowledge prevented his country from 'harbouring fears that otherwise might have arisen.'

Moreover, technological change was more essential for the United States than for the Soviet Union because the former was far more dependent upon reliable photographic and electronic intelligence in the light of the 'closed' nature of the Soviet state and the geographical remoteness of many of the strategically important areas of the Soviet Union. Most of this intelligence had to be obtained from low earth orbit, making satellites highly vulnerable to anti-

---

* A sideways-looking target indicating radar intended for the US Army and USAF for the purpose of battlefield management which came into service in the late 1980s.

satellite weapons. This is not the place to discuss methods of defending or destroying space vehicles, and in any case the technology and tactics of conflict in space during our period were still in their infancy. Nevertheless, because of the value of close-look strategic reconnaissance in times of international tension or in war, protection of these vehicles must assume a high priority.

As for sensors, aerial photography has improved to such an extent that resolutions as good as 15–30 centimetres from an altitude of 100 miles can be obtained. Innovations in infra-red and FLIR have made it possible to obtain real time intelligence in conditions of poor visibility and even at night – a great bonus for corps and army commanders. At the same time, it is salutary to remember that, throughout our period, the discerning human eye continued to be, in certain circumstances, the most reliable sensor of all. For in cloud, fog or mist, electronic methods of detection may be at an disadvantage.

It was on account of improved sensors that electronic intelligence began to rival the collection of visual intelligence in importance. It has now become commonplace for the superpowers and their allies to intercept each others' military communications, monitor military radar signatures, and conduct radar search over the oceans. Finally, as a result of the ability of sensors to collect so much information, the methods of processing and analysing photographs and other data have had to be reviewed and here too, as in communications, the latest data-processing techniques have been invaluable.

. 5 .

MOVES AND COUNTER-MOVES
IN LAND WARFARE

From the start of the Cold War it was assumed by NATO and the Warsaw Pact powers that the main conflict, should a 'hot' war begin, would take place on a battle field in central Europe. To this end was the planning of operations directed and it was here that the greatest confrontation of military force ever seen in peace time was assembled. At the same time several of the Western Alliance states – Britain, France and the USA, and towards the end of our period, the Soviet Union – were compelled to divert their attention to internal security operations in former colonies or dependencies like Indo-China, Kenya or Malaya, or were called upon to intervene for ideological reasons in countries like Korea, Vietnam, or Afghanistan, which threatened to upset the precarious equilibrium between East and West. These became almost major conflicts encroaching heavily on the economic resources of the countries involved. Meanwhile throughout the period the political cauldron in the Middle East simmered and from time to time boiled over.

Sometimes these operations required tactics and special equipment quite different from what had been intended for war between highly industrialised countries. Yet more often than not, they were the seed bed or testing ground for new types of equipment, as in the Middle East or Vietnam, providing an opportunity for trying out sophisticated weapon, deception and information technology, and so frequently speeding the rate of technological advance.

Effect of Changes in Strategy on Ground Weapons

Strategy for a war on the Central Front in Europe was always over-shadowed by the possibility of nuclear weapons being used. How to get off the nuclear hook was always at the back of the minds of weapon designers. Our period falls naturally into three phases. The first began in 1949 with the formation of

NATO to resist Soviet aggression. For the next 18 years, the ground forces were merely intended to act as a trip wire. Soviet preponderance in manpower and armour could only be overcome, it was believed, by strategic nuclear weapons. By the mid-1960s, however, the Soviet ability to strike at the American heartland with nuclear weapons deprived the trip wire strategy of any credibility. From December 1967 onwards, therefore, a new strategy known as 'Flexible Response' was introduced. This relied primarily upon the use of conventional weapons in the first stages of the defensive battle with escalation to battlefield nuclear weapons if the conventional response was in danger of being overwhelmed, and further escalation up the nuclear ladder as necessary.[1] This strategy assumed that political moves to halt the fighting would be put in hand as soon as the conventional stage began. In short, it was a more sophisticated form of deterrence, designed to reduce the likelihood of a strategic nuclear exchange to the minimum.

It was, in fact, rapid advances in information technology and the introduction of much more accurate weapons to deal with tanks and aircraft that gave credence to proposals to modify the strategy of 'Flexible Response'. These took two forms and were classified under the heading of 'Deep Attack'. They were intended to counter the Soviet strategy of a sudden penetration of NATO's forward defences and a rapid advance into Western Europe to forestall 'full mobilisation and reinforcement from the United States and to bring about early military and political collapse.'[2] One proposal was devised in the early 1980s by US Army officers dissatisfied with the doctrine of 'active defence'. Instead they offered the doctrine of 'AirLand Battle' (ALB), noted on page 79, in which counter-attacks would be made up to a distance of 60–100 miles or more into enemy territory, the object being to delay and disrupt enemy reinforcements, forcing them to fight at a time and place advantageous to the defender. It anticipated the Soviets using nuclear and chemical weapons, enabling the US Army to take the offensive and fight the battle on its own terms. This imaginative but potentially hazardous concept involved the mass use of helicopters of all types and massive close air support and air interdiction. It was, in fact, the first serious attempt to produce a tactical doctrine in which the ground and air forces were totally enmeshed in a single plan. The ponderous mobility of mechanised forces was replaced by the speed and flexibility of air-mobile operations.

A rather more cautious strategy called 'Follow on Forces Attack' (FOFA) was devised at Supreme Headquarters Allied Powers Europe (SHAPE) and was introduced in November 1984 after five years gestation. Again, the intention was to disrupt Soviet deployment by interfering with the enemy's reinforcement measures, his attack routes and critical lines of communication. Significantly, it did not anticipate the integrated use of conventional, nuclear and chemical weapons, nor was provision made for preemptive strikes. Both these doctrines assumed dependence on the latest technology as applied to reconnaissance aircraft, C^3, surveillance equipment and guided weapons.

Soviet strategy followed a somewhat similar pattern, reverting from an emphasis on nuclear to a fresh interest in the possibilities of conventional forces.[3] In the late 1950s, the artillery branch gave way to the nuclear rocket forces and infantry were downgraded in favour of tanks which, it was thought, might survive on a nuclear battlefield. At the same time, the concept of the offensive in depth, which emphasised mechanised infantry, was reinstated. This doctrine had been evolved in the 1930s by the great Marshal Tukhachevsky, who then became a victim of Stalin's notorious purge of senior officers and the doctrine was purged with him. After the fall of Stalingrad, the doctrine was revived in time for the great Russian sweep forward after the Battle of Kursk in 1943, only to be purged yet again after the war was over. In 1967, the appointment of Commander-in-Chief of Ground Forces in the Soviet Army was revived. In the same year, the Soviet Union conducted her first exercise emphasising conventional rather than nuclear combat, and from then on Soviet tacticians stressed the importance of ground forces other than tanks, and there was even the suggestion that tank divisions should be merged with motorised divisions. The Soviet reaction to ALB and FOFA was to speed up the time taken to commit their Second Echelon forces. It was virtually a revival of the Second World War 'operational group' in which a concentration of tanks and mechanised troops was assigned to a leading commander, given the best equipment and used to strike deeply and quickly into the enemy's rear. This new OPERATIONAL MANOEUVRE GROUP would be a heavily armoured force reinforced with artillery, air assault elements and aircraft. Its task would be to seize important objectives, destroy operational reserves, interfere with command and control, and generally disrupt NATO mobilisation and reinforcement – just as Tukhachevsky had foreseen and taught.

The purpose of this chapter is to show how conventional weapons like the tank, artillery and short range equipment used by the infantry were changed by new technology, how new weapons like guided missiles could counter the threats of aircraft and tanks, how the helicopter could be used as a combat as well as a load-carrying aircraft, how surveillance and deception techniques were changed by the exploitation of the electromagnetic spectrum, and, finally, to consider whether automation has been able to solve problems of the supply of food, fuel and ammunition without which any army in the field must wither.

From Heavy Gun Tank to Main Battle Tank

After the Second World War the tank continued to hold pride of place on the battlefield. But the campaigns in North Africa, Normandy, and on the Eastern Front demonstrated the growth and lethality of anti-tank weapons, ranging from airborne rockets to mines and portable anti-tank guns. If tanks were to be able to carry out their battlefield role of providing direct fire, they had to be able to withstand more devastating munitions. They had to be provided with thicker armour and more powerful guns for encounters with their opponents. They had to be provided with thicker and better shaped armour and more powerful guns to enable them to engage and destroy their potential opponents at longer ranges. The Germans had learned this painful lesson when they encountered the Russian *T-34* in 1941 during their invasion of the Soviet Union. This simple but reliable medium tank introduced the sloping glacis plate and sloping sided turret to tank design, thereby acquiring added protection for no increase in weight. Its hard hitting 76 millimetre gun easily penetrated the lightly armoured German Mark IIIs and IVs. The German reaction was immediate and a new medium tank, the *PANTHER*, was put in hand incorporating many of the design features of T-34 but being larger in order to incorporate a new long barrelled 75 millimetre gun of immense hitting power. This new tank, which was produced in record time, complemented the slower but heavier TIGER, already in service and carrying the dreaded 88 millimetre gun. These two tanks far outclassed the tanks of the Western Allies in general use although, towards the middle of 1944, a small number of harder hitting tanks appeared and, at the turn of that year, the excellent British COMET, well capable of tackling *PANTHER*, came into service. The war over, however, the armies of the West realised that they would have to be ready to fight against the formidable Soviet successors to T-34.

The British, like other nations, began to design new tanks. As they saw it, tanks were required for close quarter fighting and for encounter battles and had to be equipped with a gun firing both armour-piercing and high explosive ammunition. The tank's armour had to withstand rounds from anti-tank guns fired from the front and from less powerful anti-tank guns and infantry close range weapons fired from the flank. Tanks also had to withstand nuclear blast and radiation. That they could operate in such an unfavourable environment in reasonable safety was confirmed during a number of atomic bomb tests carried out by the Americans in the 1950s. All these requirements led to an increase in armour, making the tank much heavier than hitherto. At the same time, the tank had to be able to move reasonably quickly and so had to have more powerful engines and wider tracks for cross-country movement.

The growth of the heavy gun tank into the main battle tank, its armour, munitions and propulsion must now be described.

British tanks had not performed well in the Second World War and reliance had to be placed on American models. Now, with the backing of Field Marshal Montgomery, the first post-war CIGS, who wanted a single type of main battle tank capable of highly mobile operations and of the support of infantry in a more deliberate attack, was the opportunity to make a fresh start. Already, before the war, it had been appreciated that the Army should have a 'common purpose' tank with a basic hull, suspension and automotive system readily adaptable for various roles. In 1946, the solution seemed to be the 'universal tank' (or FV201 as it was designated).[4] But in a short while, experience of Soviet tanks in Korea, including the war-tested *T-34/85* and the *JOSEPH STALIN 3 (JS-3)*, the latter equipped with a 122mm gun, led to the temporary abandonment of the 'universal tank'. Instead the General Staff ordered two types: a medium gun tank and a heavy gun tank (the FV214). The latter was required for two tasks: the defeat of the heaviest Soviet armour and to take on armour and heavy self-propelled guns used by the Soviets in the 'over watch' role at long range.

At the outset, the medium gun tank was to be an up-dated CENTURION (designed as early as 1943) firing APDS shot which had a higher velocity than any other contemporary tank gun. However, the increased protection of Soviet tanks called for a more effective weapon than the 20 pounder – the earlier marks of CENTURION. Design of a 105 millimetre gun was undertaken by a team at the Armament Research and Development Establishment led by Stephen Coppock and Permutter, a Belgian engineer who came over in 1940, They found that by reboring the 20 pounder to 105 millimetre it would fire APDS shot and HE shells, retaining the same chamber. This brilliant piece of improvisation allowed the weapon to have the same external dimensions as the 20 pounder but with greatly improved performance. The APDS shot, using vulcanised nylon driving bands, had better ballistics and accuracy. As there was then no service requirement for the 105 millimetre gun, a production licence was offered to Vickers who made the initial batch of guns, but in response to the Director Royal Armoured Corps, Major General H R B Foot, VC the gun was at last procured for the Army in 1958.

In the meantime CENTURION was used by the British in Korea over exceptionally difficult terrain and in extreme cold, but it gave very little mechanical trouble and incurred little damage from enemy gunfire and mines. A Canadian brigade commander reported that its armour and 20 pounder gun made it the 'best universal tank in existence.'[5] However, Major General N W Duncan, Director Royal Armoured Corps, warned against experience in Korea being applicable to a battlefield in central Europe. In the former, tanks were used as a source of mobile fire power escorted by infantry up to selected positions to assist the advance of infantry units. As a tank officer then in Korea wrote: 'The role of the tank is the sudden surprise attack with the maximum number in the least expected place.' The CENTURION remained in service until the 1970s after evolving through a series of 13 marks and changing from the 20 pounder to the 105 millimetre gun.

A number of foreign armies also bought CENTURION together with 105 millimetre guns and ammunition, including the US Army which replaced its 90 millimetre gun with the 105 millimetre, and the Israeli Defence Force. In the

1967 (Six Day) war, Israeli CENTURIONS more than proved their worth against the Russian-built *T-34s*, *JS-3s* and *T-55s* of the Egyptians. By outranging them, they could knock them out with impunity while they proved remarkably impervious to the Soviet tank guns. However, the limited size of the CENTURION 3's fuel tanks restricted their range to around 80 miles. This led to the Israelis converting their CENTURIONS to diesel fuel.

Throughout the 1950s, the arrival of the FV214 was anxiously awaited. Known as the CONQUEROR it was the heaviest tank yet built by the British. It weighed 65 tons and was equipped with a 120 millimetre gun based on an American design. It was to be used in two roles: defensively, when a limited traverse was acceptable, or offensively, to seek out enemy tanks or to counterattack them. It was believed that even a small number of CONQUERORS would improve morale in the Royal Armoured Corps and act as a deterrent in the Cold War. [6]

However, the design was not unanimously accepted. The DRPC sub-committee on anti-tank measures, chaired by Sir Frederick Brundrett, the Scientific Adviser to the Ministry of Defence, and advised by colleagues well-versed in ballistics and metallurgy, believed that the 120 millimetre gun was incapable of dealing with the latest Soviet tanks.[7] They maintained that only a 183 millimetre gun using a high explosive squash head round (described below) could knock out a tank in one go, though the projectile had to strike the tank at quite high velocity. But a 183 millimetre gun could not be fitted into the CONQUEROR; it would have to be a self-propelled gun. It was doubtful, however, whether British industrial resources could cope with manufacturing both self-propelled guns *and* tanks. Heavily-armoured self-propelled guns had been considered since the end of the war, but, in a short while, they were to go out of favour when it was appreciated that the tank must rely on its *own* armament to fight opponents. The other alternative was the anti-tank guided weapon, of which more later. A prototype of the immensely heavy TORTOISE 183 millimetre self-propelled anti-tank gun was built but, for a host of good reasons, never came into service.

Meanwhile the CONQUEROR came into service in the mid-1950s. Although equipped with the latest fire control devices and a special system for ejecting empty shell cases from the turret, it was not a success. Teething problems were never overcome and the tank was phased out of service about 10 years later without ever being used operationally. Its much vaunted adversary, the Soviet *JS-3*, went into action with the Egyptian Army and was only discarded when the concept of the heavy gun tank was abandoned in favour of a single battle tank.

Development of the new medium gun-tank and successor to the CENTURION and known as the FV4201 began early in 1955.[8] It was anticipated that seven years would elapse before it came into service. The role of the

FV4201 was again twofold: support of the infantry in a close-quarter fight and ability to engage enemy tanks at ranges of around 2000 yards. Much thought was given to the type of gun and propellant. At the outset there were three possibilities: a gun using a liquid propellant,* which seemed to offer advantages in reducing the space occupied by the gun and ammunition; a low pressure 120 millimetre gun then being developed by the Americans; or an unorthodox 105 millimetre gun developed from the 20 pounder then mounted on the CENTURION. As liquid propellants would take too long to develop and the 105 millimetre was not powerful enough the decision was taken, in 1958, to adopt the rifle-bored 120 millimetre gun using a bagged charge.

This new system consisted of a projectile (APDS or HESH), a silk bag containing the charge and an obturator (or resilient pad) to ensure the gas sealing of the breach – an essential new feature in the absence of the brass cartridge which previously performed this function. The 120 millimetre fixed ammunition had been immensely heavy and had called for a sort of pocket Hercules to manoeuvre the round within the confines of the turret and load it into the breech. The silk bag of the bagged charge is completely consumed on firing and the problem of the heavy brass cartridge is eliminated. Every system has its Achilles heel and that of the bagged charge is the inherent danger of loading an APDS charge behind a HESH projectile, the effect of which would be to burst the barrel of the gun. However, good training, effective marking and the shape of the charges go far to eliminate this risk. The 120mm gun was rifled and so had no shaped charge projectile. It fired a high velocity APDS or HESH shot, care having to be taken that an APDS charge was not loaded with the HESH projectile which would have burst. It was an admirable weapon at ranges of about 1000 yards. It relied on ballistic ranging with a 0.5in ranging machine gun. In 1981 a computer replaced the machine gun. This Improved Fire Control System, as it was called, gave the tank a good chance of obtaining 'first round kill' so vital in armoured warfare. CHIEFTAIN, the name given to the FV4201, was tested in prototype during the period 1959–62. Numerous problems had to be overcome mainly relating to the engine, the ultimate effect being to make the machine rather slower than had been intended. CHIEFTAIN did not come into front line service until 1966. Nevertheless improvements continued to be made to CHIEFTAIN putting it well ahead of other medium gun tanks in NATO,[9] which were equipped with 105 millimetre rifle-bored guns. It was another 12 years before the West Germans equipped their *LEOPARD 2* with a 120 millimetre gun. Unlike the British weapon, this was a smooth-bored gun manufactured by the *Rheinmetall Company* and firing either armour-piercing or hollow charge rounds.

---

*Instead of one large explosion, the propellant is gradually introduced into the gun after ignition so that pressure is maintained as the projectile travels up the bore.

Plate 13 CHIEFTAIN: British main battle tank designed to support infantry in a close-quarter fight and to engage enemy tanks at ranges up to 2000 yards. (*Vickers Defence Systems*)

Plate 14 CHALLENGER: British main battle tank, successor to CHIEFTAIN. It is fitted with Chobham armour. (*Vickers Defence System*)

116

Development of CHIEFTAIN'S successor had already begun in the late 1960s. By this time, the term 'main battle tank' had replaced 'medium gun tank'. The project, envisaging an entirely new type of tank, began as an Anglo-German venture. It was called the Future Main Battle Tank (FMBT) and was planned to come into service in the late 1980s. But as time went on, it became apparent that not only would FMBT be very expensive, but that before long new and more powerful Warsaw Pact tanks would be introduced to overtake it. The development of the FMBT came to an abrupt halt in mid-1980. Tanks had now become extremely expensive. By the end of the 1970s, a main battle tank could cost over £1 million. Luckily for the British, they were able to fall back on an improved form of the CHIEFTAIN – the SHIR 2 – intended for but never delivered to Iran.[10] It was fitted with a new kind of armour called Chobham (described below) and was powered by a better engine than the CHIEFTAIN'S. The gun and fire control system were virtually unchanged. This tank designated FV4030/4 was named CHALLENGER and was intended to come into service in 1985.

The British were by no means alone in encountering difficulties in developing new tanks. The Americans, caught off their guard by the Korean war, had to convert 2000 M-26 (PERSHING) tanks to M-46 (PATTON) tanks which carried 90 millimetre guns. They continued to plan for light, medium and heavy tanks, but soon began the development of the M-60 series which mounted the British 105 millimetre gun. In 1963 they combined with West Germany to develop the MBT70 which was to be armed with a 152 millimetre SHILLELAGH gun/missile system.[11] But the Germans pulled out in 1970, firstly, because the machine was far too expensive and, secondly, because they believed high velocity guns were superior to missile systems as the main armament of a tank. (The French had similar ideas and cancelled their AMX-30 tank with its 142 millimetre gun/missile launcher.) Although the Americans persisted on continuing the project on their own, it was vetoed by Congress in 1971. The US Army reverted to the well-tried British 105 millimetre gun which was mounted in the XM-1 and protected by Chobham armour.

The Russians too had had to surmount tank production difficulties. Contrary to Western expectations and predictions, it took them 15 years to deploy a new battle tank in Central Europe following the introduction of the *T-62* with a 115 millimetre gun in 1962,[12] though they were working hard on battlefield air defence systems, artillery and armoured personnel carriers. The new *T-72* began to be deployed in 1976. It was armed with a 125 millimetre gun.

Weight and Mobility

The weight of tanks increased partially because of the heavy guns they mounted (the recoil of these guns had to be absorbed by a heavy vehicle and also called for an enlarged turret ring, thereby increasing the size of the tank overall), but more because of the heavy armour needed as protection against projectiles and missiles. Consequently more powerful engines had to be installed. In the post-war years, the horse power of tank engines was more than doubled. For example, the US ABRAMS M-1 and the West German *LEOPARD* 2 weighing over 50 tons were driven by engines of 1,500 horse-power, giving them a power to weight ratio of more than 20 horse-power per ton.

During the 1960s, diesel engines replaced petrol engines.[13] At the same time the development of the gas turbine offered an alternative to the piston engine. The American M-1 was the first fully-turbined tank in service (though the Swedish *S*-tank combined a diesel engine with a small gas turbine for rapid start-up and extra power). Gas turbines offered high power to weight and power to volume ratios and had few moving parts, but they were thirsty when idling (and tanks usually spend a lot of time idling) and were expensive to build. Diesels, on the other hand were extremely powerful when supercharged and were favoured by tank designers as they produced power to weight ratios of over 25 brake horse-power per ton. To go beyond that would require a tank which was light (and therefore vulnerable), or if heavily-armoured, would need a very expensive power unit with a high fuel consumption.

As tank weights increased, so did it become necessary to widen their tracks to provide better flotation (the ground bearing pressures) to ensure mobility over soft going. At the same time, as speeds increased and more and more emphasis was being placed upon the engagement of targets by tanks on the move, so did it become essential to make improvements to their suspensions. Torsion bars were strengthened and hydro-pneumatic suspension units replaced the old style volute spring systems.

Tank Ammunition and Accuracy

Having discussed the tank in relation to the gun it had to carry, we now need to describe improvements in anti-tank munitions and the accuracy of their delivery. After the Second World War anti-tank projectiles had to penetrate frontal armour (which was usually set at an angle of 30 or 60 degrees) varying in thickness from 160–370 millimetres or side armour (set at an angle of 60 degrees) from 75 to 160 millimetres thick.[14] Projectiles continued to be divided into two categories – kinetic and chemical energy. In the former category were the tungsten carbide-cored shot, used successfully at the end of the Second World War, which, because of its high velocity (the product of its density and the use of the sabot), enabled the 83mm gun of the CENTURION to penetrate armour twice as effectively as the German 88 millimetre gun, and the steel armour-piercing shot. In the latter category were the HE hollow charge shell (HEAT), already described, and (a more recent development) the HE squash head (HESH).[15] This shell had a light case containing a high percentage of an HE filling which was intended to flatten on to the target before detonation occurred (it was originally intended to shatter concrete or earthwork bunkers). When used against thin armour, a hole was blown in the plate; against thick armour success was obtained by the detachment from the rear of the plate under attack of a scab of varying dimensions and mass at velocities ranging up to several hundred feet per second. The effects resulting from blast and concussion were intended to knock out both the tank and its crew.

As we have seen earlier, the HEAT, hollow-charge, round was first developed towards the end of the Second World War and relied upon the velocity of the explosion of its chemical filling to burn its way through thick armour. At short ranges it was extremely effective but because it could not be fired at high velocities, it soon lost accuracy at ranges over 1000 metres. However, proponents of HEAT argued that a tank would seldom engage another at above this range when fighting in Europe. The British, with bitter memories of being outgunned in the Western Desert, clung firmly to their high velocity kinetic energy form of attack. Although the British continued to use HESH rounds in the latter marks of the CENTURION and in the CHIEFTAIN, other armies, notably the American and the French, favoured the HEAT round for their new tank models introduced in the 1960s.[16]

In the next decade, however, both the APDS and HEAT rounds began to be discarded and to be replaced principally by the armour-piercing, fin-stabilised discarding sabot (APFSDS) which were used both by NATO and Warsaw Pact armies; APFSDS rounds could be fired with a muzzle velocity of 5,400 feet per second and were capable of penetrating much thicker armour than earlier types of ammunition. They had the advantage of being used in either smooth bore or rifled barrels. In the case of the latter, the incorporation of a smooth ring allowed the sabot to rotate in the rifling while the projectile itself remained unspun.

Two essential factors dominated the development of armour-piercing ammunition: shape and composition. Good shape ensured minimum loss of velocity before impact and concentrated the maximum of energy at the target. In the composition of the core, designers looked for the best combination of density, ductility and toughness. Tungsten alloys continued to be used though depleted uranium was another possibility; it was dense and ductile and likely to cause a fire inside the target tank. Target acquisition and accuracy of aim vied in importance with the ability of the projectile to penetrate armour. Three examples of post-war developments must suffice. Most important was the introduction of optical rangefinders; they were first used on the American M-47 and the West German *LEOPARD I*.[17] In the 1960s, as we have seen, laser rangefinders began to come into service. In combination with electronic ballistic computers they greatly increased the hit probability of tank guns.[18]

The importance ascribed to night fighting by the Soviet Army in the late 1950s led to the development of night sights. These were at first of an active infra-red type. Further advances were made in the next decade with image intensifier sights (see below) followed by passive imaging sights which did not reveal the source of energy from the 1970s onwards.[19] But such sophisticated devices were expensive and could absorb as much as 20 per cent of the total cost of a modern tank. Fire control instruments added another 20 per cent. Some of this expenditure, it was argued, could be avoided as the very flat trajectories of extremely high velocity rounds made range estimation rather less important for short range engagements.

The second innovation was the provision of tanks with stabilised gun controls to enable them to fire more accurately on the move. They could then travel over rough ground at the same time being able to keep their gun barrels at a constant angle of elevation. Tanks were later fitted with independently stabilised gunner's as well as commander's sights to enable them to engage targets on the move more effectively. Later the introduction of the laser rangefinder, computerised fire-control and the thermal sleeving of the main armament all contributed to much greater accuracy of fire and enormously enhanced the chances of a first round hit – something that had become of the first importance as anti-tank systems improved. In effect, most of the inaccuracies which had hitherto been largely due to human error had been eliminated as had those such as barrel droop and trunnion-tilt which were due to technical shortcomings in earlier systems.

Thirdly, the Soviet Army (and the Swedes) introduced automatic loading in the mid-1970s. Automatic loading allowed a higher rate of fire to be maintained and, perhaps more importantly, made a loader redundant, reducing the crew from four to three.[20] This saving in space decreased the volume to be protected by armour and so reduced the size and weight of the tank.

The basic design of the Swedish 'S' tank was more like that of a self-propelled gun but, by an ingenious use of the tank's hydraulic suspension and its steering, it was possible to lay the gun in azimuth and elevation and so give the vehicle the characteristics of a tank despite the loss of the turret. It was later proposed to follow this design with a tank carrying an externally mounted gun. By placing the crew within the hull, the low silhouette of the 'S' tank would be retained but the gun would have a much freer traverse whilst still being served by an automatic loading system. Whilst there is still general agreement that such a tank probably marks the best way forward, the concept presents a number of technical difficulties. Thus, although design studies have been made in Sweden and in the United States, no such tank has yet appeared in service.[21]

Protection of the Tank

Intensive efforts were made after the Second World War to make the tank less vulnerable to anti-tank weapons. Welding techniques used by the Germans and Russians long before 1939 were adopted by the British. Increases were made in thickness followed by several changes in armour layout, such as sloping armour (ultimately introduced into all armies in the Second World War) and spaced armour to create an air gap between two plates of armour in order to dissipate the effects of kinetic energy shot. It was first considered by the British as early as the inter-war years and then taken up by the Germans but was only used to a limited extent until more sophisticated forms of it were devised in the late 1960s; it was also proof against the latest shaped charge projectiles up to and including 22mm and was more effective than a single plate of vertical armour of equal weight but only the same order of efficiency as a single plate sloping at 45 degrees.

The next step was to find new materials to replace very heavy armour which had the drawback of requiring 'a large ratio of man power in production and maintenance behind the line compared with its military effect in a modern battle.'[22] The most suitable materials were titanium, already being used in the aircraft industry, plastics (first used in armour in the Second World War after it had been observed that a mastic substance resisted bullets), and fibre glass, useful as a backing to other forms of protection and which had been considered by the British in 1947 as protection against anti-tank mines; and finally, ceramics used in conjunction with other materials.

In 1947 the British began research in the use of laminated materials as armour. Its outcome in the 1970s was the now celebrated Chobham armour composed, it is believed, of laminates of armour steel separated by substances such as ceramics, aluminium, plastics or carbon fibre.[23] Compared with an equivalent weight of steel, such combinations were believed to increase resistance to attack by hollow charge weapons by a factor of at least two. Composite armour did not make the main battle tank invulnerable, however. Against a kinetic energy round it offered no greater protection than a single plate; it was bulky and, if used all over the surface of the vehicle, it greatly increased the volume of the tank; it was also expensive and somewhat harder to manufacture than conventional armour plate. For these reasons composite armour is usually reserved to increase protection of the tank's most vulnerable parts such as the glacis plate and turret front, leaving the top, belly, running gear, sides and rear no better protected than before.

The final innovation in tank armour that occurred towards the end of our period was the introduction of explosive reactive armour. This consists of a layer of explosive sandwiched between two relatively thin plates of the frontal armour of a tank.[24] When struck by a shaped charge warhead, the explosive goes off disrupting the shaped charge jet. Reactive armour was developed by the Soviet and other armies and was fitted to Israeli tanks (and called BLAZER) during their operations in the Lebanon in 1982.

Armoured Personnel Carriers

The requirement to carry infantry into action quickly by mechanical transport had long been recognised. But it was not until the Germans began to use armoured half-tracked vehicles, as opposed to unarmoured vehicles, not merely to carry troops into battle but actually to fight from them on the move, that a new dimension was given to the infantry tactics. The need for some form of protected transport for infantry was recognised by the British and Canadians in North-West Europe in 1944. Here a quantity of old Canadian RAM tanks were converted by the removal of their turrets and by clearing the inside of the fighting compartment, to create armoured 'taxis'. They were first used in Operation TOTALIZE, as the 1st Canadian Army advanced by night south of Caen, in Normandy. Thereafter, these KANGAROOS, as they were dubbed, were used extensively throughout Montgomery's 21st Army Group.

The Americans had quickly appreciated the value of fully-tracked vehicles and by the late 1940s had produced the fully-tracked M39 Armoured Utility Vehicle which was later developed into the M44 Armoured Personnel Carrier (APC).[25] Fully-tracked vehicles (M-75s) carrying a dozen men were in action in Korea. In 1955 the first amphibious APC was introduced, to be followed five years later by the M-113 with a low silhouette and much lighter in weight, mainly due to the fact it was the first military vehicle to be built with aluminium armour. The drawback to these vehicles was that they were no more than 'taxis' ferrying troops into action, having no more than a machine gun for self-protection. The British followed suit with their FV432, later adapted as a maintenance carrier signals vehicle and ATGM carrier. But the inability of the troops to see out of the vehicle was a serious disadvantage and a lot of time was wasted when they had 'de-bussed' and were trying to re-orient themselves on the ground.

The French and the Germans, on the other hand, concentrated on making a tracked armoured carrier from which infantry could fight. The West German *MARDER* transporting 10 men and armed with a 20 millimetre gun was the first Western Mechanical Infantry Combat Vehicle (MICV) and was the most successful. However, it post-dated the Soviet *BMP-1* (*Boevaya maskina pekhoty*) carrying eleven infantrymen and which could be used for combating tanks and for crossing ground contaminated by a nuclear strike. It was able to bring into action an anti-tank guided missile (ATGM), a turret-mounted 73mm anti-tank gun and at least one RPG-7 anti-tank grenade launcher carried by a trooper within. Nevertheless, improvements in ATGMs, manifested in the Yom

Kippur war, appeared to put the *BMP* at risk. If too dangerous to employ on the battlefield, a possible alternative was to use them in daring surprise raids on the enemy's rear, making use of their high speed and good anti-tank armament.

Tracked and Wheeled Reconnaissance Vehicles

Both sides produced some very good wheeled reconnaissance vehicles during the Second World War – notably, the German 8-wheeled armoured cars, the American GREYHOUND and the British DAIMLER – the latter having a very long career, from 1939 until well into the post-war era. From 1945, it was the British, with their almost ceaseless involvement in counter-insurgency operations and brush-fire wars who had the greatest need for a small, fast, reliable scout car. The FERRET soon became known wherever their troops were deployed. So too did SALADIN, a six-wheeled car with a fine 76 millimetre gun. However, the need for a superior cross-country performance on the Central Front in Europe led to a change of policy and the creation of the family of vehicles known as the Combat Vehicles Reconnaissance Tracked (CVRT). Of these, the SCORPION, mounting the same gun as SALADIN, came to prominence in the Falklands Campaign, where its remarkable flotation properties enabled it to move over ground so soft that even the infantry were having difficulties. The CVRT series introduced a valuable new feature in that they have a water-crossing capacity, through the use of a flotation screen, the propulsion when afloat coming from the vehicle's own tracks. Principally for Home Defence purposes, the British also produced FOX, a four wheeled car with exceptional cross-country performance. The French Panhard series of cars have given yeoman service in many countries of the world, particularly in the 1950s and 60s during the troubles in Algeria. The Germans, reverting to past policy, have a new 8-wheeled car of high quality.

Introduction of the Anti-tank Guided Missile

While it was acknowledged that the tank itself was the best form of defence against another tank, tanks needed infantry and artillery support and the necessity to operate in numbers made them conspicuous and vulnerable. The Second World War had been responsible for revolutionising the anti-tank gun and providing it with velocities to penetrate ten inches of armour up to 1000 yards range. But again, guns were conspicuous as they were easily located by their muzzle flash and the smoke and dust they created; they were handicapped by having to be towed by a vehicle.

As we have seen, German guided missile experiments included a wire-controlled weapon for use against armour. This missile and its designers were appropriated by the French who seem to have been the first to recognise that a shaped charge warhead guided electronically to the target might well prove more effective than shorter-ranged tank guns.

ATGMs, either mounted on an armoured or non-armoured vehicle or carried by an infantryman, were to be developed extensively in the post-war years. The former were intended to take on enemy tanks standing off beyond the range of other anti-tank weapons and bringing down harassing fire. Such targets were usually engaged at ranges of 2000 yards and over. ATGMs handled by the infantry had to deal with targets up to a range of 1000 yards.

Nevertheless it had to be recognised that compared with anti-tank guns, ATGMs suffered from a number of disadvantages. They had a slow rate of fire; when restricted to travelling at subsonic speeds they were not as fast as a high velocity shell in reaching the target; a severe limitation was the question of 'minimum range' – that is to say, the distance needed for the controller to 'gather' the missile and begin actually to 'fly' it. This distance could sometimes be as much as 500 yards; to handle them required considerable skill; they were susceptible to ECM; and, finally, one missile was much more expensive than a round fired from a gun, so that firing several of the latter was more cost-effective than launching one missile. The ultimate 'fire and forget' anti-tank weapon has still to be achieved, although missiles are becoming less dependent on operator skills.

The French, eager to revive their arms trade, took the lead in developing ATGMs in Europe.[26] Taking advantage of German experience with wire-guided missiles, they developed in the 1950s the man-portable SS-10 and SS-11 (range 3,500 yards) able to penetrate 60 centimetres of thick armour and ENTAC, which was more successful and had a range of just over one mile. The former were sold to foreign armies, including the IDF, which deployed but did not use them in the Sinai campaign of 1956. The French went on to produce two types of helicopter-borne second generation ATGMs in the 1970s in collaboration with the West Germans – MILAN and HOT. The West Germans produced their own second generation ATGM in 1960, the man-portable COBRA which had a maximum range of over 1,700 yards.

The British, on the other hand, dragged their feet in ATGM development. They needed two weapons, one a heavy long range weapon to take on the heaviest type of tank and a man/vehicle portable weapon to give protection to the infantry. MALKARA came into the first category. Carried by and launched from an armoured vehicle, it was a wire-controlled weapon in which launch and control were inseparable and it was intended to knock out the heaviest Soviet tank at ranges of 300–6000 yards. Development began in 1952 and was divided between Britain and Australia causing innumerable problems for the agencies responsible for the launcher vehicle, the gyroscopes, the warhead and the fuse.[27] The missile also had to be air-transportable. Although there were doubts about the efficacy of the 60 pound HESH warhead, on the grounds that armour could easily be developed to resist it, it was too late to fit a HEAT warhead, unlike later types of ATGM. MALKARA was carried on an armoured truck called HORNET and entered service in 1962, but was not regarded as a valuable weapon.

The successor to MALKARA was intended to be another wire-controlled weapon (ORANGE WILLIAM) but with control and launch taking place at two different places (to meet the possibility of having to fire across a water obstacle). The fire controller would be in a FERRET armoured car about two miles away from the missile. Again, it was intended to knock out heavy tanks at ranges of 300–6000 yards. Early development by the Fairey Aircraft Company was slow and led the Controller of Munitions to complain in 1959 that in four years from then the British would have the only army without a long range anti-tank weapon apart from the WOMBAT (a 120 millimetre recoilless gun).[28] ORANGE WILLIAM was cancelled but the basic features of its design were incorporated into the wire-controlled SWINGFIRE, a much more useful weapon designed by the British Aircraft Corporation from 1960. Its name was derived from its ability to be turned through large angles (up to 45 degrees after launch). On account of this asset, it had its own unique integral simulator to assist in training crews. Its maximum range was around 4,400 yards and it entered service in 1969. An infantry version of SWINGFIRE was also produced.

Plate 15 SWINGFIRE: British long range anti-tank guided missile. It can be turned by the controller through wide angles (up to 45 degrees) after launch. (*Royal Aeronautical Society*)

125

British short range ATGMs also took time to emerge. Again, the British had to turn to the French for an example. Yet as early as 1951, the Guided Weapons Division at the RAE conceded that while the French SS-10 was well-engineered it 'was unlikely to be sufficiently accurate and would in no way meet War Office requirements, though it would be an advantage if some weapons could be made available for further analysis.'[29] As European cooperation at that time had not advanced very far, the specimens were not forthcoming.

Due to the initiative of Vickers Armstrong, who had privately designed a weapon called VIGILANT, the British Army was provided with a man/vehicle portable ATGM. VIGILANT was eventually produced by the British Aircraft Corporation (an amalgamation of the leading British aircraft companies which took place in 1960). It was the first missile to have velocity control, ie the response to commands varied with the range, so giving a constant apparent velocity for a given command, thus making the operator's task much easier. Its 5 inch hollow charge warhead could penetrate most armour up to about 800 yards range. VIGILANT entered sevice in 1953.

Like the British, the Americans were concerned about the need to protect their armoured formations with ATGMs. In 1959 the US Army began to develop a light tank (SHERIDAN) with a 152 millimetre gun which would

Plate 16a TOW: US-designed wire-guided anti-tank missile. It can be launched either from an APC or from a tripod ground mounting. (*Hughes Missile Systems Group*)

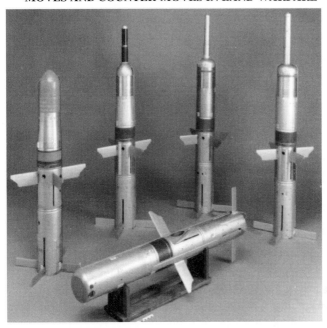

Plate 16b TOW: the missiles. Clockwise from left: Basic TOW, Improved TOW (with a telescoping probe for stand-off detonation), TOW 2 with heavier warhead, TOW 2A with tandem warheads. Foreground, fly-over, shoot down TOW. (*Hughes Missile Systems Group*)

be capable of firing both missiles and shells.[30] The missile was called SHILLELAGH and it had a maximum range of over 1000 yards. SHERIDAN was intended to be a combined armoured reconnaissance/airborne assault vehicle, but its dual function led to it being unsatisfactory in either role. The gun/launcher was also mounted in the M60-A2 tank, but again proved to be disappointing because it tried to combine two separate functions.

More successful and easier to operate was an ATGM called TOW (Tube-launched, Optically-guided) which could either be launched from a tripod on the ground or from an armoured personnel carrier. Unlike SHILLELAGH, which was infra-red-guided, TOW was wire-operated and the firing of a rocket motor left a signature considerably less than that of the recoilless anti-tank gun that it replaced. Its maximum range was about 4000 yards and the time of flight over that distance was about 15 seconds. This second generation ATGM was the most widely distributed missile of its kind.

Like its counterparts in the West, the Soviet Army was not lax about developing vehicle-borne ATGMs. In the early 1960s, their SNAPPER, SWATTER and SAGGER missiles were introduced; they were all wire-controlled and had a maximum range of 2000 yards and over. As will be shown, they were used with some effect, by the Egyptians in the 1973 war.

By the beginning of the 1970s, the advantages of the ATGM, such as its ease of production and now relative cheapness, its relatively light weight, and its high hit probability, led some enthusiasts to claim that it would supersede the tank. Moreover, the new attack helicopter then being introduced could carry ATGMs and the helicopter advocates were quoted in support of this claim. Their argument was based on the misleading results of trials in Germany in which 18 armoured vehicles were assumed to have been 'knocked out' for each helicopter destroyed, though conditions had actually favoured the helicopter.[31]

Second Thoughts on ATGMs

The first major test of ATGMs in action came in the Yom Kippur war of 1973. Both the Egyptian and Syrian armies were quite lavishly equipped with Soviet missiles, many of the SAGGER variety and RPG-7 grenades. These weapons were used to repulse an Israeli counter-attack against Egyptian forces advancing from the Suez Canal. The first reports of the Israeli tank casualties were exaggerated; it later transpired that about 30–40 tanks out of a total of 810 were knocked out by ATGMs.[33] The hand-held RPG-7s, of which there were many more than the SAGGERS (scattered throughout the Egyptian and Syrian forces) accounted for a number of tanks. Altogether the Soviet weapons many of which may have been rockets accounted for 8.25 per cent of all kills. The remaining casualties were accounted for by tank guns. It is interesting to note that the total Egyptian losses to armour amounted to 900 AFVs while the Syrian losses amounted to 1,050.

After 1973, a rather more sanguine view of ATGMs was taken. The ability of the high velocity gun to hit a tank more quickly than a ATGM was recognised as being more important than the certainty of scoring a hit (for tank guns could be manually loaded and fired more rapidly than even the most up-to-date supersonic missile). Moreover it was recognised that in Central Europe at least, tank actions were unlikely to place at ranges of much more than 1000 yards. (In the Second World War tank actions usually took place at little more than 800 yards). At such short ranges, missiles would be saturated. Again, by the mid-1970s the advantages of the ATGM at long ranges were being overtaken by terminally-guided artillery projectiles. Fired from self-propelled guns, they were able to engage moving targets at distances of over four miles. The tops of tanks were especially vulnerable to these projectiles. Even so, ATGMs were given a new lease of life when fitted in helicopters flying nap-of-the-earth and engaging tank units which had broken through the main defences.

Other Types of Anti-Tank Weapon

Infantry were, of course, extremely vulnerable to attack by armoured vehicles and recoilless guns and rocket-launched grenades were pressed into service as anti-tank weapons. The Germans had used recoilless guns and the Americans introduced their 57 millimetre and 75 millimetre recoilless guns towards the end of the Second World War. Both offered the possibilities as anti-tank weapons. The British needed something better than their 17-pounder anti-tank gun which, although useful at 1000 yards range was too heavy and lacked mobility.* Hence their development of recoilless guns for use at battalion level like RED PLANET, MOBAT and WOMBAT. A useful latecomer in the field was the Swedish 84 millimetre *CARL GUSTAV* firing a HEAT projectile which could penetrate up to eight inches of armour. Unfortunately these weapons all had the disadvantage of a back blast which was both dangerous and conspicuous.

Rocket-launched grenades were developed by both the Americans and the Russians. The US M-28 was a 3.5 inch launcher to which was attributed the destruction of seven T-34 tanks in the course of the Korean campaign.[32] The Soviet RPG-7 saw service, as we have seen, in the Egyptian Army.

The Continuing Threat from Land Mines

The Korean war provided a reminder to the Western powers of the threat of land mines both to personnel and tanks which, as we have seen, demanded such an effort to master in the Second World War. Thus a post-war tank could be brought to a halt by 15 pounds of TNT, breaking a track or damaging the suspension, belly armour or engine. A larger mine could distort the whole hull of an armoured fighting vehicle (AFV), thereby rendering it beyond repair. Alternatively, mine fields could channel enemy armour into areas where they could be dealt with by anti-tank weapons. Or minefields could be laid to give protection to infantry positions.[34]

Land mines, and especially anti-personnel mines, have been used in most of the post-war conflicts, but have never proved impassable and usually have been overcome within hours by a determined force. On the other hand, they are extremely difficult to clear, especially in the case of non-metallic mines, as was found in the Falklands and Afghanistan wars. Both these wars showed the appalling consequences to civil life, long after hostilities ceased, of broadcasting mines without charting the minefields where they were laid.

In the 1950s, the British Army gave priority to the development of heavy

---

* In Korea it was considered to be a 'white elephant', clumsy and difficult to dig in.

and light anti-tank mines able to stop all kinds of tracked vehicles including the heaviest type of tank. The carefully planned and patterned minefields, familiar to troops in the Second World War no longer met the needs of modern mobile warfare. Mines now had to be laid rapidly by mechanical means, or projected from a vehicle, The British resolved this problem by evolving two systems. One, called RANGER, was a multi-barrelled projector mounted on the back of a truck or tracked vehicle capable of discharging anti-personnel mines up to a distance of 100 yards. The approaches to a river crossing could thus be mined from the opposite bank or tracks denied to enemy infantry groups.

Anti-tank mines can also be sown by the BAR MINE layer. The layer is towed behind an APC with its conveyor projecting into the towing vehicle. As the layer progresses, a plough blade cuts a furrow through the earth. The Bar Mines are then placed on the conveyor and as they pass through the layer body the fuse is activated automatically. Once the mine has been placed in the ploughed furrow, two disc wheels bury it and smooth down the earth surface. Up to 600 or 700 mines can be laid in an hour using one vehicle and a three man crew.

Mine clearance techniques were meanwhile being renewed. Infantry need a passage about a yard wide while tanks and other types of vehicle need a minimum of seven to eight yards to pass safely through a minefield. Apart from electromagnetic devices operated by hand, rollers attached to the front of armoured vehicles can make a path through a minefield. They replaced the Second World War flails and were much favoured by the Warsaw Pact armies. The latter also devised mine ploughs, mounted on the horns of selected tanks, in a manner similar to the rollers just mentioned. An ingenious British device called the GIANT VIPER consists of a long hose filled with plastic explosives. The hose is fired by rockets from a trailer towed by a tank or APC. The hose is stabilised in flight by three parachutes. Once on the ground, the plastic explosive contents are fired from the towing vehicle. A path will then be cleared about 8yds wide and 200yds long.

The mine is only one ingredient in a defensive system. In the Western Desert in 1941–42, the Germans perfected the coordinated use of barrier minefields (of mixed mines) and anti-tank guns. However, they also demonstrated how vital it was for any obstacle to be covered by artillery fire: without it, the barrier merely becomes a delaying factor, not a means of actually destroying the enemy.

There are, of course, several other methods of inhibiting enemy movement. They are the cratering of approaches to bridges or causeways, the laying of dummy minefields (though likely to be visible on aerial photographs) and, finally, the construction of earth or sand barriers and the deliberate flooding of areas – all strategems used in the Iran-Iraq war and in many an earlier campaign. These 'passive' barriers employing military and civil engineering resources, in fact, proved to be more effective than mines.

Eclipse of the Tank by the Helicopter

The helicopter was to pose a serious challenge to the tank. From 1945, the tank had formed the fulcrum of the ground offensive; it had acquired more fire power, mobility and protection through the lavish application of technology. Yet, from time to time, its usefulness was questioned by a number of military thinkers who felt that equipping tanks with ever more effective anti-tank weapons was the antithesis of the tank's proper role on the battlefield. They looked forward, as some of their inter-war predecessors had done, to the replacement of a heavy mechanised manoeuvre force by a highly mobile air-mechanised force which included light infantry supported by artillery. The basis of this air-mechanised force* was the helicopter; its unexpected evolution from an army support aircraft to a combat aircraft must now be described.

The emergence of the helicopter as an essential combat weapon – after a long period of gestation – is comparable to the arrival of the tank on the battle field of Flanders in the First World War. In the case of the helicopter, Vietnam was the equivalent of Cambrai. The helicopter is basically a mobile lifting device with a remarkable hover performance. This is further enhanced by an ability to take off and land vertically. The possibilities of such an aircraft were perceived as early as 1918, particularly as a spotter for artillery fire. But during the inter-war years, the development of rotorcraft for military purposes was virtually neglected. In Spain, Juan de la Cierva pioneered the autogiro (a fixed wing rotorcraft). Although the British Air Ministry's Director of Scientific Research had observed that 'we have been inclined to look upon rotating wing machines as something rather humorous',[35] de la Cierva's demonstration of his C-6 autogiro at Farnborough convinced the Air Ministry sufficiently to persuade them to order a number of these new-fangled aircraft.

However the first true helicopters able to take off directly were developed by Igor Sikorsky in the United States. His R-4 machine demonstrated the full potential of the helicopter and his S-300 built in 1942 was the first to incorporate a main and tail rotor design. He was closely followed by Anton Flettner of the *Focke-Wulf* Company whose FW-61 was first demonstrated indoors in 1936.

In the Second World War, rotorcraft were used to a very limited extent for communications purposes by the Germans and the Americans. The British

---

* The term 'air mechanisation' appears to have been coined by General von Senger und Etterlin, a former German cavalry officer and Commander-in-Chief, Allied Forces Central Europe. A prolific writer on tactics, he was known for his forward-looking views.

used autogiros for calibrating radar stations. In the war years, the aeronautical engineer and designer Raoul Hafner, then the leading exponent of rotorcraft in England, proposed an ultra light rotary wing glider launched from an aircraft and steered by its pilot to land at a given point. This scheme, which envisaged the landing of light tanks in this way, had to be abandoned.

Technical Developments

After 1945, development of rotorcraft was sluggish until the Korean War when they were recognised as being valuable machines for cross-country move-ment, either evacuating casualties, carrying supplies, or moving small parties of troops into fire positions. While the main interest in development was in the States, the British did not altogether lag behind. The Cierva Company, for example, built the AIR HORSE (W11) which had three rotors of 47 feet diam-eter, arranged in the form of a triangle with one rotor leading in forward flight. Unfortunately, an accident put an end to this venture,

During the 1950s and 1960s, extensive development of helicopters took place and there was inevitably controversy over the most efficient design; whether, for instance, single rotors were more useful than tandem rotors. But it was the development of the gas turbine that brought the helicopter into greater favour. If helicopters were to carry heavier loads they had to have more power. Compared with the petrol engine, the early gas turbines were able to provide much higher power-to-weight and power-to-volume ratios. This was particularly so of the free turbine (introduced in the late 1950s) which dis-pensed with the need for a clutch in the transmission system; a drawback in all reciprocating engines. The British Westland Company built the first turbine-powered helicopter called the WESSEX; its first flight was made in the summer of 1958. In the same year the Bristol Aircraft Company's twin-turbine engined BELVEDERE went into production – the first of its kind. Though the BELVEDERE was difficult to handle, it could carry a 6000 pound load, which was quite respectable for that time.

Further attempts had meanwhile been made to improve lift with rotor tip tur-bojets. In 1951 O L L Fitzwilliams, chief designer of Westland, who had been investigating the possibility of carrying 50-ton tanks by helicopter, suggested that the tip turbojet would offer a reasonably low fuel consumption and, in the absence of a mechanical transmission system, a very low specific weight, especially for large rotors. However, technical problems had to be overcome before this form of drive was adopted.

Helicopter designers also benefited from the current development of strong, light weight composite materials which not only reduced the weight of the machine but allowed the structural engineer to produce strong lightweight rotor blades which were aerodynamically efficient. Semi-rigid titanium rotor hubs brought about simplified, lightweight, responsive control systems. Helicopters have benefited from fixed-wing aircraft improvements and have thus improved their manoeuvrability and lifting power. Such improvements paved the way for the combat helicopter.

Military Applications: from Support to Combat

The military advantages of the helicopter were perceived by the major powers at a fairly early stage of their post-war development. A British aeronautical engineer visiting the States in August 1945 reported that 'it has been proved that the helicopter can carry out many tasks which are beyond the scope of other aircraft' and it was now feasible to 'build helicopters of much larger size and to lift much greater loads than was generally thought possible a few years ago.'[36]

At that time, three possible military roles were considered: light or ultra light machines would be used for artillery spotting or liaison; larger machines would lift cargo (up to 10,000 pounds) and troops; a general purpose helicopter might be used for internal security operations or for a 'hot' war. As just noted, a strong boost to helicopters was given by the Korean war. Remembering that they had used light aircraft for liaison and evacuation of casualties in Burma in the Second World War, the Americans, faced with poor communications in Korea, naturally turned to the helicopter. There was already a promising helicopter industry in the States (largely *Sikorsky's*). The possibilities of the helicopter as a close support vehicle were not slow to be appreciated by the Russians (after seeing what the US marines had done at Inchon), Stalin himself assembled leading helicopter designers and ordered at a high priority (with dire threats of punishment if the deadline was not met) large passenger carrying helicopters which could be used to lift follow-up forces and supplies.

In Malaya meanwhile, the British had to deal with eliminating terrorists in jungle country with poor communications. General Sir Gerald Templer, the High Commissioner and Director of Operations, was one of the first senior British Army officers to appreciate that helicopters could be used for 'operational as opposed to medical evacuation purposes'[37] and badgered the War Office until he was given ten *Sikorsky* 55s flown by Royal Navy pilots. Although climatic conditions reduced their payloads, helicopters dropped parachutists into primary jungle; landing zones were then cleared and troops and supplies were ferried in by helicopter.

In spite of their proven value in Malaya, the Army, unlike the Navy, was slow to accept helicopters. A Chiefs of Staff working party, reporting in the summer of 1953, gave priority to the light helicopter used for air observation post duties. It conceded that the Americans had an appreciable lead in development having acquired experience from early types of helicopter 'produced in numbers'. Thus it was vital to obtain experience with British designs. Lack of cooperation between the Services was another obstacle. The RAF was unwilling to deal with aircraft which had no combat value. It regarded helicopters as 'expensive, complicated and irrelevant aircraft, inherently unreliable and difficult to maintain.'[38] The Army recognised their value as load carriers over the battlefield, so dispensing with road-bound trucks, but was concerned about their vulnerability to attack from the ground and from the air, and to their inability to operate at night. A judgement on such matters could only be obtained from experience. At last, in 1954, a joint Army-Air Force experimental helicopter unit (JEHU) was formed to find out whether helicopters were 'a practical, efficient and economical means of solving the Army's problem of mobility, organisation and administration in the field in a future war.'[39]

Three years later, after the 1957 Defence Review, the question of helicopter control was solved when the Army was made responsible for its own air operations and light liaison aircraft. The RAF controlled the medium and heavy lift helicopter capability for the Army.

The technical developments described above made it possible for helicopters to have greater endurance and to carry five to ten ton loads. Coinciding with, and later stimulated by, the Vietnam war, the concept of the combat helicopter was born. Guns and rockets were strapped on to so-called helicopter 'gunships' and used against Viet Cong positions in Vietnam. Rather surprisingly, the loss rates were low, compared with fixed wing aircraft, and demonstrated that combat helicopters could sustain continuous operations in the battle area, and that many machines after being shot down were repairable. But current types of helicopter were too slow and it was only when the AH-1G HUEY COBRA was introduced that the true attack helicopter went into action. It could dive at high speed like a fighter bomber and therefore, it was concluded, could be used as a 'tank-buster'. Indeed, as early as 1963, the French had equipped *ALOUETTE* helicopters with S-11 missiles for operations in Algeria.

As we have seen, the value of helicopters in the anti-tank role was somewhat exaggerated, judged by experience in the Middle East. However, helicopter development did not stand still, Helicopters were becoming less vulnerable with the fitting of armour, under floor fuel tanks and honeycomb structures to quench fires when hit. They were also becoming less obtrusive with flat canopy surfaces to reduce glint, and mast-mounted sights above the main rotor enabling the helicopter body to be hidden behind cover.

Furthermore, more sophisticated air defence systems had forced fixed wing aircraft to fly either about 200 feet above the ground or to fly at very high altitudes. Attack helicopters flying nap-of-the-earth, making use of hillsides and trees and moving faster than battle tanks, might well alter the course of the battle, especially when armed, as was the US APACHE, with eight HELLFIRE missiles (the replacement for TOW).

Plate 17 APACHE: US combat helicopter. Combines fire power mobility and defensive hardness. It flies nap-of-the-earth. Fixed wing aircraft avoid it or risk possible destruction. (*Royal Aeronautical Society*)

Plate 18 CHINOOK: US-designed medium lift helicopter. During the Falklands War in 1982, one CHINOOK moved over 1000 tons of freight and 15,000 troops. (*Royal Aeronautical Society*)

135

Soviet doctrine for combat helicopters encapsulated this philosophy with the phrase 'The infantry boot is to the tank tread as the tank tread is to the helicopter rotor.' The Soviet intention was evidently to break 'the ground friction of the tank, and elevate the average velocity of movement of the tank battle of the past, which parallels the armoured vehicle battle to battle velocity of about 20mph, and ascends to several hundred feet and makes the blade to the tread as the tread was to the boot.'[40] From this it might be inferred that combat helicopters would assume more battlefield roles including combat with fixed wing aircraft.

American military theorists in the 1980s believed that even the relatively slow speed of helicopters could be turned to their advantage. According to the ALB doctrine, 85 per cent of battlefield missions were within three miles of the forward line of troops. Because of this and the need to fly safely, nap-of-the-earth, speeds in excess of 170 knots were not yet required. On the other hand, helicopters still presented an infra-red signature, but could defend themselves by making use of chaff or smoke in addition to their very low flying capability.

Though greatly favoured by the soldiers, the high cost of attack helicopters meant that they got a lukewarm reception in Britain from the Treasury. However, the role of the medium lift helicopter for transporting troops and supplies across the battlefield continued to be accepted as being of the utmost importance. By 1978, a medium lift helicopter was required by the British Army in succession to the WESSEX able to carry a 9½ ton load, primarily the FH-70 howitzer, and the ability to lift 38 troops in one go. This requirement was fulfilled by the US CHINOOK tandem rotor helicopter. It was to prove its worth in all the phases of the Falklands war. After the destruction of four CHINOOKS in their transport ship, the one remaining aircraft flew 107 hours, with virtually no maintenance, and in doing so moved over 1000 tons of freight and 15,000 troops.' According to the Ministry of Defence Scientific Survey, it was 'a critical force asset, for without its ability to keep the smaller helicopters supplied with fuel, these could not in turn have supplied the artillery ammunition to the guns; which were essential for the advance and eventual victory.'[41] At last the British Army, hampered by an innate conservatism and by parsimonious defence budgets, had perceived, long after the Americans and the Soviets, the value of helicopters as a revolutionary way of providing fire power, mobility and flexibility, now enhanced by improved protection.

Guided Missiles or Artillery? Introduction of the Tactical Surface-to-Surface Missile

The doctrine for artillery up to the end of the 1940s was to use it to bring down quick and accurate concentrations of fire in support of the assaulting infantry. The advent of radio made an enormous difference to the application of artillery fire. Not only was the response time greatly reduced but the use of a common artillery grid made for much greater flexibility in switching large numbers of guns on to a single target or group of targets. But from the 1950s onwards, the battlefield was transformed by two new factors. First, the threat of nuclear attack in forward areas called for increased tactical dispersion, both laterally and in depth. Ranges of artillery weapons had to be increased to maintain the principle of concentration of fire. Secondly, commanders of armies in the West realised that they were likely to be greatly outnumbered in the field and needed a weapon of great power to deal with heavy concentrations of enemy personnel and weapons.

Surface-to-Surface Missiles (SSMs) could take on targets at ranges of from 30 to 100 miles, far beyond the capability of the heavier types of artillery. They could also be used against targets normally engaged by close-support aircraft but which, under conditions of bad weather or an adverse air situation, would be immune from attack. Typical roles for such weapons in attack would be preparatory bombardment to destroy defences, weapons and materiel; in defence, defensive fire in depth to break up preparations for attack, while general tasks included counter-bombardment, harassing fire and isolation of the battlefield in conjunction with the tactical air force. The degree of accuracy demanded was to get the warhead to within a hundred yards of the target. Ultimately, it was anticipated that a CEP of no more than five yards would be achieved. As the range of ground-based weapons increased, so did the importance of radars, drones and RPVs (discussed in Chapter 4).

The Americans, benefiting from their exploitation of the Peenemunde scientists and technicians, took the lead in developing SSMs. In 1953, HONEST JOHN, an unguided rocket with a range of 25 miles, was introduced, followed several years later by CORPORAL which had a maximum range of about 80 miles. These early SSMs were quite cheap to build but were clumsy, inaccurate and had a slow rate of fire. HONEST JOHN, for example, required 15 vehicles to carry all its components, which weighed no less than 100 tons and, when assembled, could only fire six rounds a day. CORPORAL took an hour to be fuelled, erected and armed and a further 15–30 minutes to be fired from the launcher. Four hours were occupied in checking each missile. SERGEANT was the last of the first generation of US SSMs to go into service; it had a better performance than CORPORAL, having inertial guidance and a solid propellant, and could be deployed in 30 minutes; it had a range of 85 miles. The US Army was equipped with SERGEANTS from 1961–78. The second generation of US SSMs was inaugurated in 1972 by LANCE which had a range of nearly 100 miles. Altogether it was lighter and more mobile than earlier SSMs and even managed to be less costly.

The Soviet Army was developing comparable SSMs with ranges of 50 to 150 miles at the same time.

Plate 19a LANCE: US tactical surface-to-surface missile. Also used by the British Army against targets beyond the range of heavy artillery and especially when bad weather inhibits air support. (*LTV Aerospace and Defense Company*)

The British would dearly have liked to develop their own SSMs and, as early as 1945, had plans for a weapon with a range of 150 miles. But they lacked both the finance and the facilities for fundamental research. In December 1952, Sir Steuart Mitchell, Controller General of Guided Weapons and Electronic Equipment in the Ministry of Supply, who had been responsible for introducing the famous OERLIKON gun to the Royal Navy in the Second World War, was confronted by the Deputy Director of Artillery. The latter wanted to 'redress the balance in the comparative performance of Russian artillery and our own which was at present all in favour of the Russian.'[42] Mitchell had to reply that the time was not yet ripe for testing the best available American missile in the United Kingdom. In due course, however, the British Army was to order HONEST JOHNS and CORPORALS.

By the mid-1950s the British General Staff was still concerned about the increasing range and accuracy of Soviet artillery and wanted to develop their own SSMs equipped with conventional or nuclear warheads. They should have a range of 35–40 miles and be used against targets of opportunity like troop or armour concentrations or to neutralise enemy long range artillery. The weapons had to be air-transportable, as Britain still had overseas commitments. It was 'important that they should go into action more quickly and be more accurate than their equivalents.'

Two designs were submitted and contracts accepted by British aircraft

Plate 19b LANCE firing. (*FMC Corporation*)

companies. They were named RED ROSE and BLUE WATER and should have come into service in the mid-1960s.[43] But the stress laid on accuracy in the former proved to be a stumbling block, as the radar guidance system (BLUE CEDAR) was too heavy to be air-transportable and the development of an alternative inertial guidance system could not be completed before the missiles were due to go into service. BLUE WATER would have had a nuclear warhead. Progress was delayed by arguments about range, other NATO countries wanting it increased to 50 miles. In 1952, financial considerations led the British to cancel BLUE WATER and so to opt out altogether of SSM technology. HONEST JOHN was replaced by another American missile – LANCE which had a modified inertial thrust control guidance system.

But SSMs like LANCE were disadvantaged in that they were expensive because of their reliance on inertial guidance and they continued to have a relatively slow rate of fire. However, by the late 1970s, it appeared that rocket and rapid fire artillery were able to carry out the tasks of SSMs just as effectively by producing a heavy weight of fire very quickly and then moving. Their accuracy was enhanced by employing electronic distance measuring equipment (DME) which provided specific distance and azimuth information from a ground transponder and which was well endowed with fast frequency hopping and other counters to avoid the effects of jamming.

Improvements in Fire Control and Artillery Munitions

While so much effort and time was being expended on missile development, the wand of the electronic revolution had begun to transform conventional artillery weapons, giving them greater flexibility by improving fire control and endowing them with greater accuracy and more rapid fire.

Hitherto, the control of artillery fire was based on the traditional time-consuming procedure, accompanied by laborious calculations performed manually, which were necessary to solve ballistical problems. All this was now taken over by the computer. As we have seen, at the close of the Second World War the preparation of range tables was greatly facilitated by early computers such as ENIAC. The next stage was to bring the computer up to the gun to deal rapidly and comprehensively with all the meteorological and other variables that accompanied the firing of modern artillery. In the 1960s and 1970s, armies in the East and West were engaged in introducing automated equipment for this purpose.

In 1969, the British Army was provided with the Field Artillery Computer Equipment (FACE).[44] It was designed to fulfil two main tasks. First, it was able to compute all the variables involved in the meteorological data required by artillery, even making allowances for the effects of earth rotation and differing latitudes. Second, it acted as a rapid processor for the mass of variables involved in firing guns. Its simplicity of operation greatly reduced the risk of human error in battle and reduced the time required to train personnel.

FACE's adoption was almost fortuitous. The Royal Artillery wanted a non-operational computer system which would simulate an American model which they had intended to adopt, but which had run into trouble with its memory and power supply. Elliott Automation produced an automated system which was so impressive that it was decided to develop it round a more advanced data processor of intermediate technology but good enough for the purpose. It proved to be an outstanding success, so much so that in the early 1970s the Americans themselves decided to adopt it.

Developed in parallel with FACE was the Artillery Weapon Data Transmission System (AWDATS) which presented the firing data computed by FACE at the individual guns of the firing unit. The great advantage of

AWDATS was that by partially eliminating the requirement for verbal transmissions and checking back of gun firing data, the speed of reaction and thus the efficiency of the artillery system was greatly improved.

The advent of FACE gave access to a wide range of factors influencing the accuracy of artillery fire which, until then, could only be guessed at. A mass of meteorological data, such as humidity, air density and air temperatures could now be assimilated and calculated. The problem was to gather and distribute this information in time to be useful for firing the guns. The answer was to introduce into one system data processors, radar, transmitting sensor carriers (known as radiosondes) which could transmit information from RPVs, or messages concerning sound ranging or nuclear fallout. This system, known as the Artillery Meteorological System (AMETS), eliminated the long delays and chances of human error associated with manual meteorological computation. At the time of introduction, AMETS was considered to be well in advance of any similar weather data information gathering system in use by any other army.

Up to the mid-1970s, British artillery fire was controlled at the level of batteries or regiments and overall command was given only in general terms or as part of a pre-set fire plan. The magnitude of a potential artillery threat on a European front meant that the best possible use had to be made of all available artillery. From the mid-1970s, planning began on the Battlefield Artillery Engagement System (BATES) which would make enable artillery commanders and staffs to make the most effective use of their artillery resources.[45] BATES operated on a corps basis, information being passed down to subsidiary units by the digital transfer of data over combat net radio, line and trunk communications. The purpose of this coordinated information would enable guns to hit their targets with the optimum weight of fire at the right moment. Artillery commanders were able to adjust their resources to meet a rapidly changing situation. Such flexibility had not been possible in a manual system.

Artillerists had striven for greater effectiveness in their projectiles for many years. In the 1940s, the most important advance had been the introduction of the proximity fuse, used successfully against the V-1s, but less successfully when low level air bursts were fired against ground targets, the fuses were then prematurely detonated by rain or cloud. In the 1970s, laser beams, described earlier, seemed to offer a means of guiding shells to their target in the same way as missiles. More specifically, the intention was to convert short-ranged artillery like howitzers into anti-tank weapons able to hit the vulnerable tops of armoured fighting vehicles. These developments were initiated in the United States. A shell was designed with fins and wings which opened after the shell had left the barrel of a 155 millimetre cannon. The target, some three miles away, was illuminated by a laser beam operated by an observer placed at some distance from the gun. After attaining the vertex of its trajectory, the shell glided towards the target, its warhead fitted with a shaped charge. COPPERHEAD, as it was called, had not been perfected by the end of our period.[46] It was complex and expensive. The fins required a longer, and therefore heavier, shell, causing range to be reduced. A second pair of wings was added to overcome this deficiency. There were other snags. The laser operator was exposed to danger and the beam itself was sensitive to rain, wet objects, smoke, dust and physical objects like trees and bushes. Nonetheless, it was hoped that the second generation of COPPERHEAD would at least overcome some of these difficulties.

The necessity to increase range, as just noted, has always obsessed artillerists and they have exploited every promising development. The painful fact was that Warsaw Pact artillery out-numbered and out-ranged the guns of NATO's armies. Guns with a range of at least 15 miles and automatic loading were needed. The Russians were content to deploy two weapons – a gun and a howitzer, but NATO needed the maximum flexibility in the smallest number of weapons; while the ability to vary the charge necessitated some sacrifice in maximum range. The Americans, at least, had a 175 millimetre gun with a range of 35 miles.

From the 1960s onwards, experiments were made with the object of increasing range by lengthening gun barrels and improving propellants, thus giving higher muzzle velocities. It was estimated that the range of NATO artillery, then limited to ranges of 9 to 18 miles could be doubled. Rocket-assisted propulsion (RAP) would further increase this range to 24 miles. But rocket-assisted projectiles were not popular because they were inaccurate, they had a lower shell payload due to the RAP chamber volume, and they were costly.

Less complex and therefore more attractive, was a technique invented in Sweden in the 1970s known as base bleeding.[47] The aim was to reduce the drag of a shell in flight. While in flight, a shell is subjected to three forms of drag:

1 body drag caused by rotation and friction;
2 wave drag, caused by the shape of the forward part of the shell; and
3 base drag, resulting from the partial vacuum formed at the base of the shell in flight, pulling it back.

Base bleeding consists of the incorporation of combustible material into the base of the shell. While burning, this produces oxygen-deficient gases. When these are emitted through the base of the shell into the airstream, extra oxygen becomes available enabling these products to burn and thus increase the gas pressure in the base of the shell. Base drag was reduced by as much as 80 per cent and extended the range of, say, an M109 self-propelled medium gun by 4 to 14½ miles.

Plate 20 British 105 mm Light Gun, developed for overseas and airborne operations. It was admired for its performance in the Falklands War 1982. The gun crew are in NBC clothing. (*Royal Ordnance*)

Increasing the rate of fire could be achieved by automatic loading techniques and improved recoil systems. Modern guns usually fire a burst rate of ten rounds per minute with a lower sustained rate. It is worth noting that the British 105 millimetre gun, developed for overseas and airborne operations in the 1960s, incorporated some of the innovations just described. Using very high grade steels, with advanced production techniques, such as explosive forming of various components, it achieved a weight much less than the veteran 25 pounder and fired a 30 per cent heavier shell to a considerably greater range (18,500yds). It was accepted by the US Marine Corps and sold to other foreign armies. It was in its element in the difficult Falklands terrain.

Saturation Weapons

Rocket artillery with terminal guidance was able to deliver a very heavy weight of fire quickly and then move on to new positions ('shoot and scoot'). But it did not have the necessary rate of fire to match multiple-launch rocket systems. As we have observed, the Soviets made good use of rockets in the Second World War and continued to develop more sophisticated types of rocket launcher from the 1950s onwards. In 1964, their formidable 122 millimetre rocket launcher, able to fire 40 rounds, either HE or chemical, went into service and three years later was used by the Egyptians against the Israelis. In the 1970s, their *BM-27* firing 16 220 millimetre rockets filled with HE, chemicals, or fragmentation bomblets, with an effective range of 24 miles became operational.

The numerical inferiority of NATO armaments in the 1960s (which gave the Warsaw Pact divisions an advantage of 6:1 in all types of equipment) stimulated the development of rocket systems. They had the advantage of being able to be used in all types of weather and could be operated when the tactical air force had to be grounded. In 1967, the US Army issued a requirement for a long range rocket system to offset the disparity in forces on the central front. This was originally called the General Support Rocket System. A comparable British-Italian-West German project (RS80) was already underway but was abandoned in 1978 for the American system which then became known as the Multiple Launch Rocket System (MLRS). At about the same time, France abandoned her 227mm SYRA system and joined the international programme. Production was to take place in Europe and the United States. The West Germans also embarked on a 110 millimetre Light Artillery Rocket System (LARS) firing ripples of 36 rockets at ranges of seven to eight miles. However, lavish expenditure of munitions gave rise to logistical problems, the significance of which will be discussed at the end of this chapter.

The West Germans, who were unable to buy precise delivery weapons, devised several so-called area weapons which were intended to hold up an

144

Plate 21 US Multiple Launch Rocket System (MLRS). Designed to provide saturation fire over a wide area very quickly. Played an important part in the Gulf War. (*FMC Corporation*)

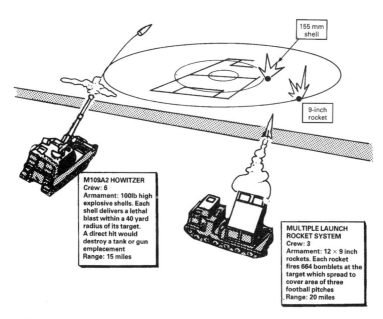

Figure 12 Comparison between the areas of impact of a medium gun and MLRS.

145

all-out conventional attack. Two of these were designed specifically to immo-bilise tanks. Known as *PANDORA* and *MEDUSA*, they were small anti-tank mines which could be projected by rockets (or alternatively dropped by air-craft). *MEDUSA* had a magnetic hollow charge capable of penetrating the underneath of an armoured vehicle. A third device called *DRAGON SEED* was similar to a cluster bomb and again could be used in rocket barrages or dispersed by aircraft.

Air Defence: Guns or Missiles?

An outstanding lesson of the Second World War was that a ground offensive could not be conducted successfully without the winning of air superiority: hence the spectacular ease with which the Germans advanced into the Low Countries and France in 1940, the tables being dramatically turned when the Allies returned to the continent in 1944. However, the leap forward made by high speed jet aircraft at medium heights, but particularly at low level, reduced the ability of defending air forces to ensure air cover. In any case, constant air cover over an army in the field could not be guaranteed; tactical aircraft were attacking defended positions or operating deeper into enemy territory against lines of communication and airfields. The need for effective ground-based air defences for ground forces therefore continued.

The German development of SAMs, limited though it was, pointed the way to future ground-to-air defence. Missiles, as they appeared to the planners of air defence in the late 1940s, would provide greater security than guns. Hostile aircraft could be followed during the time of flight of the missile and passing aircraft could be engaged effectively. Missiles were lethal at greater ranges than guns. In September 1953, the War Office concluded that the medium anti-aircraft gun had 'lost the altitude race with aircraft'.[48] Unless guns could be modernised fairly rapidly and inexpensively their effective engagement height was limited to around 20,000 feet. SAMs, due to improved radar, could deliver fire in virtually all conditions of visibility and, because of their accu-racy, the amount of ammunition required could be greatly reduced. Finally, the warheads of missiles and their fusing arrangements were more effective and lethal than current anti-aircraft shells. On the other hand, SAMs had, like ATGMs, a minimum range within which the weapon was ineffective. This was the range needed to bring them under control. And the greater the employment of radar, the more vulnerable was the equipment to hostile ECM.

The introduction of SAMs presented the British with a dilemma. They needed two types, one for home defence to be at constant readiness to destroy sustained attacks by hostile aircraft carrying nuclear weapons, and the other was for the defence of unavoidable concentrations of troops or materiel in the field in Europe or elsewhere. Clearly, priority had to be given to home defence.

The prototype weapon for this role was RED DUSTER (later BLOODHOUND) and was developed by the Bristol Aircraft company and Ferranti; it was propelled by the, as yet, untried ram jet system; tracking was provided by a semi-active radar called YELLOW RIVER and control by ORANGE YEOMAN, later replaced by BLUE YEOMAN (TYPE 85 set) which had improved anti-jamming facilities.[49] Initial development of the radars took place at RRDE/RRE. BLOODHOUND (range 49 miles) was eventually deployed to defend V bomber bases and was also installed at points near the East Coast.* Mobility was not important.The Army's SAM was called RED SHOES (later THUNDERBIRD) and was designed by Leslie Bedford of English Electric, 'an exceptionally gifted research and development engineer'[50] who had worked on fire control radar since its early days. The weapon had to be light and mobile. Its role was to shoot down medium bombers and fighters flying at subsonic speeds up to heights of 30,000 feet, at a range of 46 miles. It had the same guidance system as RED DUSTER but was propelled by a solid fuel system.

Development of the two missiles was characterised by the different approaches of their makers. Bristol used their final air frame from the start while English Electric were more cautious, testing everything before firing. Lengthy trials of both weapons ensued in the United Kingdom and in Australia. At last, by 1958, both missiles had concluded their trials. BLOODHOUND had scored a direct hit at over 30,000 feet ('the highest altitude yet achieved').[51] Both missiles were improved in second generations which came into service in 1964–65. The British Army, however, purchased only one regiment of THUNDERBIRD – far too little to sustain a production line of missiles. Both Mark 2 systems employed continuous wave radars which were less vulnerable to jamming; both weapons had longer ranges. In retrospect, the development of two SAMs by a nation undergoing severe economic difficulties was almost certainly an over-insurance.

While these missiles were being developed, an interim modern heavy antiaircraft gun was needed to provide an insurance should the SAMs not come up to expectation. This was GREEN MACE; it was intended to deal with sustained air attacks firing 80 rounds per minute in 20 second bursts with 20 second intervals for 20 minutes.[52] A fin-stabilised, discarding sabot projectile was used to give a high effective ceiling and was fired through a smooth barrel; another version had a rifled barrel and had a lower performance. One of its interesting features was the skirt on the back of the shell which carried the driving band and expanded into the bore as the gun wore. The rapid rate of fire caused severe wear and tear, however, while the gun's massive water cooling

---

* The Army's Anti-Aircraft Command was disbanded in March 1958 and the RAF became responsible for home defence SAMs.

Plate 22 THUNDERBIRD: British medium to high surface-to-air guided missile. It succeeded the anti-aircraft gun in the ground-based air defence system for the UK. (*Royal Aeronautical Society*)

system made it extremely cumbersome. The viability of THUNDERBIRD and BLOODHOUND led to GREEN MACE being made redundant in 1954.

The Americans experienced similar difficulties with their battlefield SAM. At the outset, the first home air defence SAMs (NIKE-AJAX and NIKE-HERCULES deployed in the SAGE system and later adapted to anti-ballistic missile defence) were sent to the US Army in Germany to protect vulnerable points. But the first mobile SAM for use on the battlefield was HAWK. For the first time, it had continuous wave semi-active radar guidance and a range of 21 miles. HAWK however, was cumbersome, manpower-intensive and expensive. In 1981, it was superseded by a long-range, medium to high altitude SAM called PATRIOT which had a multi-function, semi-active radar which made it possible to engage a number of targets simultaneously at ranges up to 37 miles. The apparent success of PATRIOT against the Iraqi SCUD SSMs has recently been questioned. It is possible that the debris from the SCUDs, such as empty fuel tanks and tail fins, as they re-entered the earth's atmosphere, may have acted as unintentional but effective decoys to the PATRIOTs.

So far we have discussed medium to long-range SAMs. But, by the late 1950s, ground forces urgently needed protection against attack by supersonic bombers flying at less than 500 feet at speeds of the order of Mach 0.9 or even Mach 1.3 in order to elude radar-controlled fighter defences. Furthermore, the technique of toss bombing, in which bombs were delivered under a 'g' pull, created a new problem for anti-aircraft defences. Other technical advances in the 1950s and 1960s favoured low level air attack, namely terrain-following radar, head-up displays, and cluster weapons. The tip and run attack gave way to saturation attacks at low level. One possibility of countering this threat was to use rocket-assisted shells, unguided rockets like LOKI,* and conventional rockets. Three inch LOKI rockets were capable of hitting targets at heights of 80,000ft The alternative was to design a low altitude air defence guided missile.

How did the British tackle the problem? From 1957 onwards, a small group of scientists at RSRE studied aspects of low level air defence. Two members of this group, C Barron and J E Twinn, found themselves 'surprised and distressed by the total lack of hard data and the fog of vague and contradictory opinions on the subject. Operational research itself, after its great flowering during the war, had lost its verve, and we no longer had a background of methodology or techniques to fall back on.'[53] No sooner had they embarked on a thorough analysis of how SAMs should be sited than they were called upon to advise on the suitability of an Army requirement for a SAM designated PT428. They did not take long to appreciate that too much was being expected of PT428 including the need to be effective against tactical missiles and rockets. As they later explained, 'guided weapons engineers were on the crest of a wave of enthusiasm and arrogance which comes with a technology which has not yet met its first big failure'.

After submitting a criticism of PT428, Barron and Twinn resumed their research and made a survey of several areas in North-West Germany where SAMs would be deployed. They found how difficult it was to site short range anti-aircraft weapons because of obstacles such as hills, trees and buildings. They concluded that the employment of expensive weapons would be a waste of time and money. Instead, better results would be obtained with larger numbers of low cost units.

PT428 was cancelled at the end of 1961 along with BLUE WATER. The Army decided to buy MAULER, an American SAM with a maximum range of 10,000–15,000 yards, similar in performance to PT428. All the components were mounted on one vehicle weighing about 10 tons and manned by a crew of two men. Although discouraged by the Army, Barron and Twinn 'quietly and with only one or two people assisting, began to tackle the conception of a new system' of low level air defence. They initially selected an optical guidance system on the grounds that the air threat would be far worse by day than

---

* The predecessor of LOKI was the German SAM called TAIFUN (noted on page 3) and was one of the post-war projects at the Jet Propulsion Laboratory. Work on it was cancelled after the advent of the more efficient NIKE.

by night. The missile would be supersonic and fitted with a small, simple warhead relying on accurate guidance to hit the target. This allowed the design of a smaller missile and lighter launcher which were much more effective than a missile fitted with a proximity fuse to detonate it. Their study was completed in two months but was initially rejected by the authorities in March 1962. Luckily, the two scientists found a sympathetic hearing in several senior officers and the General Staff was persuaded in October 1962 that a study contract should be placed with British Aircraft Corporation. By that time it had been decided to supplement the optical tracking system with a semi-active radar called BLINDFIRE.

Meanwhile, in 1965, the Americans had cancelled their MAULER programme (as predicted by Barron and Twinn); the RAPIER system, as it was now called, stood alone. Although its maximum range (7,436 yards) was slightly less than MAULER, it had a maximum operational height of 9,800 feet. The fire unit was towed by a one-ton Land Rover which carried an optical tracker and three crew. A second vehicle towed the radar unit and a ¾-ton Land Rover carried crew members and stores. Ammunition was distributed between the three vehicles. By 1971, the first units were being deployed by the

Plate 23 RAPIER: British low level surface-to-air guided missile. During the Falklands War it was credited with 14 confirmed kills for 45 missiles fired. (Note the position of the controller (right) separated from the actual missile site). (*Royal Aeronautical Society*)

Army and the Royal Air Force Regiment. A tracked, semi-armoured version for use near the battle area was introduced some years later.

RAPIER proved itself in the Falklands war. Its crews were known by the troops trying to form a beachhead at San Carlos Bay as the 'most popular guys around.' Later they provided cover to the advance on Port Stanley. They were credited with 14 confirmed kills with only 45 missiles fired.[54] RAPIER was also a commercial success and was exported to twelve nations. It 'obtained about half the export market for this type of weapon, with sales roughly equal to those of its rivals put together.' These were the French *CROTALE*, intended for the defence of mobile targets, the Franco-German *ROLAND*, an all-weather missile, and the American CHAPARRAL, originally earmarked as a stand-in tactical SAM for NATO forces.

The designers of RAPIER later claimed that it combined three features which had never been made to work before, namely: 'an unmanned, multi-function surveillance radar; automatic control of a supersonic missile to a sight line; and a guidance and control system so accurate as to allow a direct hitting missile design.' Finally, they reckoned that there were three useful lessons to be learned from its development:

1 proper application of operational analysis;
2 the importance of the scientist advancing his own view and arguing for it; and
3 insistence on low cost which could, and did, lead to elegant design.

PT428 and MAULER, on the other hand, were not properly subjected to cost restraints; hence they were much more of a pedestrian design than RAPIER.

While RAPIER was the Army's principal defence against low-flying aircraft, a 'light weight self-defence SAM was also needed', according to a working party set up under Professor R V Jones to study the problem of air defence in the period 1975–85. BLOWPIPE (optical guidance) produced by Short Brothers fulfilled this role and was even approved by the RAF who 'initially saw in it the means by which every British soldier might be able to shoot down every low-flying British aircraft.'[55] BLOWPIPE was credited with nine kills in the Falklands – fortunately all Argentine. Its American counterpart was the infra-red-guided STINGER which also performed well in the Falklands and was used with success in Afghanistan by the Mujahidin against Soviet aircraft.

It would be wrong to assume from this catalogue of sophisticated SAMs that became available in the 1970s that the anti-aircraft gun had gone out of favour. Quite the contrary. SAMs have three weaknesses. They tend to be ineffective at altitudes below 1000 feet because of the difficulty of getting good radar coverage below that height, especially at distances over two miles from the missile site. Secondly, their complexity makes them relatively slow to respond to

Plate 24 BLOWPIPE: British man-portable short-range surface-to-air guided missile. A light weight point defence system for the infantryman. (*Short Brothers*)

intruder aircraft when compared with anti-aircraft guns. Thirdly, each missile site has a limited number of rounds available for immediate use. Ideally, a combination of SAMs and anti-aircraft artillery makes a potent defence against aircraft.

The Soviets were quick to seize on this point. They developed two multi-barrelled, radar-controlled anti-aircraft guns; the first was the *ZSU57-2* with a calibre of 57 millimetres and two barrels with a maximum range of 2½ miles in 1957. Eight years later came the *ZSU23-4* with four barrels, able to fire 4000 rounds per minute, as opposed to the mere 240 rounds per minute of its pre-decessor. It is worth noting that the electronics of the *ZSU23-4* were still based upon valves. However, the system was so well designed that the weapon was extremely robust and reliable. Its main draw-back was the speed with which it ran out of ammunition.

This weapon, handled by the Syrians in the assault on the Golan Heights in the Yom Kippur war, won admiration from military observers. The beleagured Israeli ground forces were deprived of the air support to which they were accustomed.[56] On the afternoon of 7 October 1973, the loss of Israeli fighters due to the *ZSU23-4s* had become intolerable . It was only by flying just above the ground, delivering their weapon load, and pulling away before their sil-houettes were acquired by the Syrian radars that they were able to provide some support. The Israeli pilots were also surprised by the sophistication of the enemy's electronic defences. However, they were very quickly able to acquire ECCM pods from the United States to fit to their aircraft with which they could jam the radar-directed SAMs and anti-aircraft artillery.

The 1973 war demonstrated that troops in defence with an inferior air force could parry low level attacks with SAMs and anti-aircraft guns. In a case where the defence had a powerful air force as well as an effective ground defence, units would be able to withstand an air assault. The attacker would have to fall back on ground artillery. It was significant that after the 1973 war, the Israelis, who hitherto had relied heavily on close air support for offensive operations, began to increase their number of artillery units. At the same time, Israeli military aircraft manufacturers were driven to reassessing the design of future strike aircraft.

Technology and Infantry Weapons

'While machine power counts more than man power in the gross . . . it would nonetheless seem that within the reduced scope of the infantry's role, the value of the skilled individual fighter has increased . . . an infantryman can seize or create many opportunities for vital intervention on the modern battlefield . . . by his readiness to take advantage of the diversion caused or the power given by artillery fire, tanks, smoke, fog, darkness.'[57]

So wrote that revolutionary infantry officer, Captain Basil Liddell Hart over 50 years ago. In retrospect his observations (as far as conventional warfare is concerned) would seem to be still appropriate. Yet the infantryman was ever the 'poor relation' when it came to sharing out new equipment. His rifle (in the case of the British) was virtually the same weapon in 1945 as used by his forebears in 1914. He was still using the Vickers machine gun, introduced in 1912; the 3 inch mortar was little more than an advanced model of the weapon used in Flanders in 1917–18. His anti-tank weapons would make little impact on a Soviet *T-34*.

The search for a lighter, more effective individual weapon for the infantry-man was led by the German Army which, some years before the Second World War had appreciated that the weight of the rifle and its ammunition could be reduced and yet would still be able to kill at the relatively short ranges of around 400 yards or under that might be expected in modern war-fare. It was the outcome of German studies – the *Sturmgewehr* light automatic rifle firing a 7.92 x 33 millimetre *Kurz* round – that won the admiration of the Western Allies and the Russians during the war. However it was the Soviet Army that proved to be more receptive to the qualities of the German auto-matic rifle and developed the famous *AK47*, designed by Mikhail Timofeyevich Kalashnikov.

In contrast, American and British rifle development was slow and led to interminable arguments over the standardisation of ammunition. After the war, the US Army was still equipped with the M-1, a light weight rifle introduced in 1936. This was intended to be replaced by the M-14 rifle. The British weapon descended from a rifle designed by a Belgian, Dieudonne Saive, who before the war worked for the *Fabrique Nationale*; it was called the *Fabrique Nationale Fusil Automatique Léger* (FNFAL) and had a high rate of fire and an accuracy up to about 300 yards. When adapted by the British in 1947, it was known as the EM-2.[58]

When NATO was formed two years later, it became essential to standardise the rifle round, each army then having its own calibre. Two more years elapsed before the Americans, British, French and Canadians realised that they had a common interest for an interchangeable round for the infantry weapon. The common requirements were agreed in September 1951 and the four nations, now joined by Belgium, undertook simultaneous studies with exchanges of information. The eventual choice lay between a 7 millimetre round favoured by the British and a heavier 7.62 millimetre one favoured by the Americans who wanted a round that would be suitable for both a new rifle and a new light weight general purpose machine gun. In the interests of the Alliance, the British agreed to cancel their revolutionary EM-2 design and adopt the 7.62 round which would fit into the FNAL. In December 1953, NATO agreed on the common round and the British discarded their time-honoured Small Magazine Lee Enfield for the FNAL.

The Americans, however, did not adopt the FNAL, but continued to use the 37 year old M-1, at the same time going on developing the M-14. This programme did not receive the high priority it should have had and at last fell victim to the rationalisation programme of Robert McNamara on 23 January 1963. Instructions were given to replace it with the M-16 but when in a few years time the US Army was committed to fighting in Vietnam, the need for a new rifle became urgent and in the ensuing haste a botched model emerged. This was replaced by an improved version called the M-16A2.[59]

By the early 1970s, the Soviet Army had begun to introduce a new family of individual weapons. NATO had to prepare to meet the challenge and new studies were put in hand. The most interesting new weapon was the high velocity ARMALITE (AR-15) firing a small 5.5 millimetre round; it was the brain child of Eugene M Stoner. Ironically, the British were able to evaluate the rifle without the political and economic restraints imposed by NATO and they adopted it in advance of the US Army; it was especially useful in an internal security role. The Americans had by this time come round to accepting smaller calibres for their individual rounds weapon and in 1971 adopted the M-16A1 with a 5.56 millimetre round. The British, after looking at smaller calibres, agreed to adopt the Belgian 5.56 millimetre SS-10 round with a steel core. It was to be used in their latest individual weapon, the XL70E3 which had a maximum range of 430 yards. Such was the state of play at the end of our period.

The sub-machine gun (SMG) was first introduced for military use during the Second World War, again due chiefly to German initiative although in America, the Thompson 0.45 inch weapon, beloved by the Chicago gangster, was available to the Army. The SMG was invaluable for close quarter fighting, in built-up areas and for commando-type operations and was retained by all armies in the post-war period. The British replaced their highly utilitarian and unreliable STEN 9 millimetre weapon with the STERLING or L2A3, for use not only by the infantry but also by tank crews and artillerymen. The need for a silenced version for use by Special Forces, led to the production of L3A1. A night sight can be attached to this weapon.

The American proposal for a general purpose machine gun has been mentioned briefly. Generations of British troops had used the Vickers water-cooled machine gun and its reliability was an argument in itself for retaining it. But conditions on the battlefield were changing and, once again, the Germans had anticipated them with their MG-34 and MG-42 machine guns; artillery fire had become more accurate, making a machine gun able to fire over 2000 yards redundant. From 1963 onwards, the medium Vickers machine gun was replaced by the GENERAL PURPOSE MACHINE GUN. This weapon was based on the West German Army's decision to combine light and heavy types of machine gun into one model fulfilling both roles. The BREN light machine gun, stand-by of the British Army since 1939, gave way to a belt-fed automatic weapon (the L4A4) in 1957, but the new gun had a fault, in that the belt picked up dirt. It was gradually replaced by the GPMG.

Mortars were lethal weapons in the Second World War and were believed to have accounted for about 50 per cent of ground casualties. Both the Germans and the Italians produced longer-ranged weapons than the British whose 3 inch mortar was the standard medium for the infantry in that war. After a long period of haphazard development, the British increased its range from 1,600 to 2,790 yards, slightly better than the equivalent German type. On the other hand, the Germans out-classed the British 4.2 inch mortar, introduced in 1941, being able to fire a bomb with their mortar up to 6,500 yards as opposed to the 4,100 yards of the British weapon. A serious disadvantage of the mortar was that its high angle of fire made it susceptible to radar detection, but it was capable of inflicting severe casualties on the battlefield and a well-trained mortar unit could produce a considerable volume of fire at very short notice.

After the war, attempts were made to improve the somewhat primitive external ballistics of the mortar. The fin-stabilised bombs had an unfortunate propensity to drop short – often down to half the nominal range – thus inflicting casualties on friendly troops. Intensive research at the US Army Ballistic Laboratories at Aberdeen, Maryland, under the direction of Serge Zarodny, succeeded in improving the design of mortar bombs by reducing what was called 'spin yaw resonance';[60] the flight of the bomb was made far less hazardous and greater ranges could be obtained. At the same time, mortar barrels were constructed with improved types of steel capable of withstanding higher external pressures at equal or less weight. The mortar's base plate was better able to withstand recoil by being made in two places with a ring. Finally, when automation of equipment began, the improved ballistics of the mortar made it possible to devise fire control systems like the British Mortar Data Computing System (MORCOS) which could store and display all the information needed to deal with up to ten separate targets.[61]

With improved stability and construction the British, Americans and Canadians agreed on a calibre of 81 millimetres for their future infantry mortars. The British design was accepted as it withstood prolonged firing, thanks to the use of improved materials; it was accurate and could be carried by a crew of three. Partly because of Zarodny's research, the British mortar attained a range of over 6,500 yards and proved itself in the appalling terrain of the Falklands. The Americans adopted it for their forces. Their own 81 millimetre model could be carried on a tracked or wheeled vehicle, but vehicle design does not meet the need to absorb a vertical recoil. The ground does it better unless it is very soft ground unable to provide enough bearing, as in the Falklands. The Soviet Army introduced mortars with ranges comparable to those of the British 81 millimetre, but they tended to be less accurate than field artillery.

Improving Methods of Detection on the Battlefield: Radar

In Chapter 4 we discussed advances in airborne methods of reconnaissance and surveillance. This section will be devoted, first, to the changes in *ground-based* methods of surveillance on the battlefield and, secondly, to the efforts made to improve the soldier's vision at night.

Army radar and infra-red equipment in the Second World War were virtually restricted either to fire control of anti-aircraft batteries in the first case, and to fire control of tank guns and small arms in the second. After the war there was, in Britain at least, little effort made to pursue new techniques. Recognition that such complacency must change came about in the mid-1950s. We noted earlier how worried the Army Council's Scientific Adviser was that 'hitherto our approach to the question of battlefield surveillance and allied subjects has been piecemeal . . . The emphasis has tended towards the purely scientific rather than to a combined technical and military approach to the study.'[62] He recommended that a working party from the Army Operational Research Group should 'study all promising methods of collecting and handling battle-field information.' Two officers were later appointed to make an investigation and the following summer a visit was made to the States to discover what the US Army was doing. After a fairly detailed inspection of work being done by the US Office of Signals, the British visitors concluded that there was 'as yet no clear recognition of priorities in requirements and desired characteristics.'[63] Operational requirements for information in the field still had to be determined in Britain and the States.

What were the needs of battlefield surveillance? In the first place greater depth of coverage on all levels from battalion to division and corps and army. The yardstick should be the weapon range 'plus 20 per cent.' In terms of battle frontage, a battalion should now cover up to 3,500 yards, a division up to 15,000 yards and a corps up to 40,000 yards. The aim of new equipment (radar and infra-red) was to identify armoured and unarmoured vehicles, either moving or stationary, and the movement of individual soldiers.

Taking radar first, three types of battlefield radar were evolved after the mid-1950s.

1 Radar for short ranges up to one to three miles. Such a device was used at company or platoon level and was carried by one man and weighed less than 20 pounds. The operator could identify moving targets by listening to the Doppler signal, even determining whether the target was running or walking. The wave length for operation was around 3–20 centimetres. (The same wave lengths also applied to the other two types of radar.)
2 Portable short range radars weighing 66–114 pounds covering a distance from three to six miles were used at brigade or battalion level.

Plate 25 CLASSIC: British battlefield surveillance system for areas which cannot be covered by direct vision or patrolling. Consists of two units – the sensor (seen here) and the monitor. (*Racal Comsec Ltd*)

3 A medium range radar, usually mounted on a vehicle, located moving or stationary targets up to 12 miles and could also be used for the direction of artillery fire.

Long range guns are useless, particularly for counter-battery fire, without the means of target acquisition. It was fortunate therefore that the first ever gun-locating radar (ZENDA), devised by the British for their successful towed FH70 155 millimetre gun and its self-propelled version (which later had to be abandoned for financial reasons) was never made because their NATO partners rejected it on grounds of cost. This drove home the lesson that when a new weapon system is ordered the accompanying equipment needed for target acquisition or for transporting munitions must also be included in the total cost package.

The introduction of Doppler radar was essential for battlefield surveillance. Doppler radar could differentiate between fixed and moving targets by detecting the apparent change in frequency of the reflected wave due to the motion of the target or the observer.[64] By 1956, manportable radars (Moving Target Indicator) able to detect personnel and vehicles at ranges up to several miles were already in operation. The Americans had by then adapted a mortar locating radar (AN/MPQ-10) able to detect vehicles at a range of 25 miles.

However, due to lack of stimulus, progress was slow and not until the 1970s did sets which could be quickly dismantled and transported by helicopter, truck or transport aircraft become available. The elimination of clutter from ground obstacles and the prevention of jamming was to some extent achieved by the introduction of Doppler, continuous wave and possibly millimetric radar. Of equal importance, was the ability to maintain and service sets more efficiently than before. Ways of locating artillery, rocket or mortar positions by radar continued to be developed and rapid electronic scanning provided non-stop coverage of a sector. Sets of this kind (like the US AN/TPQ-37) could locate gun positions at ranges of 18 miles and beyond. The British mortar detector CYMBELINE, which replaced a much heavier equipment called GREEN ARCHER, could detect a bomb of 81 millimetres calibre up to 11,000 yards away while a 120 millimetre bomb could be detected up to 15,000 yards. The maximum range of CYMBELINE was over 21,000 yards. Finally, the arrival of three dimensional radar able to deduce height, range and azimuth in digital format provided enhanced warning of low-flying aircraft, cruise missiles and tanks.

Nevertheless it was very difficult to make tactical radars impervious to ECM; the enemy would always be near enough to jam or put a set out of action by physical destruction using shells or missiles to home on to the radar's antenna. RPVs could blanket radars as the latter were tracking aircraft movements.

Aids to Night Vision: Infra-red and Television

The hours of darkness in warfare have traditionally been a time for recuperation, for replenishing stocks of food, fuel, ammunition, and above all for rest. For that reason the night is often chosen to launch a surprise attack or to make an enveloping movement. But only in the post Second World War years has it been possible for technology to magnify the soldier's field of vision at night. Artificial moonlight, created by shining searchlights on low cloud, was used to illuminate the battlefield at night in North-West Europe in 1944–45 on many occasions and, more recently, searchlights assisted the Soviet Army in anti-guerilla operations in Afghanistan. Although artificial light can be controlled, it arouses the enemy's suspicions that something is afoot.

The alternative is to exploit the infra-red range of the electro-magnetic spectrum. Infra-red devices offer far less detectable means of seeing in the dark.[65] The first useful night viewing equipment was the image converter tube fitted in the fire control systems of tanks, anti-tank and infantry weapons. The image converter tube is a photoemissive device that converts an infra-red image into a visible image. An optical system forms an image of the scene on to the cathode of the tube. Photoelectrons leaving the cathode form an image of that scene that is re-imaged on to a fluorescent screen. When struck by an electron, this screen emits visible light. In this way the original infra-red image is converted into a visible one. A magnifying eyepiece increases the apparent size of the image without appreciable loss in its brightness.

Image converters were first used in the fire control systems of German tanks on the Eastern front and proved to be remarkably effective in night actions.[66] They were never used in the Normandy battles, probably because it was thought that they were too easy to detect and would only invite counter-measures. The Germans also used them for driving vehicles at night. The Americans attached an image converter to their sniper's rifle, giving it an accuracy initially up to 80 yards and then to 150 yards and used it in the Pacific theatre of operations.

After the war, both the British and the Americans went on developing infra-red-based night vision devises, priority being given to the fire control systems of tanks and anti-tank weapons. The CHIEFTAIN was fitted with a powerful infra-red external light which, combined with infra-red night sights, gave it a very effective night fighting capability. Extensive research on behalf of the US Army was carried out at the Bendix Research Laboratories at Southfield, Michigan and at the US Army Night Vision Laboratory at Fort Belvoir.[67] The outcome was the remarkable image intensifier (II) which amplified diffused starlight, moonlight and radiation from the upper atmosphere, allowing an observer to see clearly without the use of a vulnerable searchlight. Although there was an initial doubt that noise in the system would drown out the intensified signal, image intensifiers were subsequently fitted into a variety of weapon systems. In Britain the SCORPION and FOX armoured reconnaissance vehicles were the first to be fitted with image intensifier night sights.

II's were used in Vietnam from 1965 and on the basis of experience in that war, the US and other armies began to develop a variety of image intensifiers. They included a 4 pound individual weapon sight which could detect moving troops at 328 yards, a 33 pound medium range equipment for outposts, which, given the right terrain, could discriminate moving men in starlight at 13,000 yards, and a longer range crew-manned device for company and battalion use. Such equipment enabled small units to become, as a military analyst wrote, 'viable defensive entities able to protect themselves in poor visibility and even see far enough to fire anti-tank weapons at night.'[68] Tanks were also fitted with image intensifiers for night driving, surveillance and target acquisition. By the 1970s night vision sights enabled tanks to fire at ranges up to 2000 yards and vehicles could be driven with vision up to 200 yards ahead.

At the same time, the armies of the Soviet Union and the Warsaw Pact had probably put an even greater effort into designing night vision equipment than the Western Alliance. It is worth noting that two excellent books written by Polish and Hungarian officers were published and widely distributed. The Hungarian volume even advised the individual soldier on how to avoid detection by image converters. The West became aware of all this progress in the 1973 Yom Kippur war, when the Syrians made good use of Soviet-made night vision devices to engage Israeli tanks on the Golan Heights; as it happened, exhaustion after two nights of continuous bitter fighting compelled both sides to withdraw and recuperate before resuming action in daylight.

We have already discussed the employment of FLIR sensors in airborne reconnaissance and surveillance equipment which were widely used in Vietnam. They could, of course, also be used as night vision devices on tanks, armoured vehicles, crew-served weapons and RPV. Many of the FLIR variants designed for ground forces are hand-held or tripod-mounted devices that have their own built-in displays.

Television itself had offered possibilities as a military sensor as early as 1939, but its poor definition, low range and cumbersome equipment discouraged interest for the time being. After the war, American and British scientists began to look for cameras 'suitable for observation and reconnaissance in which high definition, high sensitivity and a wide field of view can be obtained from apparatus fitted into light aircraft and helicopters'.[69] Another possibility was to equip remotely-controlled reconnaissance vehicles with TV.

Efforts to improve definition in the form of pick-up devices were made by a small group of scientists under V K Zworykin at the laboratories of the Radio Corporation of America (RCA).[70] Before the war they had developed a camera tube called the orthicon* which opened up the possibility of televising sporting events. But from 1942 onwards, the RCA Laboratory was encouraged by the military to develop a more sophisticated camera tube called the image orthicon. A miniaturised version called MIMO (Miniature Image Orthicon) was installed in test bombs, the descent of which was guided by the aircraft which had dropped them. After the war, image orthicons became the work horse of live TV broadcasting and were used in difficult lighting situations. They were, in turn, superseded by the isocon which, in company with image intensifiers, led to the development of low light level television.

As in the case of image intensifiers, low light level television could intensify the weak light emitted by the stars enabling a viewer to see an area almost as clearly as in daylight. It has been used mainly for night flying, in tactical night operations, or in poor visibility.

Seismological devices (used as long ago as the First World War) have also been investigated in the cause of battlefield surveillance and have yielded two British systems: the Terrestial Observation Battlefield Intruder Alarm System (TOBIAS), able to detect a person at 150 yards, and the Remotely Monitored Battlefield Sensor System (REMBASS).

Camouflage and Deception

The intensive work put into devices to detect troops and their equipment inevitably kindled a fresh interest in camouflage and deception. The aim of camouflage has always been to frustrate one of the principal aims of reconnaissance, which is to obtain information about numbers and types of weapons and their locations, not to mention dumps, airfields and other military installations. Modern airborne cameras and rapid photographic interpretation in the Second World War made it necessary to take camouflage much more seriously than before, though the need to camouflage had, of course, existed throughout the history of warfare.

After the war, techniques had to be developed to obstruct detection from radar, infra red and, eventually, laser devices.[71] Paints and nets, which continued to be the basis of camouflage, were designed to reduce the degree of radar or infra-red reflectivity described on page 101. Nets made of new materials such as saran and polyvinylidene, were used for this purpose. They had to merge into the background against which they would be used. In Western Europe, for example, fighting would take place in woodland, heath, and over cultivated fields. Nets were therefore given light-reflecting chlorophyll properties similar

---

* The name orthicon is made up from the Greek 'orth' meaning straight added to the term 'iconoscope', familiar to scientists, to describe the linear relation between light and signal output which has been observed.

to the foliage against which they were disposed. Arctic warfare presented different problems. As snow has a high ultra violet reflectance, nets had to have a similar response and equipment like skis and snow-traversing vehicles had to be covered with paint of a high ultra violet reflection value.

Camouflage nets have always needed to be fire resistant when exposed to muzzle flash from artillery. Now they were liable to be exposed to heat flash from an atomic explosion. New techniques were developed, not only by government research establishments but also by commercial firms which specialised in this new branch of military equipment. Some of these new techniques were put into practice in Vietnam and in the Arab-Israeli wars. In 1973, for instance, the Egyptians made extensive use of camouflage and decoys to conceal missile sites and armoured vehicles.

Deception was an allied topic demanding scientific and technical application. In the latter part of the Second World War special units were formed to operate deception equipment. As is well known, one of the great *coups* of deception took place in 1944 when the Germans were persuaded that major landings would be made in the Pas de Calais rather than in North-West France. Deception units also operated effectively in South-East Asia. Their equipment ranged from dummy aircraft, tanks, guns and other types of vehicle to battle noise simulators. Their purpose was to represent weapons in common use by an army or to simulate gun or rocket fire, or specialised equipment like rocket-launchers, field artillery and anti-tank guns. Vehicles fitted with loud speakers were required to produce, in realistic volume and quality, sounds that would emanate from tanks concentrating in the forward area or bridge-building operations. In addition to visual and sonic deception, equipment was needed to simulate the characteristic features of radio set transmissions. There also had to be a capability for radar deception.[72] Such equipment would simulate large concentrations of troops and their paraphernalia, or dumps, buildings and important static installations. It was important to prevent dummies from being distinguished from the real equipment which they represented by radar of any frequency.

Logistics

All the multifarious types of weapon that have been described would be useless without an assured supply of munitions, fuel and spares for vehicles and tanks, food for the army, and medical supplies for the tending of casualties. This activity is known as logistics and may be broadly defined as 'the science of planning and carrying out the movement and maintenance of forces.'[73] The greatly increased mobility and dispersion of modern armies and the complex, and frequently sensitive, nature of their weapons make logistics even more important. Although the Soviet Army engages in regular reviews of its logistical systems, strangely enough, in the West the tide of automation has left this subject comparatively dry. This may be due to a tendency acquired during the Cold War to equate logistics with cost effectiveness, weapon standardisation, and a desire to integrate support services rather than to improve the actual efficiency of combat units.

The main requirements of an army in the field are fuel and munitions of all kinds. NATO, in the early 1950s, decided to ensure a constant supply of fuel for its combat forces by building the Central European Pipeline System (CEPS); it was modelled on the war time PLUTO that so effectively supplied the Allied armies in Europe in late 1944–45. The primary function of CEPS was to satisfy the needs of forces engaged on the Central Front. By 1970, some 6,300 miles of pipeline and storage for 70 million cubic feet of oil had been completed. Separate pipelines replenished the vehicles of forces in Italy, Greece and Turkey. But outside Europe, where minor wars took place, improvisation was the order of the day. Sometimes they had unpredictable results, as in the Falklands, where fuel was carried ashore in jerricans which subsequently were not returned to base, causing difficulties in maintaining a continuous supply. Elsewhere the introduction of new laser and surveillance equipment required the production and refilling of gas cylinders at very low temperatures: one more item to the list of essential supplies.

Ammunition supply causes more headaches to the logistician because expenditure rates almost invariably exceed predictions. Munitions come under the term 'organic support', the generic name given to the supply of combat forces in the field. In general, it covers the number of vehicles, the number of days' supply and the recovery and repair organisation (specially needed for tanks and APCs). The core of this system is the motor vehicle. Military transport and its load-carrying capacity have hardly changed since the Second World War. Cross-country vehicles have been developed and have been used extensively in minor wars but they are expensive items of equipment. Trucks have, however, tended to proliferate since the Second World War, especially in the armies of the West. By the early 1970s, NATO divisions were employing 50 per cent more trucks than their opposite numbers in the Warsaw Pact, probably as a result of the inherent defensive and therefore static nature of Western strategy in the early years.[74]

Vehicles inevitably create jams and, when caught in bottlenecks by air attack, delays will occur. Schemes were introduced to try and reduce the conglomeration of transport in the battle area. One of them was the British Demountable Rack Offloading and Pick-up System introduced in the 1970s. Another attempt to relieve the hard-pressed vehicles of combat units was the Royal Corps of Transport Intermediate Replenishment Groups. The helicopter was also ideal in a logistical role and it became all-important from Korea onwards. Computers helped to speed up the control of supplies of electronic stores and spares. But, in general, the application of data processing systems to logistical problems has, in Britain at least, proved to be 'painfully slow'.[75]

Successful operations in the field depend on the speed of the concentration of troops; it is essential to deploy logistical and support capabilities into the forward area without delay. Hence the need for regional facilities including interoperable stocks, as in Western Europe. In the Middle East wars it was found to be of vital importance to deploy stores as close as possible to the troops needing them or to the forward edge of the battle area. Another feature in the Middle East and in Afghanistan was the failure of many munitions and weapon systems to operate in the harsh conditions of desert, marsh and mountains, a fact which not only reduced weapon lethality but greatly increased consumption. In the 1973 war and the Iran-Iraq war, adequate fusing and/or temperature tolerance would have sharply reduced the need for artillery ammunition.

When fighting guerilla forces or Third World troops, sophisticated armies tend to underestimate, as in the case of the North Vietnamese, their ability to rely on primitive logistical systems. Such troops are able to operate with limited supplies of stores and weapons: in Afghanistan, where supplies were slow in reaching the guerillas, every bullet was precious. But in the West, good logistics is a force multiplier and can be used as a substitute for lack of troops and weapons.

Conclusion

So far new weapon systems for the ground forces have been described mainly in the abstract. How did they perform under the stress of battle? The minor wars of the later 1970s and early 1980s provide some interesting lessons.[76]

Tanks

The early set-backs suffered by the Israeli armoured brigades at the start of the Yom Kippur war in 1973 led some military analysts to suggest that the day of the tank was over. To say this was to ignore the massive tank battles that followed after the Israelis had realised their folly in divorcing their armour from its essential all arms support – particularly infantry. This failing rectified, the whole position changed and some magnificent victories were won. The defence of the Golan Heights against the very courageous Syrian tank forces, which were in overwhelming strength, demonstrated what courage, professionalism and superior night fighting equipment could achieve. The failure of the armour in the Iran-Iraq war might also have given grounds for doubts about the future of the tank, but that failure was due almost entirely to total incompetence. It is now generally accepted that the manoeuvrability, fire power, and protection of the tank continues to make it an essential weapon. Improvements in tank design, particularly in protection and night vision, have tended to offset the improvements achieved in the lethality of anti-tank weapons. The ability to recover battle casualties and repair them quickly, so that they can be committed once more to the fight, has become almost as important as the improvements in the tank's fighting capacity.

Anti-tank Weapons

The German *PANZERFAUST* proved conclusively the value of the cheap, mass-produced, hand-held short range anti-tank rocket, available to every infantryman. The requirement survives today, since virtually every ATGM has a minimum range (the distance needed to get the missile under control). The hand-held weapon bridges the gap. Cheap, easy-to-operate rocket launchers have long been favoured by Third World countries rather than expensive, sophisticated PGMs intended for operation by well-trained crews.

In contrast, the Falklands campaign showed the value of the handy, crew-served ATGM (in this case MILAN) for countless battlefield tasks which call for direct fire but are beyond the scope of small arms. These include the attack on field defences, pill boxes and buildings – against all of which the chemical energy round is lethal.

The great strides made in night vision have added enormously to the effectiveness of ATGMs and make a major contribution to the concept of the 24-hour battle. Both in the defence of the Golan Heights during the Yom Kippur war and, much more recently, during Operation DESERT STORM in the Gulf, the possession of a good night fighter capability proved decisive.

Helicopters

The helicopter first came into its own in Vietnam where it not only gave added mobility to the ground troops but made a significant contribution to logistic support and casualty evacuation. Offensively, attack helicopters gave new, intimate close support to ground units and provided a valuable reconnaissance presence. The considerable power of that support was brilliantly demonstrated in the Gulf war in 1991. The helicopter is vulnerable to ground fire and its handling calls for a very high standard of tactical flying, normally in a state of air superiority. The high cost of helicopter operations has meant that only those nations with very substantial defence budgets have been able to use them on the scale that would make air-mobile operations viable. It is worth noting that the logistic support of a single CHINOOK helicopter was such a force multiplier in the Falklands that it made a major contribution to victory.

Surface-to-Surface Missiles

Much attention was paid in the first half of the period to long range SSMs and
their employment against troop concentrations or communication centres.
However, their role in minor wars was confined to inflicting terror on local
populations (whose morale was usually strengthened) and because they could
deliver nuclear or chemical warheads they served as a deterrent to a small
nation's will to fight.

Artillery and Multiple Launch Rocket Systems

Post-Second World War experience has shown that artillery fire has been
most effective in the first few minutes of engagement; follow-up fire with
ordinary ammunition had little killing effect and rarely had significant tactical effect; the rolling barrage indulged in by western armies demanded
resources far beyond those available for small countries. On the other hand,
the range, fire power and coverage of the MLRS has made it an ideal weapon
for attacking large numbers of moving troops, although in most cases it has
been used for battering hostile forces dug in, or holding built-up or rough terrain positions.

Surface-to-Air Missiles

SAMs, of all the PGMs described above, have probably been the most used
and the most effective in Vietnam and the Middle East wars. Their main purpose has been to shoot down hostile aircraft, but damaging them so that they
could not perform assigned missions, or intercepting their attack pattern, has
often been just as valuable. In small wars, light, low-level weapons like
BLOWPIPE, RAPIER and the Soviet *SA-7* were all used effectively against
modern aircraft. On the other hand, the heavier SAMs like HAWK were less
effective after 1973 when their crews often either lacked the training needed to
operate them properly or they had inadequate C^3I resources.

Anti-Aircraft Artillery

Anti-aircraft artillery, combined with low cost SAMs, continue to have an
important role to play in deterring low-level air attack. Dual purpose mobile
anti-aircraft guns like the US Army VULCAN, can bring down the helicopters,
which may now form the spearhead of a ground offensive.

Night Vision

When guided weapons first appeared, they were almost totally ineffective in conditions of poor visibility, due to smoke, weather or darkness. Modern technology has made great strides to overcome this. Low level SAMs, like the British RAPIER, for example, have a good all-round capability as have new anti-tank systems. Liddell Hart once wrote: 'Darkness is a friend to the skilled infantryman, if a source of confusion to the unskilled.'[77] That was half a century ago but it remains as true today as ever. However, today's infantryman has night vision aids to help him – but so does the enemy in many cases, so that skill is now at a greater premium than ever. We have seen how important a night fighting capability is to the tank and to the anti-tank weapon system. The soldier can now fight 'round the clock.' The 24-hour battle day has become reality with all the added stresses and strains that that involves. The whole tempo of warfare has changed in consequence.

Training

The enormous strides in battlefield technology which our period has seen make new demands upon the skill and professionalism of the individual soldier, be he commander or crew member. Just as technology has enabled the individual or the team to which he belongs to have a much more significant impact upon the outcome of an operation and has put at his fingertips far greater powers of destruction than any experienced by his forebears in arms, so have the consequences of failure through ignorance or incompetence increased proportionately. This has put a new premium on both individual and collective training. Yet the very nature of many new weapon systems makes such training ever more expensive and often more difficult to conduct for lack of space and facilities. Much is now being achieved by simulation but simulators too are enormously expensive and, in general, can only serve to teach and practice techniques. Field training remains as important as ever, whilst the need to practice personal skills almost daily has never been higher.

. 6 .

CHEMICAL AND BIOLOGICAL WARFARE

Toxic agents have been used in one form or another throughout the history of warfare. It was the growth of the chemical industry in Europe at the end of the 19th century that made it possible for armies to embark on chemical warfare on a large scale. In the First World War although the high commands on both sides were reluctant to resort to using poison gas, not so much on ethical grounds but more that it was an 'ungentlemanly' weapon, poison gases were discharged in large quantities on both the Western and the Eastern fronts. Like the employment of tanks, the purpose was to use gas to break the apparently unsurmountable deadlock of trench warfare. The most effective toxic agents used were mustard gas and phosgene. The former was persistent; it penetrated the skin causing severe blisters, but did not necessarily cause death. The latter according to the degree of concentration caused asphyxiation from which the victim could die. Both these agents were disseminated from shells, projectiles and bombs.

The Unpredictable Threat of Chemical Warfare

But just as the manufacture of toxic agents was relatively easy, given an advanced industrial infrastructure, so was the development of protective equipment such as face masks (called respirators by the military), impregnated clothing, and ointments for the skin. Although the employment of toxic chemicals on the battlefield, provoked (and continues to provoke) feelings of revulsion, in the First World War at least, gas was not a decisive weapon. Gas discharged from ranks of cylinders depended on the wind blowing it in the right direction and could thus upset other arrangements for an attack, while special weapons like projectors or gas shells had to be devised to put the gas where it was wanted. Nor did gas cause more casualties than shells or bullets.

On the Western Front, for example, it has been calculated that deaths attributable to poison gas were not more than three to three and a half per cent of the total casualties on both sides. According to the most recent assessment, gas was more than a wartime scientific curiosity, but not a significant addition to the weaponry of armed conflict.[1]

Nevertheless, after the First World War chemical weapons were to take their place alongside the other two weapons that had achieved significance in modern warfare – tanks and aircraft. Gas had become a major threat which, for armies in the West, it was wise to acknowledge and to take appropriate offensive and defensive measures. Moreover, apart from being quite easy to manufacture, toxic agents used on the battlefield, unlike high explosive, did not cause wanton physical destruction. They were most effective as a weapon of surprise to overcome an enemy unprepared and ill-equipped to meet that form of attack (as were the Abyssinians in 1935 when bombed with mustard gas by the Italians). At the same time, there were disadvantages to the use of chemical agents. After being stockpiled for some time, they were liable to deteriorate and become dangerous; their supply in bulk on the battlefield was an additional strain on the line of communication, and they required specialists to handle them.

Chemical and biological weapons (the latter to be discussed later) were outlawed by the Geneva Protocol of 1925 signed by most of the great powers (though signed but not ratified until 1975 by the United States). The Convention ceased to be binding if an enemy failed to respect it. It is still in force and provides the basis for the international prohibition of chemical warfare. But chemical weapons continued to be studied and measures for making troops immune to them developed at the chemical warfare research establishments of Britain, France, the Soviet Union and the United States. After the Nazis came to power in Germany, experiments in toxic agents were, as we shall see, secretly resumed (Germany after all was the first to use poison gas in the First World War). Poison gas had by then become a favourite subject for writers forecasting the horrors of air bombing in a future conflict and made a powerful impact on current opinion. So much so that with the likelihood of another European war drawing nearer, several nations, but Britain especially, as its cities were the most vulnerable to air bombardment, decided to equip its citizens with gas masks.

Poison gas was never used in the Second World War. Allied policy was not to use chemical weapons except in retaliation. This was publicly confirmed by President Roosevelt on 10 June 1943 in a notable statement. Preparations for the eventuality of chemical warfare were made in the meantime.[2] Large quantities of bombs filled with mustard gas and phosgene were stockpiled and plans were made to use them against selected German cities. However, the possibility of using them was only once considered by the British – as a measure of retaliation against the V weapons in July 1944 when, for a moment, it seemed possible that life for those living in London might become extremely unpleasant. The consensus of opinion among the British Chiefs of Staff was that chemical agents should not be used. (Some months earlier they had been concerned lest the Germans drench the Normandy beaches with mustard gas.) Nevertheless full details of bomb loads and force requirements for an all-out retaliation on German cities were prepared for that summer. Early in 1945, with the prospect of defeating Germany clearly in sight, the British Chiefs of Staff agreed that the 'production of gas and the charging of gas weapons should be discontinued' subject to the Prime Minister's approval. Churchill endorsed their recommendation and asked that all those who had worked on chemical warfare weapons should be thanked for their efforts. As far as the war in the Far East was concerned, the possibility of using chemical (and even bacteriological) weapons in support of amphibious landings was considered (the Japanese had had no qualms of using both kinds of agent in China and Manchuria), but the verdict went against the proposal on the grounds that gas was too unreliable and unpredictable for operations so dependent on precise timing.[3]

Like the Allies, the Germans had stockpiled considerable quantities of mustard gas and phosgene and had the same reservations about their employment. Probably gas was only seriously considered for use against the Russians, but the likelihood of Russian retaliation and the German inability to prevent heavy air raids over the *Reich* made the initiation of chemical warfare very risky. The possibility of Allied air attack with chemicals was considered and somewhat ineffectual attempts to equip the German population with gas masks were made in the latter stages of the war.

Evolution of Nerve Gases

However, since the mid-1930s, the Germans had been developing in great secrecy novel and far more deadly gases than mustard and phosgene.[4] Responsibility for them lay with the *Waffenamt Prüfwesen 9*, a branch of the German Army's Weapons Department, and the firm chosen for the secret production of toxic agents was the Anorgana Company, a subsidiary of the *Montana Industriewerke* financed and controlled by the General Staff. Full scale trials took place in the Forest of Falkenhagen near Fürstenberg on the Oder, south-east of Berlin. Discovery of a new toxic agent arose quite fortuitously out of research on organic fluorine compounds which might be used as insecticides at what was then the *I G Farben* laboratories at Wuppertal/Elberfeldt. Dr G Schrader, the head chemist, at first encountered a negative response; he then turned his attention to the more promising organic phosphorus compounds. In December 1936, he found that one of them, a cyanogen phosphoric acid amide, was extremely toxic. In accordance with an official decree of 1935, requiring that inventions of possible military significance should be reported to the War Ministry, Schrader submitted a sample of the toxic compound, which he called tabun, to the authorities. Its military value was quickly appreciated and the patent applications covering it were made secret. At the outset of war, work on poison gases was not pursued with much enthusiasm. However, with the prospects of victory lengthening, a full scale production plant for tabun was built at Dyhernfurth near Breslau in Silesia in April 1942. Some 12,000 tons were stockpiled there by the end of the war.

In the meantime, Schrader had gone on to study an even more toxic substance than tabun which became known as sarin, but because it was so difficult to manufacture, only a small quantity was produced before 1945. A third and even more lethal substance, called soman, was independently prepared by Richard Kuhn, a Nobel laureate, in 1944, but there was no time to do more than make a preliminary sample of the product.

The prospect of an Allied invasion of Europe in 1944 led the Germans to pay greater attention to the production of chemical weapons, because of the great industrial capacity of the Allies, which, if needs be, could be turned to making poison gas. However, the devastating and ever more accurate bombing of German industrial targets in the autumn of 1944 induced Speer (in charge of armament and war production) to request that the production of toxic chemicals be reduced in favour of propellants and explosives badly needed by the hard pressed army. Henceforward, supplies of tabun were drastically reduced and work on the other nerve gases restricted.[5]

The Germans were convinced that they had more to fear from gas attacks on the Eastern front as they felt sure that the Russians were following the same trail towards organic phosphorus compounds for military purposes. It was known by chemists that Professor A Y Arbusov, winner of a Lenin prize for chemistry, had published results of his studies in this field as long ago as 1934. Thus, as soon as the Red Army launched its final offensive into East Germany in 1945, the Germans made every effort to deny their small but potent stocks of nerve gases to the enemy. A team of experts from Anorgana, under a senior army officer, was despatched to Dyhernfurth to obliterate the plant and the existing stocks of tabun before the arrival of the Russians. Although the team afterwards claimed to have carried out their mission, the Russians captured a number of the scientists working on the project and persuaded them to reveal their secrets. The Silesian plant had apparently resumed operation by 1946.

Allied chemists were some way behind in evolving organic phosphorus compounds. Several were actually synthesised in British and American laboratories, but nothing of military value appeared. After discovering the extent of the German developments, the British promptly acquired the undestroyed stocks of tabun, along with those of high quality mustard gas.

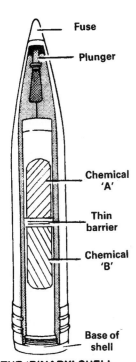

Fuse

Plunger

Chemical 'A'

Thin barrier

Chemical 'B'

Base of shell

THE 'BINARY' SHELL
Two non-toxic chemicals are kept apart in an artillery shell until impact. When they mix they form a deadly nerve agent. Can be fired from most artillery pieces

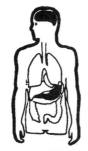

NERVE AGENTS:
Sarin, tabun and soman affect nervous system causing sweating, vomiting and convulsions

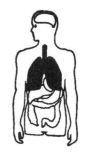

CHOKING AGENTS:
Phosgene irritates lungs,which fill with liquid. Known as ''dry land drowning ''

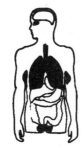

BLISTER AGENTS:
Mustard gas inflicts burns, especially in the groin and armpits, and sears eyes and lungs

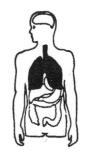

BLOOD AGENTS:
Hydrogen cyanide enters through the lungs, blocks oxygen in the bloodstream and chokes victim to death

Figure 13 Chemical warfare agents.

Characteristics of the Nerve Gases

No time was lost by the Allies after the war to examine and develop the German nerve gases.[6] Each was given a code name: tabun was called G-A, sarin, G-B and soman, G-D. What made them more deadly than earlier gases was their extreme toxicity (sarin was 30 times more toxic than phosgene) and their virtual undetectability as they had no smell and were invisible. Small doses could be put in shells and, after dispersion, could cause death in one to ten minutes by anyone inhaling them. Phosgene, in contrast, took 4 to 24 hours to kill. Even for troops not affected 'the effect on morale of witnessing convulsive deaths in the field and of uncertainty whether minor symptoms might not be the prelude to more serious consequences would undoubtedly be considerable.'[7] Moreover, in low level doses, nerve gases could cause myosis (darkness of vision).

Nevertheless, looked at cold bloodedly, the G agents offered considerable offensive potentialities and even an alternative to atomic weapons, especially when carried by aircraft. One 1,000 pound cluster bomb filled with nerve gas could cover a '200 yard square'. Even at non-lethal levels, nerve gases could restrict the movement of troops by compelling them to wear masks and protective clothing. Two subsidiary types of nerve gas need to be mentioned: G-E and G-F; the former was less toxic and less volatile than sarin; the latter had a toxicity comparable to G-E and was the first compound used by the British when attempting to meet the requirements of a persistent nerve gas. Development of both these agents appears to have been abandoned by the end of the 1940s.

Sarin and soman, on the other hand, were successfully developed and stockpiled in the West in large quantities, mainly at the US Army's chemical research establishment at Edgewood Arsenal, Maryland which had been in existence since 1917. It was now the headquarters of the Chemical Warfare Service (later the US Army Chemical Corps). It was here, and later at other testing grounds, that the Americans tried out new variants of toxic agents. By 1956, large amounts of sarin had already been stockpiled.

On a much smaller scale, the British also developed and produced G agents. In 1946, the Chiefs of Staff declared that during the next five to ten years (ie up to 1956) 'we must be in a position to wage chemical warfare from the start of hostilities.'[8] The British equivalent of Edgewood was the Chemical Defence Experimental Establishment at Porton Down which had also been created in the First World War and kept in being ever since. A production plant in existence since the 1920s was situated at Sutton Oak on the Lancashire coast. On 21 June 1946 the Chemical Defence Advisory Board, composed of a number of well known chemists and physicians and staff officers, reported that the work at Porton had now 'shifted from *ad hoc* investigations under war conditions towards more fundamental problems and the study of basic principles directed towards the development of ideal designs of weapons and equipment.' In the immediate future, the offensive and defensive aspects of the G-agents were to be exploited as they were 'of great potential promise' and demanded 'special techniques differing considerably from the methods hitherto employed for existing chemical warfare agents.'[9] Suitable weapons for discharging nerve gas were to be developed for the three services.

The Cold War underlined the need to keep an option on chemical warfare weapons. Thus, in 1949, the British Defence Committee agreed that the captured German stocks of tabun should be retained until research could 'provide something better'[10] and instructed the Inter-Services Committee on Chemical Warfare to 'keep under review the possibility of replacing weapons charged with mustard and phosgene when efficient weapons for the discharge of tabun had been developed.' Two years later, the DRPC considered the possibility of increasing nerve gas production at Sutton Oak from one ton a week to 'a full scale 50 tons a week.' In 'normal circumstances' they were not prepared to recommend such an increase, but 'in view of the present emergency (the Korean War) and the fact that gas represented an extremely potent tactical weapon' they agreed that 'from the scientific view the risk should be accepted.' Subsequently, there was some argument between RAF staff officers as to whether the funds alloted to nerve gas production might not be better spent on 'all-out atomic development', but others pointed out that 'nerve gas is the tactical counterpart of atomic strategic weapons' and warned 'lest we should get too strategic-minded and be found wanting at the battle for the Rhine crossings'[11] (ie in the event of the Soviet Army overrunning West Germany).

In 1952 the British Government decided to transfer the production plant at Sutton Oak, situated in what had now become a densely populated industrial part of the country, to Nancekuke near Portreath, a remote site on the north coast of Cornwall. Here an 'experimental full scale unit' with a capacity for producing 50 tons of sarin a week and a corresponding unit for charging weapons would be established. The plant at Nancekuke would, it was hoped, 'enable the UK to be in a position to wage retaliatory chemical warfare with the most effective weapons available.'[12]

As the scale of the nuclear capabilities of the superpowers increased, so that any thought of a nuclear exchange became incredible, the arguments in support of chemical attack grew stronger – chemical weapons were not destructive of buildings, did not have to contaminate the area attacked, like nuclear fall-out, and could be more localised. Thus it was perfectly feasible, from a purely military point of view, to attack through an area which had been subjected to chemical infestation a few hours earlier, without any of the hazards of disruption and contamination which were the inescapable products of a nuclear attack, no matter how limited in scale. So it was hardly surprising that the

Western Allies, knowing of Soviet policy towards chemical weapons, should follow suit – even if only, as with nuclear weapons, to counter-balance a threat and so, hopefully, to reduce greatly the risk of a move to chemical warfare whilst, at the same time, being in a position to respond to a Soviet chemical attack in kind.

Discovery of the V-Agents

No more than two years elapsed before British chemical warfare officers learned of a new type of nerve gas even more deadly than the G-agents. This again arose out of the search for commercial pesticides using the organic phosphorus compounds. Studies along these lines were pursued all over the world including the Soviet Union, the USA and West Germany where Schrader, who had discovered tabun and sarin, was still working. But it was probably the compound called Amiton, discovered by R Ghosh and J F Newman, both chemists working for ICI, that was the first in the field. Amiton was too toxic, especially through the skin, to be of any commercial use, but the staff at Porton was informed of its existence and it became known as a V-agent. According to the Chief Superintendent at Porton, V-agents promised to mark a major advance in the history of chemical warfare.[13] They killed rapidly and were 10 times more toxic than sarin. Their most remarkable property was their extreme toxicity through the skin – 'a drop the size of a pin head allowed to stay on the skin will kill a man. Unlike GB, a [V-Agent] evaporates very slowly and would therefore have to be disseminated in the forms of droplets or aerosols.' Whereas, in the case of G-agents, it was necessary for a large number of guns to build up a lethal coverage over a comparatively small area, when using a V-agent, surprise was not essential. A V-agent produced its effects by liquid contamination and required only a small amount of artillery, firing over a period of time, to 'build up the necessary coverage of defended areas. This basic distinction from [G-agents] has to be kept firmly in mind throughout any consideration of the potentialities of V-agents as a weapon.' V-agents would be particularly useful against widely-dispersed troops using the minimum amount of ammunition. Two or three 25pdr shells charged with a V-agent 'might well be expected to cover an area of 5,000 square yards, ie a modern platoon position with a concentration sufficient to kill most of the men in it.' Used strategically, the 'lethal coverage of 200 square miles is estimated to be possible with the use of a single aircraft.'

However, there was need for a good deal of further research. There were many V-agents to choose from and one was needed to fulfil the standard of stability required in battle and ease of manufacture. The Americans were informed of the new compound and by 1958 they had selected V-X for manufacture. Full scale production of this agent began in April 1961 and continued until 1968. Meanwhile, the Canadians tested the performance of V-agents in the field on their remote range at Suffield, Alberta . What they needed to discover was the 'efficiency of dispersion by [shells], the behaviour of droplets and aerosols in penetrating field works, etc and the degree of access to the person by actual penetration of the clothing or by a ventilation process, of typical droplets produced by various weapons'.[14]

Weapons Used for Nerve Gas and Other Chemical Agents

Essentially, NATO's policy for using chemical weapons in the 1950s was twofold. First, knowledge by the Soviet Union that NATO possessed them would impose on the Soviet armed forces the inconvenience of having to protect themselves and, second, should the Soviet Union, or any other potential enemy, embark on chemical warfare, the Allies would be in a position to retaliate in the same manner. As for requirements, chemical agents were needed:

1 to exploit the special characteristics of gas, namely penetration and duration of effect;
2 to neutralise or harass when that could be done more certainly or economically by gas than by other means;
3 to be part of the normal equipment of artillery, engineers or infantry and capable of being used for chemical warfare with a minimum of special training. Unlike the US Army[15] (which had its own, and sometimes vociferous Chemical Corps), the British believed that special chemical warfare units for the offensive use of gas were undesireable.

The doctrine of flexible response in 1967 confirmed that NATO should retain the capacity for retaliating with chemical weapons, but that the enemy's chemical warfare capability was to be deterred primarily by conventional and nuclear means.[16]

Insofar as nerve gas weapons were concerned, British requirements were for anti-tank* and anti-personnel in that order. In both cases 'the primary object was:

1 to liberate the nerve gases so as to achieve the greatest effective concentration in the shortest possible time, and
2 subject to 1 the design should aim at providing ammunition which should be as similar as possible to high explosive ammunition of the same calibre both ballistically and in sound and appearance of burst.[17]

---

* Anti-tank nerve gas weapons were not intended to penetrate armour and no attempt was to be made to combine the effect of armour-piercing and nerve gas ammunition.

The most potent ground weapons for the discharge of chemical weapons agents in the immediate post-war years were artillery, mortars, rockets, with the likelihood of guided weapons coming along to supplement them. Devices such as proximity fuses were valuable to cause low level bursts over defended positions. In the 1950s, rockets were held to be effective weapons for toxic agents as they did not have to withstand explosive propellants. In the Second World War the US Army had experimented with 7.2 inch rockets and a small bazooka rocket, both of which were intended to discharge chemical agents. The British had designed a 5-inch rocket which was designed to throw a bomb (which could be filled with mustard and/or phosgene gas) to a range of around 4,000 yards covering a frontage of 700 yards. However the multiple rocket launcher designed some thirty years later, described in Chapter 5, gave the ground forces the same capability as a ground support aircraft. Two of these launchers could put down a lethal dosage of sarin over a square kilometre in less than half a minute.

Far greater ranges could, of course, be attained by the use of missiles. The payloads of the V-2 class of rockets were too small to hold adequate quantities of toxic agent and their low rates of fire made them incapable of putting down an effective blanket of gas. But with the advent of nerve gases, requiring relatively small amounts of agent, chemical warheads became feasible. The Soviet Union was probably the first to develop nerve gas missiles in the early 1950s. In the West, nerve gas warheads for HONEST JOHN and LITTLE JOHN had been developed before 1958. When they came into operation, SERGEANT and LANCE SSMs were also intended to be able to fire gas warheads. But work on the warhead for LANCE was cancelled in 1970.

As just indicated, in the pre-missile period, gas bombs carried by aircraft had a greater charge/weight ratio compared with that of army weapons. And ground support aircraft were able to deliver surprise dosages of toxic agents over large areas. Typical targets included troop concentrations, gun positions, lines of communication, airfields, and the saturation of bridgeheads or beachheads. The calibres of bombs charged with gas ranged from 500–1000 pounds. Larger bombs merely saturated the ground with too much poisonous liquid. For this reason, the most effective airborne weapon was the cluster bomb, as already noted. Ways were sought to increase dispersion of gas. The answer was to replace a conventional bomblet with a spherical one provided with small, carefully-shaped vanes that would impart horizontal motion to the bomblet after ejection from the cluster unit. By such means, the lateral dispersion of the bomblets over the target area was greatly increased. At the same time, a much more economical use of the agent was achieved. The other weapon was the spray tank, which was only accurate when used at low levels and therefore made the aircraft vulnerable to anti-aircraft fire. This problem was overcome to some extent with the arrival of helicopters flying nap-of-the-earth over the battlefield. Another approach was to drop large containers from aircraft spraying gas as they descended.[18]

The possibility was also considered of using the strategic bomber force to attack cities in the Soviet Union (in the case of the RAF the attack of an average-sized German city such as Frankfurt was to 'continue to be used as the yardstick for determining the bomber effort required').[19] The 'V' bomber force was not expected to be able to attack targets in the Soviet Union until the early 1960s.

However, by the end of the 1950s, the British government decided to stop the production of offensive chemical weapons or of providing storage facilities for those of Allied countries. President Eisenhower likewise renounced the use of chemical weapons in 1960. But the Kennedy Administration's emphasis on flexibility of conventional as opposed to nuclear weapons gave a new boost to planning for chemical warfare. A comprehensive programme for improving the chemical and biological warfare capacity of the United States Services was initiated. It concentrated on the development of munitions charged with both G and V-agents and included artillery (both army and naval), rockets, guided missiles, bombs and spray tanks. Altogether, around 30,000 agent tons were stock-piled; some two-thirds stored as bulk agents for filling new or re-usable munitions. Most of the chemicals were retained in the United States, but about 435 agent tons, loaded into artillery rounds, were kept in West Germany under United States control.[20] No comparable step was taken by the other members of NATO.

Binary Munitions

During the early 1960s, the United States began to investigate a new method for disseminating chemical agents. This was the concept of binary munitions.[21] Binary munitions are a variation of chemical munitions, filled separately with two non-toxic components which form a toxic chemical agent when they are mixed in the process of employment (ie when fired or released). This gives them a degree of safety over other types of chemical munitions when being loaded, handled, transported or stockpiled. The binary concept had been considered for some years past, principally in the States, but its advantages as a weapon, as opposed to safety of handling, were not immediately perceived by the military. Why was the binary system important? The main reason was that it provided field commanders with a broader range of ammunition, allowing them greater flexibility in matching their weapons to immediate battlefield requirements.

But the safety factor just mentioned could not be ignored. Stockpiling of toxic chemicals had always been hazardous. The binary principle offered a practical solution. Once again, the idea was not new. In 1909, it had been applied as a way of harnessing nitroglycerine (extremely dangerous to stockpile) for use in artillery shells. In this method, the binary components were nitric acid and glycerol which had to be mixed under the influence of compressed air just before the shell was fired. The method was rediscovered in the Second World War and was applied to chemical weapons, primarily to prevent bombs being dropped from aircraft from exploding too quickly and releasing a cloud of toxic gas.

The binary munitions programme began with laboratory studies around 1954 and, in the early 1960s, the Defense Department let a number of development contracts to industry. The US Army wanted binary projectiles for 155 millimetre artillery and the US Navy a large aircraft bomb. In 1968, development of aircraft cluster bombs charged with G-agents began. Both the binary components were liquids, suggesting that the emphasis continued to rest on weapons filled with G-agents.

But in spite of the advantages offered by the binary route, these munitions were not easy to produce. In the first place, chemists experienced difficulty in obtaining pairs of low toxicity chemical compounds reacting together in a matter of seconds to produce a high yield nerve gas and, on the other hand, sufficiently stable to survive prolonged periods of storage. Secondly, the handling of toxic chemicals was very dangerous, as they were liable to react with biochemical substances in the human body, thus exacerbating toxic effects. Thirdly, it was necessary that the chosen chemicals should be liquid at ambient temperatures (the involvement of solid chemicals complicated the mechanics of binaries). Altogether, the matching of suitable compounds proved to be much more complicated than anticipated.

These difficulties experienced by the scientists in the laboratories were paralleled by a reluctance in American political circles to embark on a fresh programme of chemical warfare weapons. Some members of the National Security Council, for example, thought that using such weapons as a form of deterrent was a 'false and dangerous concept.' In 1975, therefore, the US government ruled that no further lethal chemical weapons should be produced until binary munitions were in a fit state to be stockpiled. However, should a crisis arise, making it necessary to resort to chemical weapons, existing stocks of G and V-agents in the States would be used and the current political restraints on transporting nerve gases would be overruled allowing stocks to be moved rapidly to Europe.

No more than five years later, Western intelligence gatherers perceived that the Soviet Union had been taking a more than lively interest in chemical warfare and the Army had introduced a new policy for chemical warfare weapons. Whereas in the 1960s and early 1970s, they were to be used *en masse* as in operations in the First World War, their application was now to be more selective.[22] Chemical weapons would be used in conjunction with attacks by raiding groups against key targets like command centres, port facilities and vulnerable depots where supplies were being stockpiled.

The potential to launch a chemical offensive in the West still lay in the hands of the Americans, though the French armed forces had a limited chemical and biological weapons capability. Despite their earlier doubts on the viability of a chemical deterrent, the Americans decided to launch an augmented pro-gramme for ground and air weapons charged with binary munitions. The most substantial item on the programme was the BIGEYE 500 pound spray bomb, though a binary warhead was to be designed for the new multiple rocket launcher system intended for NATO.

This fresh interest in chemical weapons led the US Congress in April 1985 to ask the President to appoint a commission to review and report on the 'chemical warfare posture' of the United States.[23] The commission was headed by Walter Stoessel, a diplomat, but most of his colleagues leaned towards the promotion of chemical weapons. So it was not surprising that the commission came out strongly in favour of the binary munitions programme as a form of retaliation, should the need arise, against the formidable Soviet stockpile of what were believed to be mainly *unitary* weapons. The commission also tried to scotch popular fears that the nerve agents stored over the past 25 years were deteriorating. Tests had confirmed that there was only a small diminution of potency and reports that stored chemical munitions were becoming dangerous or leaking were 'exaggerated or inaccurate'. In the event, it was due less to the Stoessel Commission than to forceful and skilful lobbying of the United States Congress by the military that led to the former approving most of the binary weapon procurement programme for 1986*, though prohibiting weapon assembly until October 1987, to allow current chemical weapons reduction talks to succeed. General W B Rogers, SACEUR, was particularly vocal on the need not to neglect chemical weapons. These, especially the BIGEYE spray bombs, had been given an important role to play in the AirLand Battle doctrine as a means of achieving surprise. At the very least they would force the enemy to don masks and protective clothing and would cause havoc if used against selected targets in proximity to the battle area.

How real was the Soviet chemical warfare threat? The answer at present can only be speculative. According to the Stoessel Report 'US intelligence agencies have for years virtually ignored the chemical and biological threat. Lately some improvement is evident but not enough to provide detailed and up-to-date knowledge of Soviet chemical weapons capabilities.'[24] Intelligence estimates are notoriously exaggerated so as to justify increases in defence expenditure, and in the case of chemical and biological warfare it was all too easy to stoke

---

* Congress voted on this just after an American airliner had been hijacked over the Mediterranean – putting the senators in a belligerent mood.

up the emotions of the politicians. But the Soviet Army had always affirmed that chemical weapons were a normal ingredient of any land battle and not a special one. Furthermore, chemical warfare was on the curriculum of many schools and colleges within the Soviet Union. Despite Soviet denials, by the 1980s the Soviet Army had undoubtedly deployed large numbers of rockets, aircraft bombs, mortars and artillery for action on the Central Front. Evidence also existed that instead of stockpiling chemical munitions, Soviet policy was to fill empty munition cases for missiles, warheads, bombs and projectiles from bulk stocks brought up by special tankers, instead of relying on stockpiles of chemical munitions. Another interesting point to emerge was that, compared with the role of the US chemical warfare units, it appeared that only ten per cent of the Soviet chemical troops were dedicated to chemical warfare tasks, their main purpose being to discover radiation and to carry out fallout decontamination to enable Soviet forces to operate over a nuclear battlefield*

Protection against the Effects of Chemical Weapons

The traditional protection against the effects of toxic agents included respirators, protective clothing, alarm systems, medical countermeasures and decontamination After the Second World War, all these items had to be reviewed and brought up to date on account of the new threat from nerve gases.[25]

The function of the respirator is to protect the eyes, breathing passages and lungs against likely field concentrations of all war gases including biological agents and radioactive materials, ie radioactive dust, smoke, gases or any other possible form of radioactive material. The respirators used in the Second World War were inadequate against the more dangerous nerve gases and biological agents. An apparatus was required which, for all practical purposes, eliminated leakage. The respirator had to be more comfortable to wear during long periods; it had to be lighter and, above all, it needed to be more efficient in keeping out gas: a leakage factor not greater than one in one million was required. The wearer also had to be able to speak into a radio or telephone microphone without the need of special microphone attachments, and he had to be able to handle all types of weapons and sighting instruments in current use. He needed a better and wider field of vision than previous designs. Finally, he had to have a device which enabled him to drink liquids.

To satisfy these demanding requirements much time and technical knowledge were needed. One problem was the improvement of the particulate filter

---

* In March 1987, the Soviet Union at last admitted, for the first time since 1938, that it possessed chemical weapons. In the following October, chemical weapons were put on public display.

Plate 26 Nuclear-chemical-biological warfare suit for the British Army. (© *British Crown Copyright 1992. Reproduced with the permission of Her Britannic Majesty's Stationery Office*)

which was a crucial component of the mask. Filters tended to lose some of their retentiveness when water seeped through the mask or after prolonged exposure to aerosols containing a high proportion of liquid droplets. These serious defects were to some extent remedied by introducing asbestos filters and hydrophobic surfactants in the preparation of the particulate filter and, subsequently, through the introduction of microdiameter glass and plastic fibres. Adequate filtration of aerosols no longer presents a serious problem.

A new British service respirator incorporating some of these requirements was ready by the end of the 1950s. It was the S-10, however, introduced towards the end of our period, that had goggles of thick ground glass enabling the wearer to sight weapons and devices permitting him to use a field telephone or radio microphone and, most important for use in a hot climate, a facility enabling him to drink from a water bottle.

For the protection of the clothed body, an all-purpose garment was required to replace the existing gas cape which would combine the functions of a rainproof, groundsheet, gas cape and part of a bivouac shelter. Secondly, an all-purpose suit was needed to reduce the hazard of contamination both from chemical and biological agents and atomic weapons. The British Mark 3 suit, although uncomfortable to work in provided some features that permitted air to circulate round the body – an advantage not found in similar suits in service elsewhere. Finally, an improved form of impregnated clothing was needed to protect the body against poisonous droplets and vapour. The Americans developed a clothing impregnant known as CC-2 that was able to decompose mustard gas to some extent. The British relied on carbon as an impregnant which absorbed the toxic agent rather than decomposing it. Neither of these garments would be proof against nerve gases if exposed against them for long periods, but it was unlikely that troops would be allowed to remain in an contaminated area for any length of time. Special clothing was not expected to prevent nerve gas casualties altogether but it could reduce their number from an intolerable level to a tolerable one. A special ointment was used to protect the exposed skin against any poisonous liquid or vapour and to neutralise any poisonous liquid falling on the body, clothing, equipment, or weapons.

Decontamination

For decontamination on a larger scale, eg for weapons, vehicles, airfields and bridges, bleaching powders were the preferred solution. Superchlorinated bleaching powder was the most common general purpose decontaminant used by armies in the West. It was effective against G-agents but not V-agents. For protection against the latter, the Americans found that a solution called DANC (acetylene tetrachloride) was effective. But this solvent was very toxic and a search for better liquid decontaminants was called for. Bleaching powder decreased in efficiency in cold weather, clogging spray nozzles. Other kinds of decomposition agents were investigated such as catalysed hydrolyses and oxidations of various types. The Americans devised an alkaline hydrolytic composition called DS-2 which was effective down to temperatures as low as minus 25 degrees Centigrade but it was expensive to manufacture.

Detection of Nerve Gases in the Field

The fact that nerve gases could not readily be detected by the senses made a field detector an urgent requirement. But warning devices tended to be complicated and expensive. By 1955, the British had developed a portable battery-operated alarm which was stable, sensitive and reliable.[26] This field detector for G-agents made use of a peroxide/benzidine colour test with an impregnated illuminated paper tape. Air was drawn through the paper, a brown stain being produced in the presence of nerve gas. This stain, by reducing the amount of light reflected by the paper surface, produced a photoelectric signal which, in turn, operated a warning signal. Unfortunately, it was more effective in testing suspect atmospheres than actually giving warning of a gas attack.

In the early 1980s, the British army was looking forward to receiving a new detector called NAIAD which was composed of two units, one was the detector and the other a remote alarm unit which could be placed up to at least 500 yards away from the detector. Thus a unit in the field could be given some warning of the approach of toxic agents. The complete NAIAD system had the advantage of not weighing more than 14 kilogrammes.

Medical Countermeasures against Nerve Gases

Finally, in the event of troops being taken by surprise by a nerve gas attack and unable to don their masks or protect their skins in time, medical antidotes were devised to reduce casualties. They took the form of auto-injectors and were carried by each soldier so that in an emergency he could give himself a nerve gas antidote if he felt the symptoms of nerve gas poisoning appearing (provided of course he did so quickly). The chemical used in the injection was atropine which by 1957 had been found to relieve a moderate dose of sarin and which could also minimise the effects of other G and V-agents. With this type of medical countermeasure fatalities (but not casualties) from some (but not all) types of nerve gas might be cut down by perhaps a third.

Biological Warfare: Second World War Developments

So far, in modern warfare, bacteriological agents have only been used by one army – the Japanese – in operations in China and Manchuria from 1936–1940:

the evidence for this is extremely sketchy, much of it being obtained from Japanese officers on trial for war crimes after 1945. Biological warfare has been defined as the use of agents[27] 'causing death or disease in man, animals or plants following multiplication within the target organism. Biological warfare agents thus include pathogenic microorganisms and ineffective materials derived from such microorganisms.' It was therefore a strategic rather than a tactical weapon because of its delayed effects. What makes an effective bacterial agent? It had to cause either death or disease with a reasonably low concentration; it should be amenable to mass production; it should be reasonably robust and stable under production and storage conditions, in munitions and during transportation; it had to be capable of efficient dissemination; finally, after delivery, it had to have a low persistence, surviving only for a short time, thereby allowing prompt occupation of the attacked area by the advancing troops.

The use of pestilential agents in war goes a long way back in history. They have been used from time to time as an inexpensive but effective means of exterminating enemies. In the 14th century the Mongols hurled plague-infested carcasses over the ramparts of a city they were besieging. A 16th century Italian military treatise describes a method of filling cannon balls with diseased materials for delivery against an enemy. As late as 1763, British troops in North America infected Indian tribesmen with smallpox in an attempt to reduce the population. In the First World War microbiological research was not sufficiently advanced to develop disease-carrying weapons, but the obsession in the inter-war years over aerial bombardment of cities included speculation on the use of bacteria-charged bombs. The truth was that the military were far from being convinced that biological weapons or, for that matter, chemical weapons were more effective than conventional weapons of destruction. Both could be used devastatingly in retaliation against an aggressor by a sophisticated opponent. At that time, not only the inability to manufacture and stockpile biological agents but the means to deliver them accurately was far from being assured and for self-defence it would be necessary to provide vaccines on a very large scale both for troops in the field and for the civilian population.

Even so, both sides during the Second World War paid some attention to the possibility of biological warfare occurring. In the spring of 1940 the distinguished bacteriologist, P G (later Sir Paul) Fildes, a Fellow of the Royal Society, persuaded the British Government to form a small group of scientists under the Medical Research Council to assess the threat posed by microbiological agents and to devise methods for the protection of the civil population.[28] This group under D W Henderson went to Porton and carried out research throughout the war, both from an offensive and from a defensive aspect. One of the experiments was the testing of an anthrax device on the island of Gruinard off the west coast of Scotland, which was to attract much attention from the media 36 years later.[29] In 1944, an Inter-Services Sub-Committee on Biological Warfare, chaired by Lord Hankey, was set up to control research. Assisting him were the well known scientists, Professor E C Dodds, a biochemist Sir Howard Florey, the developer of penicillin, and Lord Stamp, a bacteriologist.

When chemical and biological weapons were being assessed as a possible means of retaliation against the V weapons, Hankey's committee declared that, even if the claims for the lethality of anthrax were substantiated, there was no likelihood of stocks being available before mid-1944. There was, the report continued, 'no known prophylactic against N [the code name for anthrax]. If it can be used in practice, the effect on morale will be profound.'[30] The report concluded that the Germans would be extremely unlikely to initiate biological warfare. Scientific opinion held that if biological weapons were ever used, they would be more likely to feature in sabotage or covert operations than in bombs or projectiles launched on the battlefield. Much of the research and field trials were directed with these possibilities in mind. After the Americans came into the war, close liaison was established between Porton and the American bacteriological research centre at Camp Detrick, Maryland. The Canadians, who were concerned about the possibilities of German sabotage teams operating over North America, also joined in.

Investigations in Germany at the end of the war confirmed that the Nazis had never seriously contemplated embarking on biological warfare.[31] Research into using bacteria for military purposes, particularly for destroying animals and crops had nevertheless been put in hand. In 1943, this work was coordinated by a Dr Kurt Blome, an academic and competent organiser but not a bacteriologist. Some interest was taken in his work by Himmler, whose mind was already engaged with ideas for the destruction of the Jews in the gas chambers. Early in 1945, a research centre was set up at Posen in East Germany for the study of bacteriological agents. Blome was apparently told by Field Marshal Keitel, chief of staff to Hitler, that the Fuehrer had strictly forbidden any offensive preparations for biological warfare and Keitel added his own opinion that it was a 'foolish method of waging war.'[32] Probably the reason why research was ever begun was the German belief that the Russians had made extensive preparations for biological warfare and had actually tested airborne bacteriological weapons in a remote corner of the Soviet Union as early as 1938. Strangely enough, the Germans were, it seems, also aware of the British tests on Gruinard Island as well of bacteriological studies being conducted by the Americans and the French.

Effect of DNA and Genetic Engineering on Biological Agents

After the war, the lead in discovering suitable agents for biological warfare was taken by the United States. Compared with Porton, Edgewood had 'a vastly greater amount of equipment available' and it was also able to draw extensively on extramural research; the expenditure on this alone ran into 'several million dollars.'[33] Moreover, to British observers, the link-up between chemical warfare and microbiological research was very much closer in the United States and Canada since they were responsible to a common director. Porton, however, continued to complement the fundamental studies of the American workers, concentrating mainly on the toxicological side. The most likely employment of biological agents still seemed to be of a clandestine nature, possibly enabling 'a single aircraft to attack effectively tens of thousands of square miles.' Yet in 1956, after 10 years of work, Henderson, the Director of the Microbiological Research Establishment, had to confess that it 'could point to little concrete information on biological warfare, but a considerable volume of knowledge on techniques had been acquired.'[34] Henderson's principal task had been to discover what agents an enemy would be likely to use and then to find out what steps could be taken for immunisation. 'There was evidence that bacteria, under certain circumstances, were poor agents but there was also evidence that they could be protected against physical and other conditions so that they could remain virulent.' Much more effort had to go into the study of virology.

However, the great break-through made by the discovery of deoxyribonucleic acid (DNA) in 1953, advances in experimental aerobiology, and the introduction of genetic engineering, made the production of bacterial agents much more feasible. DNA, for instance, 'allowed the induction of random genetic changes and the more or less random transfer of genes among related bacterial strains or species.'[35] These important advances in microbiology made it possible to consider as BW agents viruses such as Yellow Fever or Lassa Fever which had hitherto been considered to be too dangerous or difficult to handle. Previously, most of the agents considered for use against personnel had been bacteria like anthrax or brucella.

The fresh interest being taken in biological warfare weapons led to the Convention on the Prohibition of the Development, Production and Stockpiling of Bacteriological (Biological) and Toxin Weapons and on their Destruction signed and ratified by the major powers on 10 April 1972 and which was intended to reinforce the 1925 Geneva Protocol. But soon a number of infringements were reported, notably by Soviet forces in Afghanistan and by Vietnamese forces, with Soviet assistance, in Laos and Kampuchea. Investigations, however, were inconclusive and provided no firm evidence on which to base a charge of breaking the convention.

Anti-Crop Warfare

Destruction of an enemy's source of food, like the use of poisonous agents, has its antecedents in the history of warfare. In the first half of the 20th century, the destruction of crops by airborne incendiary devices was considered as, for example, the proposal that RAF Bomber Command should set alight the German harvest fields. But the possibility of retaliation as well as the strong aversion of the air commanders to employ aircraft badly needed for other tasks on such dubious missions led to the proposal being abandoned.

After the war, advances in herbicides and pesticides provided an opportunity for military scientific advisers to take the possibility of anti-crop warfare more seriously. Both Americans and British embarked on a search for suitable agents, the former taking the matter more seriously and forming a Crops Division at Camp Detrick. Among its subjects for study was the possibility of 'employing anti-crop warfare against the Soviet Union.'[36] The aim was the development of a universal anti-crop agent to reduce the yield of 'narrow-leaved as well as broad-leaved crops at very low temperatures.' In the late 1940s, several effective herbicides for attacking broad-leaved food crops, such as sugar beet, sun flowers, beans and cotton were discovered, but no agent that would destroy more vital crops like rice, wheat, oats, rye and millet.

What was needed was a chemical agent which could destroy both narrow-leaved and broad-leaved crops, was capable of being easily absorbed by plants, and was not subject to extreme cold. Towards the end of the 1950s the most promising agent was the 2-ethyl ester, a liquid with a freezing point of approximately minus 30 degrees Centigrade which had a special propensity for destroying rice and millet. The other agent was a fluorophenoxyacetic acid called KF mainly useful against narrow-leaved crops. Discovery of a real universal anti-crop agent was still far from being achieved.

Meanwhile the biologists at Camp Detrick were working on pathogens which would induce stem rusts in wheat and rye and blight in potatoes and rice.

Problems of Disseminating Anti-Crop Agents

Dissemination of these chemical and biological agents was far from easy. Before the arrival of long range ballistic missiles, the launching of attacks with these agents against strategic targets could only be made by long-range bomber aircraft. When the British Air Staff was called upon to undertake crop destruction missions, they commissioned a study with Japan as the hypothetical target. It was estimated that 120,000 tons of agent and liquid solution would be needed to destroy by spraying only one third of the Japanese rice crops. This would absorb the equivalent of 36,600 sorties by piston-engined LINCOLNS –

at that time (the early 1950s) the only long range bombers available. Taking into account all the other tasks which the bombers were required to tackle such a 'method of strategic warfare was out of the question.'[37]

The Americans concentrated on the technical aspects of spraying targets in the battle area with aircraft flying at heights of no more than 200 feet. Various types of spray tank were developed which were able to distribute an agent uniformly over the target area at 'the minimum rate of application required to achieve its purpose.'[38] An aircraft carrying two Aero 14A spray tanks, each containing 90 gallons of agent, was able to lay a swathe 7000 feet wide and eight miles long (ie about ten square miles) when operated under favourable conditions.

The distribution of biological agents was most easily achieved by charging aircraft bombs. An example of these was the US M-115 bomb which held four cylindrical paper containers filled with feathers impregnated with rust spores. But these weapons could only be launched by relatively slow-moving, and therefore vulnerable, aircraft and the bombs contained no heating device to prevent the spores being damaged by freezing. Before the end of our period, more efficient bombs were designed with electric heating pads to maintain an optimum storage temperature for the spores.

Use of Anti-Crop Agents and Defoliants in War

The only time that agents similar to those just described were extensively deployed in action was in the Vietnam war from 1961–1971. According to American statistics, over 90,000 tons of herbicides were dropped by air, primarily for the purpose of defoliation. The intention was to clear jungle or undergrowth to prevent ambushes, expose enemy strong points, and to improve friendly fields of fire.[39] For some years past, tests had been carried out at the Avon Park, Florida and Fort Richie, Maryland.

However, a precedent for using chemicals for these purposes had been set, albeit on a very limited scale, by the British nine years earlier. The Malayan government, at the instigation of General Templer, already seen to have been an innovator in novel methods of warfare, decided to experiment with anti-crop and defoliating agents as a means of suppressing the activities of the communist guerillas. These agents were to eliminate 'roadside vegetation at possible ambush points and [to destroy] bandit crops in jungle gardens.'[40] Although the War Office expressed some doubts as to whether spraying would not infringe the 1925 Geneva Protocol, officials in Malaya felt that anti-terrorist operations were an internal security matter and not 'war' in the international sense. The main agent used was sodium trichloracetate – a non-toxic chemical, and spraying took place from vehicles, light aircraft, and eventually a MUSTANG fighter, all at very low levels.[41] It was soon appreciated that helicopters were a much better type of aircraft for the purpose and preliminary trials took place in England but never actually in the field. In the long run it was doubtful whether the experiments were worth while; flying at such low heights was both difficult and dangerous. The use of these agents would, the Air Staff believed, be appropriate only in a limited war.

Limited warfare was indeed what the Americans had in mind since the mid-1950s having appreciated that sooner or later they were going to be involved in fighting communism in South-East Asia. American observers had, in fact, studied anti-guerilla tactics first hand in Malaya; one of them, Richard Nixon, was to become deeply involved in Vietnam as President of the United States. When American forces became inextricably tied down in their arduous campaign against the North Vietnamese and the Viet Cong, there was a call for herbicides both to prevent ambushes on the line of communication and to destroy the enemy's rice fields. The use of these agents was given wide publicity and revived the horrors of chemical warfare until then somewhat overshadowed by nuclear weapons. The most common agents used were called ORANGE I and ORANGE II (2,4-D and 2,4,5-T esters), some 57,000 tons being expended.[42] According to Vietnamese estimates, some 12,400 square miles of forest were destroyed. A number of long-term cases of illness were also attributed to the use of herbicides but so far they remain unproven. Eventually, doubts over the value of anti-plant operations both from a moral and a military point of view began to be felt, In 1967, a Rand Corporation study declared that crop destruction was hurting the civilian population far more than the enemy, but it was not until 26 December 1971 that President Nixon curtailed the herbicide programme.

Irritant Agents

The use of tear gas weapons has for long been considered part of the armoury available for riot control; they were usually in the form of grenades. In recent years they have begun to appear on the battlefield. At the end of 1964, American troops were authorised to use tear gas in Vietnam and, by the end of the fighting, had expended some 8,600 tons of irritant agents, mainly of the CS (o-chlorobenzalmononitrile) variety (popularly known as the 'mighty mite') dispersed by the M-106, an agricultural sprayer. These CS agents were also used in grenades, rocket launchers and in cannisters lifted by helicopter. The purpose was to flush the enemy from the fox holes, bunkers and other types of cover.[43]

Use of Chemical Agents by Third World States

Although the Soviet Union and the United States possessed the largest stockpiles of chemical warfare agents and chemical weapons, virtually all the documented or alleged use of lethal chemical weapons since the First World War have occurred outside Europe and have not involved direct contact between the major military powers of the day.[44] By June 1985, about 16 countries, including the United States and the Soviet Union possessed chemical weapons. Two months earlier a British Minister of State for Defence said that most of these countries were in the Third World. It would be wrong to assume that the sophisticated nerve agents that have been described above alone constituted a serious threat or that they had to be delivered by ballistic missiles or high performance aircraft. First World War toxic agents can effectively threaten an enemy who does not possess proper protective equipment. Nor is it difficult to obtain adequate offensive equipment (agricultural appliances like the 'mighty mite' used in Vietnam is one of a number of possibilities). The production of nerve agents is so closely allied to the production of organophosphorus pesticides being imported by or actively manufactured in Third World countries that there is no obstacle to their acquisition by the military. In fact certain pesticides in high concentrations could be used as chemical warfare agents, producing both a physical and a psychological impact. The latest or most lethal types of agent do not necessarily have to be used. Another factor making it easier for countries to develop chemical weapons is binary technology which, as explained above, facilitates the production and storage of pairs of chemicals which are relatively harmless individually but lethal when combined. Again, progress in genetic engineering can simplify the process of evolving bacteriological agents.

It is generally agreed that an offensive chemical warfare capability could be a plausible deterrent to a nuclear weapons threat, making the former the 'poor man's atom bomb'. Yet the use of chemical weapons since 1945 has not been a decisive factor. For the most part reported incidents have never been confirmed, as in the Yemen war of 1963–1967. But the Iran-Iraq war of 1980–88 provided much more substantial evidence. After the Iranians launched an offensive in the direction of Basra in March 1985, the Iraqis warned the former that they intended to repel the offensive by using chemical weapons. At the outset, tear gas was used but as the Iranians ignored the warnings more lethal agents were brought into play. Apparently nerve, blister and choking gases were discharged from air and ground weapons on some 32 occasions. Although a large number of Iranian troops were killed or injured by chemical weapons, their employment had a negligible effect on the course of the war. It was estimated that up to the end of 1985 approximately two per cent (7,000 men) of Iran's total casualties were caused by chemical weapons.[45] In the latter stages of the war, Iran retaliated with chemical agents, though to a lesser degree. A total figure of 45,000 casualties has been given for both sides.

Conclusion

Chemical warfare remains something of a bogey. Though not used in the Second World War, afterwards the Allies hastened to exploit the nerve gases which, on account of being featureless, offered opportunities for surprise on the battlefield or to halt an overwhelming attack. Although chemical weapons were more or less universally renounced, except for use in retaliation, extensive stockpiling took place mainly in the United States and the Soviet Union. The NATO powers for all practical purposes stopped production of toxic agents after the 1960s, though sensibly continuing to take defensive measures which implied testing the offensive capabilities of new toxic agents. Yet chemical and biological weapons have not been integrated into the war plans of the armies in the West to the same extent as tactical nuclear weapons. Why was this?

First, we have seen that the technical problems in the matching of suitable compounds in binary munitions and the problematic duration of the stability of toxic agents when stockpiled have put chemical weapons into a particularly hazardous category of their own.

Secondly, methods of dissemination, while greatly improved with the development of missile warheads, artillery munitions, and aerial cluster bombs are still to some extent dependent on favourable climatic and meteorological conditions. Surprise is not always possible, though it should be noted that on the one occasion that chemical weapons have been used recently to any extent (in the Iraq-Iran war), the intention in the first place was to deter by warning of their proposed uses.

Thirdly, once the element of surprise has gone, a sophisticated enemy will be prepared for a future attack even though, at the same time, he will be handicapped by having to move and fight wearing his protective equipment. Since defence against chemical weapons is possible, despite severe restraints on movement, they are not an absolute deterrent like nuclear weapons.

Fourthly, the revolution in warfare caused by precision-guided munitions has to some extent robbed chemical weapons of some of their power. The ability of artillery to place shells with great precision and multiple rocket launchers to saturate a target area can achieve the same effects as chemical weapons rather more economically. Even though nerve gases may be at least twice as effective as First World War toxic agents, large concentrations are still required to put personnel out of action in an given area. The additional burden of conveying chemical agents to the forward area is unlikely to be welcomed by the quartermaster. Finally, if they are to be effective, chemical agents must have the power to penetrate the skin and clothing. Fortunately, the development of respirators, protective clothing, decontamination techniques and warning/detection systems have kept pace with the development of toxic agents.

For all these reasons, and as long as both contestants are prepared for chemical warfare, it seems unlikely that it would be used in the sort of conflict we envisage in Europe. However, in a desperate situation, when the choice might lie between the relatively local use of chemical weapons or the strategic use of nuclears, that position might well be changed. This still leaves us with the possibility of chemical weapons being used in Third World conflicts. Here it is the side which is less well-protected and less well-trained that will suffer. To date, chemical weapons have not proved decisive in such conflicts.

As for bacteriological warfare, it is more likely to be used in covert and strategic operations against a defenseless population. We have no historical precedents on which to reach a judgement.

. 7 .

SURVIVAL OF THE MANNED AIRCRAFT

Air power came of age in the Second World War. Until then, the air arm was regarded as an auxiliary to act as an eye looking over and beyond the battle-field and to reach targets inaccessible to artillery. In five years, air forces became at least the co-equals of armies and navies. No campaign could be won without air power either at sea or on land; aircraft proved themselves to be flexible for every kind of operation, whether by winning air superiority, pro-viding long or short range reconnaissance, affording close support on the battlefield, and even by sinking submarines far out in the ocean. They showed that they could act independently in a strategic role by attacking industrial tar-gets or communications in the homeland of the enemy. Indeed some of the enthusiasts of air power believed that wars could be won without engaging sea or land forces. The failure of the German Air Force to create a properly bal-anced air arm, which included strategic as well as home defence and tactical units, left the German Army in Normandy in 1944 bereft of close air support and thereafter to the end of the war in the West.

Role of Air Forces

When the first primitive missiles were launched at the end of the war, many believed that the manned aircraft would soon become obsolescent. Long range ballistic missiles with the accuracy derived from inertial guidance would destroy the targets until then regarded as the purview of the long range bomber. In air defence, the SAM would replace the interceptor fighter with improved sensors and the range and height to bring down raiding aircraft; and even in time to intercept missiles themselves.

   The prophets of wars fought by missiles proved to be wrong. Far from becoming obsolete, manned aircraft became the vehicle for delivering precision-guided missiles. Their versatility was enhanced by variable geometry structures enabling them to operate at high or low altitudes without loss in performance; and VTOL/STOL gave them the means to support the land forces more effectively by operating close to the battle area.

At the same time, manned aircraft could not ignore the improvements to air defences and ECM that had meanwhile taken place. They had constantly to improve their own protection with better weapons and sensors and the means to elude detection over hostile territory. This chapter will attempt to show how the manned aircraft in the missile age survived through improved propulsion systems and aerodynamics, and how its weapon systems were improved through new technology.

Development of Combat Aircraft: Propulsion

The Second World War was fought in the air by propeller-driven aircraft and reciprocating internal combustion engines. Excellent though these were for aircraft like the SPITFIRE and TEMPEST, they imposed an impenetrable upper limit to speeds (of around 400mph) because of the invariable collapse of propeller efficiency caused by propeller tip speeds exceeding the speed of sound. The means of attaining subsonic, transonic and supersonic speeds was provided by jet propulsion. For many years, the theoretical probability of jet propulsion had been recognised but it was not until the inventiveness and persistence of engineers like Whittle and Ohain converted theory into reality and enabled the first jet-propelled aircraft to fly that recognition became realisation and steps were taken to commission a design for a jet-propelled military aircraft. The increase in engine power was dramatic; in 1944 the power thrust of the centrifugal turbojet Derwent engine was about 3000 pounds; 13 years later it had risen to 12,200 pounds in the case of the Avon turbojet axial engine. In a few years time, still greater power was provided by the turbofan which is, in effect, a ducted multi-bladed propeller driven by a gas turbine engine. That eventually produced a thrust of 42,000 pounds in the RB211-22B engine.

Introduction of Swept Wing Aircraft

The turbojet engine opened the way to aircraft flying at subsonic, transonic and supersonic speeds with endurances of up to four hours at cruising speeds. With the ability to fly at 600mph and over, new configurations for military aircraft had to be considered because of the factor of drag. The choice lay between aircraft with swept back wings or tailless aircraft with a delta-shaped wing.

Some thought had been given to new configurations before the end of the war but, when Germany was occupied, Allied aeronautical engineers and scientists found to their surprise that the Germans were far in advance of what they had expected. Not only was advanced wind tunnel research in progress but several swept wing aircraft were standing on the ground. One of them – the Me P1101 – was appropriated by the Americans. At the same time, a great deal of information was collected by the British and the Russians. But while it was appreciated that a swept back wing would delay the supersonic drag experienced by pilots of early jet aircraft, there were some penalties, especially when aircraft had to fly at very high or very low altitudes or when great endurance was required. The British approach to high speed flight was therefore tempered with caution until a new configuration enabling changes in speed to take place without reducing the aircraft's performance had been discovered.

Enough information was obtained from the Germans to provide the basis for the new jet-propelled British interceptors: the HUNTER, SWIFT and JAVELIN as well as for the V bombers. Although one experimental aircraft (the Miles Aircraft Company's 'X' E24(33)) had to be cancelled because of limitations in size, a very extensive research programme on high speed aircraft took place in Britain, mainly at RAE where a high speed wind tunnel was already installed. Nevertheless, it was not until the Korean War and the rearmament programme that stemmed from it that the first generation of swept wing aircraft took shape. They began to come into service in 1954, not always to the benefit of the aircraft as, in the haste of production, radar and weapons did not always match up with the aircraft.[1] In fact, during the period 1948–54 the RAF had to fly the US F-86 SABRE fighter which was the principal Allied fighter operating in Korea. It was ironic that, during that period, no British fighter was able to intercept the CANBERRA light bomber (the first successful post-war British military aircraft) above 50,000 feet.

American supersonic flight development, however, was not much farther advanced than the British, although the experimental Bell X-1 was the first aircraft to exceed the speed of sound in December 1946. Plans for using rocket propulsion to penetrate the sonic zone on the lines of the formidable but hazardous *Me* 163 led into a blind alley. It was only in 1954, when the F-100 SUPER SABRE became operational, that the Americans had a supersonic fighter. That year, the French brought the delta wing MIRAGE into service and the first British supersonic fighter (the F23/49) later known as the LIGHTNING made its maiden flight on 4 August 1954. But another six years would elapse before the latter entered service in the RAF as an all-weather interceptor.

Tailless Aircraft

The alternative to swept wing was the tailless aircraft, A good deal of research on such an aircraft had taken place before the war, particularly that conducted by the distinguished British aeronautical engineer, G T R Hill. However, post-war development by de Havilland's led to disaster and the death of three test pilots and this configuration, with the exception of the VULCAN bomber, was abandoned.[2] Better results were achieved in the States and led to the F-102 (CONVAIR) and F-106 (DELTA DART) which proved to be useful interceptor aircraft after being introduced in the 1960s. As just noted, the French experiments led to the Dassault MIRAGE. In general tailless aircraft were less manoeuvrable than swept wing fighters and provided a limited field of vision for the pilot.

First Jet Fighter Combats

The Soviet Air Force, also benefiting from the German experience, had progressed in supersonic aircraft technology, but beginning like other air forces with subsonic types, The sophistication of the *MiG15* caused some surprise when it appeared over Korea and took part in the first exclusive jet versus jet combat. To some extent, its agility was due to the sale to the Soviet Union by Britain of 25 Rolls Royce Nene centrifugal turbojet engines and 30 of the lower-powered Rolls Royce Derwent engines. The *MiG's* performance in some respects rivalled the US SABRE though the latter had the advantage of a better fire control radar. The Soviet Air Force's first supersonic fighter was the *MiG19*, which made its first appearance in 1953.

Variable Geometry Aircraft

The concept of variable geometry derives from the fact that swept back wings are very effective in delaying and reducing transonic drag but, as just suggested, they held penalties both for high as well as for low level performance. The object of trying to design a variable sweep aircraft was to enable wings to be swept back for high or fast low level flight but swept forward for take-off and landing and for long range missions.

A number of proposals were made during the 1930s in Britain and Germany for aircraft with movable wings. Hill designed a tailless aircraft known as the PTERODACTYL on account of its supposed resemblance to the prehistoric flying lizard. In January 1930, he filed a patent for adjusting wings of an aircraft in a 'fore and aft direction during flight.'[3] A similar idea had occurred to the German rocket engineer, Rheinold Tiling. In 1949, another British engineer, L E Baynes, patented a variable sweep for the main planes and the tail plane. After extensive wind tunnel tests on models, Baynes claimed that he could obtain a speed ratio of ten to one. This implied that a supersonic aircraft would be able to keep in the air at 150 miles per hour and probably make a safe approach to land at 200 miles an hour, much higher than the approach speeds of existing jet airliners whose speed ranges did not then exceed, at the best, seven to one. His idea failed to attract the attention of the authorities.

It was, however, Barnes Wallis, head of the Research Department of Vickers Armstrong, well known for his wartime inventions of the 'bouncing bomb' and the five and ten ton TALLBOY and GRAND SLAM bombs used with spectacular results against battleship, viaducts and submarine pens, who had probably given more thought to the problem of reducing aerodynamic drag (at first in connection with the vast hulls of airships) than anyone else. Wallis's idea became known to the Air Ministry and Ministry of Supply as the Wing Controlled Aerodyne – an aircraft with wings attached to the rear of the body. The idea germinated after Wallis had studied components of a German V-2 smuggled out of Europe and sent to RAE. He believed that if the compressed graphite vanes in the V-2 jet nozzle were used to deflect the jet downward, the rocket would be given a horizontal trajectory. This was the starting point for his thesis on adjustable wings mounted near the end of the body. On August Bank Holiday 1944, Wallis arranged for the total compressed air supply of the Vickers factory at Weybridge to be diverted into the six foot open jet wind tunnel so as to obtain measurements on the stability of a model V-2 and thus establish the importance of keeping the wing mounting aft. Wallis patented his invention on 6 May 1946, but on the recommendation of Ben Lockspeiser, Chief Scientist in the Ministry of Supply, it was kept on the secret list.

Unlike Baynes, Wallis unfortunately knew influential men like Tizard and Sir Thomas Merton, who had also been a wartime defence scientist and was now a director of Vickers, as well as members of the Air Staff like Sir Ralph Cochrane, who had come to recognise Wallis's prickly but undoubted genius through his wartime work. They believed, mistakenly, that here was a design of potential military importance. The SWALLOW, as the Wing Controlled Aerodyne (WCA) became known, was also a tailless aircraft.[4] It provided for a two position wing with a moderate degree of sweep back at subsonic speeds and a larger amount at supersonic speeds. Wallis claimed that it offered a better lift/drag ratio than any other comparable development. The airmen were naturally attracted by Wallis's proposal for an aircraft which could be used either as a bomber or a fighter, able to fly at 114mph at stall with wings fully spread to over 1615mph at cruising speed, and to have a short burst capacity of 3106mph with wings fully laid back at over 70 degrees. The range for the fighter type was 5000 miles, enabling interception of enemy bombers to take place well away from the British coast, while the range for the bomber version was 11,000 miles enabling it to cover all important strategic targets in the Soviet Union, and, if need be, to fly from England to Australia without violating the national sovereignty of any country. These proposals were never substantiated and the WCA remained a 'paper aeroplane'.

Wallis was given a modest subvention by the Ministry of Supply to support his work, which remained under Vickers. But as the years went by, without a manned prototype being built, doubts began to arise even in the minds of Wallis's supporters.[5] Admittedly, he had flown models of SWALLOW by remote control and, in doing so, had, according to himself, 'made the most significant advance in control since the Wright brothers had their brilliant concept of twisting the wings.'[6] The trouble was that Wallis kept changing the shape and objective of the project. By 1953, with the need to control defence expenditure, SWALLOW came under searching scrutiny for the first time.

Wansbrough Jones, Chief Scientist of the Ministry of Supply, provided the Treasury with a well-balanced criticism of Wallis's ideas. Conceding that a variable geometry aircraft has 'far more to commend it than solely its novelty', he believed that Wallis had 'suffered from too much personal patronage and unbalanced encouragement from Lockspeiser and Tizard and members of the Air Staff and then had been blowing hot and cold.'[7] There was criticism from other quarters of Wallis's idiosyncratic and highly personal leadership and his inability to delegate responsibility, which merely discouraged some of the competent, independent-minded members of his staff and forced them to leave.[8] It was also believed that his age was beginning to tell (he was then in his seventies) and that his intellectual powers were on the wane. Even those members of the management of Vickers who had hitherto loyally supported him began to doubt whether his plans would ever come to fruition. The real engineers at Vickers had never supported him.

Nevertheless, SWALLOW was kept alive by the Air Staff's requirement for a very long range reconnaissance aircraft (eventually the TSR2) which fitted in with Wallis's ideas. The Ministry of Supply, while sceptical of Wallis, *was* interested in the 'problem of the two position wing' and wanted him to concentrate on 'getting an aircraft to fly and to keep off the other ancillary problems.' Arnold Hall, Director of RAE, and member of a panel set up by the Ministry of Supply in 1954 to decide whether Wallis should be given more money, said that 'with certain provisos, Wallis's work should be supported to the maximum possible extent.'[9] But after the major defence expenditure cuts three years later, financial support for SWALLOW was withdrawn in March 1957. Vickers continued to provide money, though they were not prepared to build the small aircraft that Wallis wanted.

Research on variable geometry had also been going on for some time in the States at the Langley Field Laboratories under the Deputy Director, John Stack. It was believed there that Wallis's concept offered 'a major step forward in aeronautical design and we cannot afford to ignore it.'[10] A team was sent to visit Vickers on 11 August 1958, but they soon realised that the wing hinge problem had only partially been solved and that it would hamper the performance of the aircraft at high supersonic speeds. Although the Americans toyed with Wallis's concept for the remainder of 1958, their views of him coincided with those of the Ministry of Supply, namely that he had 'no experience in the real problem of transonic and supersonic flight.'[11]

Meanwhile the USAF wanted a tactical strike fighter (later called the Tactical Fighter Experimental – TFX) able to fly at tree top height against precise targets over 900 miles away. This was, in effect, the prototype of the F-111 – the first variable geometry combat aircraft to fly. It contained the most modern airborne radar to enable it to attack unseen point targets; the latter were reached with the aid of automatic terrain-following equipment using pre-scanned, stored ground profiles and terrain avoidance, so that it could fly at the very low levels that were now required in an electronically-hostile environment. The F-111 became operational in 1967 and took part in the latter stages of the Vietnam War, where it successfully made a number of precision attacks against communications targets.

But this was only accomplished after surmounting a number of fearsome obstacles, both political and technological, not to mention the escalating expenditure of the project. The F-111 became a victim of the rationalisation programme imposed by McNamara in the early 1960s (briefly described on page xxix). It even encountered hostility from the USAF which, at one point rejected the plane and only retracted its decision after pressure was placed on it from its own Scientific Advisory Board. The opposing requirements of the

Plate 27 F-111: the first variable geometry fighter/strike aircraft built for the USAF. It has been employed in the long range strike role since the end of the war in Vietnam. (*Royal Aeronautical Society*)

USAF and the US Navy constituted another difficulty. The former was primarily interested in a strike aircraft, the latter was far more concerned about the need for an interceptor which could provide cover for the fleet. McNamara insisted on a joint Air Force/Navy fighter. Although two separate types of aircraft were eventually built, the F-111 was never used purely as a fighter, but some oddities were common to both types, such as the US Navy's demand for side by side seating.

Technically, much time was spent in deciding on the position of the swing wing pivots and on a major redesign of the Pratt & Whitney engine. British aircraft designers, like B O Heath (later associated with the TORNADO) criticised the F-111's wing pivots. Another contentious point was the undesirable increase in the aircraft's weight in order to give it a bomb-carrying capacity and to accommodate all the ECM equipment that was an essential concomitant. But in spite of the setbacks experienced in the development of the F-111, it proved to be a revolutionary aircraft and it demonstrated that variable geometry aircraft could be built in a wide range of sizes and weights.

The Soviet Air Force was to benefit from the development work at Langley Field. Its *Su19* (FENCER) fighter/ground attack aircraft was, in fact, closely modelled on the F-111. Moreover, at the end of the 1960s, the Mikoyan design team produced two variable geometry aircraft, the FLOGGER (*MiG23*) which had a combat range of 600 miles, and the FEARLESS – an interceptor which did not evolve beyond the prototype stage.

A Solution to Deficiencies in Tactical Aircraft: the TSR2

It was soon realised that ballistic missiles, though easily dispersed and relatively invulnerable to attack, were most unsuitable for meeting the needs of conventional or limited war. The fighting in Korea and Indo-China provided abundant evidence for the need to update fighter and close support aircraft. In 1956, Britain experienced such a limited war at Suez. The ground attack aircraft in service with the RAF proved to be inadequate and the need for some kind of multi-role aircraft became glaringly obvious. 'We must depart from the time-honoured practice of taking a front line interceptor and dressing it up with ground attack weapons to become a fighter bomber', Sir Geoffrey Tuttle, Deputy Chief of Air Staff, told the Air Council in July 1957.[12] He continued:

'The history of this practice in the jet era alone makes dismal reading. Our early METEORS in the Second Tactical Air Force (1945) and METEORS 8 in Korea were relatively ineffective in the ground attack role, and today our SWIFTS and HUNTERS are gravely restricted in the fighter reconnaissance and ground attack roles overseas. In the recent action in Egypt, the limited range of the VENOMS made it necessary to operate them on a sortie profile

Plate 28 Air Marshal Sir Geoffrey Tuttle, Deputy Chief of Air Staff and Member of the Air Council, 1956–59. Responsible for operational requirements of the RAF, he pressed for long range, tactical-strike aircraft and supervised the introduction of the first automated ground surveillance radars for the defence of the United Kingdom. (*Air Historical Branch, Ministry of Defence*)

which gave the maximum early warning to the enemy. Against even moderately determined opposition, this could have had disastrous consequences. Moreover, even operated in this highly vulnerable manner the VENOMs could not reach the main bulk of the Egyptian Air Force's *ILLYUSHIN 28s* [twin jet bombers] which had been moved to Luxor (570 miles from Cyprus). By 1965, a developed F-23 [LIGHTNING] is likely to be the only modern fighter available, but there is no reason to suppose that it would be any better following adoption.'

Such forthright criticism by Tuttle and his colleagues led the Air Staff to seek what was to be called a tactical strike/reconnaissance aircraft, capable of carrying either high explosive or tactical nuclear bombs in close support of the ground forces and at the same time fly on deep reconnaissance missions which would be 'a decisive factor in the conduct of operations.'[13] It should also be able to fly all-weather electronic reconnaissances. It should have an adequate range of around 1100 miles to permit effective operation from the limited number of overseas bases, or, in global warfare, from outside the highly vulnerable tactical area. An ability to operate from short runways or dispersed strips was also highly desirable. The new aircraft would need to be operational by 1964, replacing the CANBERRA which by then 'would be incapable of defeating the hostile defences that could be mounted in the zones in which tactical warfare may be waged [in the mid-1960s].'

Coming in the wake of the swingeing cuts imposed by Sandys in 1957, the Tactical/Strike Reconnaissance 2 (TSR2), as it became known, was considered by the Air Staff to be the 'last boat for the shore'[14] to use a nautical rather than an aeronautical metaphor. On 1 January 1959, the contract for the TSR2 was awarded to Vickers Armstrong and English Electric. Its complex design, navigation and weapons systems caused development to be farmed out to a number of companies. Committees replaced the 'brains and decision-making mechanism of the chief designer.' The TSR2 was to have a crew of two and had to be able to take off from rough strips no longer than 1,800ft (though it did not have VTOL capability), and fly at supersonic speeds. It held a veritable cornucopia of electronic equipment, including a fully automatic navigation system, automatic terrain-following and sideways-looking radar, the latest high resolution radar, active linescan, and full photographic reconnaissance equipment.

But the TSR2, from which the British Air Staff had expected so much, was beleaguered by one setback after another, such as the closing down of English Electric's guided missile plant at Luton, while control of the project was split between the Ministry of Aviation and the British Aircraft Corporation. Technical problems arose causing the programme to lag, and costs soared.

Opposition to the TSR2 emerged from several quarters at a high level.

When the operational requirement for a tactical strike reconnaissance aircraft was originally mooted by the Air Staff, the NA39 (BUCCANEER), a high speed, low altitude strike aircraft had been submitted by Blackburn, the aircraft manufacturers, as a possible candidate. Though rejected by the Air Staff, the BUCCANEER met with the approval of the Chief of Defence Staff, Lord Mountbatten. Another opponent of the TSR2 was Sir Solly Zuckerman, the new Chief Scientific Adviser, who was critical of the general management of weapons research and development. He argued that the TSR2 would only add to the plethora of combat aircraft projects awaiting approval of the Government. If the BUCCANEER could fly as well as the TSR2 at low level and fulfil the close support role demanded by the Army, why build the TSR2? He was later to point out that even an aircraft like the VULCAN, intended for a strategic bombing role, was equally capable of carrying out low level strikes, as demonstrated in the Falklands war.[15]

Now a target for high level criticism, the TSR2 flew for the first time on 27 September 1964. Three weeks later, the first Labour Government since 1951 was elected. In the spring of 1965 the new government announced further cuts in defence expenditure. On 6 April the TSR2 was finally cancelled after huge cost overruns. With the cancellation of the TSR2 it seems, in hindsight, that a great opportunity for British military aviation was lost. Nevertheless, there were compensations; a number of important technical developments arose on account of the experimental machine which at least provided a catalyst in the evolution of other aircraft. The terrain-following system was in advance of any other in the world. What the RAF needed was a system enabling the aircraft not only to hug the contours and the hollows but also the bumps, so that it should not present a target as it came over the top of a hill. The nearest approach was the American autoflite system used in the F-111, but the American forward-looking radars were primarily designed for mapping, search, and medium altitude bombing and were unsuitable for close terrain-following. The autoflite system was also used mainly in a manual flight director mode while the TSR2 mode was automatic with the flight director used for monitoring and as a back-up. Although never tested in flight on the TSR2, terrain-following systems are now used on many aircraft, but at the time it was unique.

Another important feature was the head-up display which projected essential combat data in a glass screen at eye-level and allowed the pilot to engage a target without actually seeing it, or he could identify a target, releasing his weapons manually when indicated by the computer. The stringent requirements, both for navigation and bombing and for day and night reconnaissance demanded the development of much novel equipment, some of it new to British industry. For example, a new inertial platform was used to meet the accuracy demands of the sideways looking airborne radar. [16]

The unexpected cancellation of the TSR2 made it necessary for the RAF to seek another replacement for the CANBERRA. In order to fill the gap, the British Government, in 1966, ordered 50 F-111s from the USA. Two years later, in the face of massive public expenditure cuts after the devaluation of sterling, the order for the F-111s had also to be cancelled. A searching review of British strategy led the Government to withdraw military forces from east of Suez and concentrate them in Europe. At least that meant that very long range aircraft were no longer required. For the time being, the offensive/defensive roles had to be maintained by the BUCCANEERS and, a new buy, US F-4s (PHANTOMS). Luckily for the British, an opportunity was at hand at last to build a truly multi-role aircraft.

Multi-role Achieved by the TORNADO

The growth of European collaborative military projects in which two or more countries agreed on the design and development of a major weapon system was mentioned briefly on page xxx. One of these projects was the Anglo-French supersonic strike aircraft (JAGUAR) which came to a successful conclusion, the first prototype flying in September 1968. However, the Anglo-French variable geometry aircraft, so badly needed by the British, failed to materialise on account of the secret decision of the French to develop their own variable geometry aircraft called the *MIRAGE G.*

By the end of the 1970s, Britain, West Germany and Italy required new aircraft in the strike and air superiority roles. The British wanted an interdiction/strike aircraft to replace the VULCAN and BUCCANEER employed in the nuclear and conventional strike roles and the CANBERRA for long-range reconnaissance as well as an interceptor for air defence; the Germans needed a support aircraft and the Italians put in for an air superiority fighter. In July 1969, after preliminary discussions in London and Bonn, the three nations signed a Memorandum of Understanding and agreed to produce a multi-role combat aircraft. A consortium, known as Panavia, was formed by the British Aircraft Corporation, Messerschmitt-Bölkow-Blohm and Aeritalia (Fiat). By March 1969, a joint design had been agreed. Production was to be administered by the NATO MRCA Development and Production Agency (NAMMA) located at Munich.

Initial studies by the aircraft designers led to the decision to adopt variable geometry as it would fulfil the three roles proposed for the aircraft. Thus, with the wings forward at low speed, the aircraft was

'virtually acting in an air liner mode with good take-off and landing, long range, long loiter and high manoeuvrability at speeds allowing use of high lift devices. At higher speeds there was a CANBERRA mode with the wing in the forward position loaded with stores.'[17]

In the wings back position, the aircraft could be used as an interceptor. The F-111 had proved that the variable geometry arrangement was feasible, though an improved wing pivot had to be developed by British engineers. The Rolls Royce RB199 engine was chosen to propel the aircraft; it had new types of compressor made from titanium alloys, weighing less than their predecessors and running at a high rotational speed to give higher compression ratios.

The MRCA had a target acquisition radar and a Doppler navigational radar from which data was fed into the main navigation computer. By continually collating the velocity and positional information from different sources, the computer maintained a running check on the aircraft's current and future positions. This information was integrated with the automatic pilot and enabled the pilot to fly at 200 feet along a pre-planned route at high speed without having to touch the controls. Special attention was also given to ECM by installing jamming and chaff-dispensing equipment.

Two types of MRCA were developed to suit the strike and air defence role: the Interdiction Deep Strike (IDS) version for ground support and the Air Defence Variant (ADV) for interception of enemy intruders. The IDS version was to achieve Mach 2 speeds and possess all-weather and short take-off and landing capabilities. The ADV version was based on the IDS version but with different characteristics in avionics, weapons and air frame for the benefit of the RAF. It was a technically complex aircraft with loitering and dash capabilities for interception of bombers and missiles. Combat radius of both types would range from 300–600 miles, but mid-air refuelling would be available.

Perhaps inevitably, development of the IDS and ADV prototypes took longer and was more expensive than anticipated, but the maiden flight of the IDS prototype was made on 14 August 1974 and production began two years later. Full development of the ADV began at about the same time. But it was hampered by the long-awaited arrival of the FOXHUNTER aircraft interception (AI) radar which was the first British long-range AI set and contained the new track-while-scan technique, providing a picture of the tactical situation and attack steering data. The two versions were given the name of TORNADO and began to reach their respective squadrons from 1982 onwards.

An aircraft as complex as the MRCA was bound to attract criticism.[18] As early as 1970, several nations had serious doubts about the ADV version and thought it would lack manoeuvrability compared with other NATO aircraft such as the EAGLE (F-15) or the HORNET (F-18) designed by the Americans. But the RAF held that none of the American designs could meet the long-range, all-weather capability, or the complex air defence tasks required for the defence of the United Kingdom. As for the IDS version, the RAF was again satisfied, as it had at last obtained the fast bomber with high endurance needed to replace the CANBERRA. The German Air Force was prepared to accept the RAF's twin engine, two-man crew design and found that its large payload

Plate 29 TORNADO: the European multi-role combat aircraft. Two versions were produced- ground support/strike and air defence. (*Royal Aeronautical Society*)

capacity and long range were well suited to carry the heavy scatter bombs (described on page 225) intended for use against armoured formations (though it was an expensive and complex system to be squandered in such a high risk environment). The Italian Air Force was the least well-served of the recipients; the IDS version did not fully satisfy the air superiority/ground attack role originally desired. This shortfall was evidently acceptable to the Italian Government as construction of the aircraft provided a stimulus to its aerospace industry.

Vertical Take-off and Landing

In order to follow the story of the development of VTOL and STOL, we must now go back in time.

High speed aircraft, like the LIGHTNING and PHANTOM, demand long runways for take-off and landing. But in the fluid warfare of the second half of the 20th century large airfields offer vulnerable, easy-to-find targets and may not be available in a swiftly-moving battle. An aircraft able to take off and land on short runways or even on grass strips and still be able to attack targets in the battle area became a desirability. German experiments with a machine that would take off vertically from a restricted space like the deck of a ship ended abruptly in 1943 when the drawing office of Focke-Wulf was destroyed in an air raid. In the early 1950s, interest grew in the possibility of a vertical take-off and landing (VTOL) aircraft with an engine able to give enough vertical thrust to lift the aircraft. Designs for an aircraft able to take off vertically and to transfer to horizontal flight at subsonic speeds and land vertically, began to be made tentatively by the Eastern and Western Alliances, but mainly in the States and Britain.[19]

Undoubtedly such an aircraft would be invaluable in a naval role and would dispense with the need for very large carriers (though this was the very reason why some senior naval officers were induced to condemn VTOL as it would deprive them of the chance of commanding such imposing vessels). The Army was more concerned about the possibilities of VTOL aircraft for transporting troops and supplies around the battlefield. The advantages of being independent of surfaced runways became more apparent when the doctrine of flexible response began to be absorbed, but as early as 1954, the military had appreciated that VTOL would allow ground support aircraft to operate from the forward area.

Reviewing progress on 2 March 1954, the DRPC agreed that the development of jet reaction and jet reversed thrust was 'of extreme importance'.[20] British experiments were then centred around two forms: a METEOR fitted with jet deflection boxes to give partial jet lift and the Rolls Royce 'flying bedstead' which was, in effect, a controllable platform housed in a gantry powered by two Nene engines to give vertical jet lift. The firm of Short Brothers also submitted a design to the Ministry of Supply which was believed to be technically more advanced but was more complex in its design. The 'flying bedstead' made a successful ascent for the first time on 3 August 1954, but four years were to elapse before the military advantages of such an aircraft began to be appreciated. The impetus came from Hawker's, which for some years past had been working on supersonic designs and had suffered from the numerous cancellations arising out of the 1957 White Paper. Sir Sydney Camm, head of the firm and responsible for such famous combat aircraft as the HURRICANE and the TYPHOON, had seen French experiments in VTOL on a visit to Paris. His chief designers, F W Fozard and Ralph Hooper were told to work out a design similar to those on the drawing boards of Rolls Royce and Shorts.[21] This project was given the classification of P1127. It differed fundamentally from the Short's SC1 in that *one* engine was to provide the forward and vertical thrust. This was the BE53 (Pegasus) designed by the Bristol Aircraft Company. The thrust from the engine would pass through four nozzles arranged round the centre of gravity of the aircraft. For vertical take off, these nozzles were directed downwards and for forward flight, backwards, with a controlled variation between the two positions to assist the transition. Control in the landing and take off phases was achieved by means of vertical jets, fore and aft and on the wing tip. These too were fed from the main engine.

Despite some interest in its early stages, the P1127 failed to arouse enthusiasm in the Assistant Chief of Air Staff responsible for operational requirements and even his advisers 'made it perfectly clear that we were unlikely ever to be interested in the project. However Camm has obviously done a lot more work.'[22] But pressure to continue the project came from other quarters. There were two requirements in 1959 for a strike/reconnaissance aircraft which would operate from the forward area in support of the ground forces, one a basic military requirement from NATO*, while the British Air Staff wanted to replace the ageing HUNTER by a new strike/reconnaissance plane. Linked with the NATO requirement was an American proposal for a variable geometry multi-purpose aircraft which would incorporate Bristol's BE53 engine. They had already invested money in it under the terms of the MWDP and they wanted the aircraft to have a V/STOL capability. Ironically, this American participation kept the P1127 project alive in Britain, but despite the recommendation of the United States Government's scientific advisers to go for VTOL, the Department of Defense rejected the proposal on the grounds that the technology was immature; it lacked the performance and was more expensive than conventional aircraft. Some years were to elapse before the US Marine Corps decided that a VTOL aircraft would be a useful acquisition for amphibious operations.

By the summer of 1959, the British services had at last begun to appreciate the assets inherent in VTOL technology and were no longer put off by the limited range and speed of such an aircraft, which were not essential for the kind of tasks it would be called upon to perform. Moreover, as the Ministry of Supply emphasised, 'VTOL/STOL was one of the few fields in aeronautical research in which we may be a little way ahead of the Americans.'[23] In October 1959, therefore, Hawker's were commissioned to design, develop and construct two P1127s. Should they prove successful, the anticipated date for the new aircraft to reach squadrons would be around 1965–66. On 12 April 1960, the Ministry of Aviation (as the Ministry of Supply had now become) asked Hawker's for four more prototypes although, as yet, no contract had been signed. The following month, the first BE53 engine arrived at Hawker's; hovering flight tests began that autumn and, on 22 September 1961, the first vertical lift-offs from the ground were accomplished. The next stage was to take off from a grass surface with both vertical and short take offs. They took place without damage to the engine or significant erosion of the ground. As Fozard pointed out, high performance fighter aircraft had not taken off from grass runways for 'at least two decades . . . The 30,000hp of

*The NATO Basic Military Requirement System was to prove ineffective and was replaced by the NATO Project System giving NATO status to projects agreed separately by individual states.

the Pegasus engine in V/STOL has provided a great leap forward (and upward).'[24]

Unfortunately, the P1127 could not fulfil the NATO requirement of 170 miles radius of action on account of the fuel required (much of which had been consumed in the initial thrust of take-off). Hooper therefore increased the thrust of the Pegasus engine from 15,000 to 18,000 pounds in addition to other improvements, thus enabling the P1127 to meet the Air Staff's critical sortie demands. This was accomplished within a period of two and a half years. It was not until February 1965 that evaluation trials of P1127 (now called KESTREL) began at the RAF's Central Flying Establishment. They were to lead to an operational requirement of the RAF known as the HARRIER. The first squadron to be equipped with HARRIERS was operational in 1969.

By then, the Royal Navy had appreciated that VTOL aircraft could provide air cover for amphibious operations obviating the need to depend entirely on helicopters or the presence of an expensive and vulnerable aircraft carrier. Furthermore the invention of a ski ramp for a carrier by Lieutenant

Plate 30 HARRIER: the first vertical take-off and landing aircraft built for the RAF. A maritime version was adapted for the Royal Navy. During the Falklands War, HARRIERS operating from carriers flew some 500 sorties per day. They proved effective even against the high performance strike aircraft of the Argentine Air Force. The US Marine Corps also bought HARRIER and produced their own modified version under licence. (*Royal Aeronautical Society*)

Commander D R Taylor greatly improved the Harrier's performance compared with a flat deck launch. In 1972, the Royal Navy, now that it had been deprived of its fleet carriers (and so of the PHANTOMS, which had provided cover against the Soviet BEAR long range maritime aircraft), wanted an aircraft with a radius of 400 miles. It should be able to reconnoitre over 20,000 square miles in one hour at low altitude and be able to attack ships, patrol boats and shore targets. With the introduction of what were originally called Anti-Submarine Warfare (ASW) cruisers, but were in reality ASW carriers, the Navy had a pressing need for a fixed wing capability, not only to shadow BEARS and support amphibious operations but also to support longer range forward reconnaissance cover than the SEA KING helicopter could provide. The outcome was the SEA HARRIER.

Hawker's, all along, had intended developing a supersonic twin-engine, two seat VTOL aircraft as a companion to the P1127 and evolved a new engine (the BS53/6) with plenum chamber burning – that is tail burning in the by-pass flow to the cold nozzles. In mid-1962, a joint RAF–Royal Navy requirement was issued for a supersonic strike aircraft which could be buttressed by American funds through the Mutual Weapons Development Team. Although the P1154, as it was designated, was primarily a strike aircraft, it could have been adapted as an interceptor operating from small carriers and would have been a much more powerful weapon than the HARRIER. Sadly, the Navy and the RAF were unable to agree on a common specification. The former needed a supersonic replacement for the HUNTER which the KESTREL/HARRIER could not fulfil. It was eventually decided that the Navy should buy US PHANTOMS fitted with Rolls Royce Spey engines which had a thrust of 1040 pounds. As we have seen, the Labour Government of 1964 axed both the TSR2 and the P1154, the latter on 2 February 1965. In their place the RAF was to be equipped with a mix of HARRIERS and PHANTOMS.

Thirteen years after the first RAF HARRIER squadron became operational, HARRIERS and SEA HARRIERS were the mainstay of the British air forces in the unanticipated Falklands conflict of 1982. Operating in both offensive and defensive roles from two carriers and later from an air strip at San Carlos, the HARRIERS flew around 500 sorties a day. Due to their remarkable flexibility and manoeuvrability, which compensated for a huge disparity in speed, the British pilots were credited with 20 confirmed victories, most of which were high performance *MIRAGE III*s and SKYHAWKS A-4P and A4-Q of the Argentine Air Force. Four HARRIERS were lost to ground defences and four were lost in operational accidents. This more than justified the persistence of Sydney Camm and his team in developing the first successful VTOL aircraft.[25]

Improvements in Aircraft Control

So far we have discussed revolutionary types of aircraft. Their high speed, capacity for low level flight and the sophisticated weapon systems with which they were equipped imposed severe strains on aircrew. It has been remarked that a 'pilot who is mentally saturated in a sophisticated battle area will probably not survive.' Every effort had to be made to help the pilot to function efficiently with the minimum amount of stress.[26]

The first step taken was to replace manual by powered controls. Instead of a cumbrous control column, the pilot was provided with finger tip control which also saved space in the cockpit. The arrangement of the cockpit contributed immensely to the success of a pilot's mission. Much thought and effort went into improving the ergonomics of a very small area. By the end of the 1970s, cockpits of combat aircraft had been transformed by the computer. Head-up displays (HUD), as we have seen, gave the pilot flight information and weapons delivery data, allowing him to read and digest it all without interrupting his concentration on the target.[27] The head-up display was connected to the flight control and weapons delivery computer as well as to the digital display computer and the radar. In addition, the head-up display reproduced the information appearing on the cockpit instruments, such as air speed, heading and altitude. By the end of our period, the tendency to adopt single rather than two seat strike aircraft further emphasised the importance of keeping an aircrew's work load to manageable proportions.

All-Weather Fighter and Strike Aircraft

All these improvements had been stimulated by the need for an all-weather aircraft. Low cloud will preclude many air operations or severely restrict what is possible. Visibility affects an aircrew's ability to acquire targets, deliver ordnance and deal with defences. Such limitations gave cause for concern in Korea, but over the central region of Europe, where a far more critical battle might be fought, darkness or poor visibility reigns for about half the time in the summer and three quarters of the time in winter. An aircraft was needed which would enable the pilot to see about half a mile ahead and to fly at heights of about 200–300 feet above the ground.

The British response to this problem was to develop an all-weather interceptor, the air defence of the UK being a prime responsibility. For this reason the two-seat JAVELIN was designed with the advanced electronics and AAMs of the time; it was also capable of being refuelled in flight. Unfortunately the high cost involved led to only 15 squadrons going into service, but many of the JAVELIN's specifications were transferred to the HUNTER and SWIFT. These were single-seat fighters and caused some experienced air officers to wonder whether one man could both fly and operate the electronic equipment. As just described, automation would provide the answer.

The Americans were working on the same problem, their experience in Korea leading them to give priority to a strike aircraft able to give support to the Army in any kind of weather, day or night. Foremost among the applicants for this aircraft were the US Marine Corps, closely followed by the US Navy. The aircraft which best met their need was the Grumman A-6 INTRUDER, its greatest asset being the Digital Integrated Attack Navigation Equipment (DIANE). This system allowed the pilot to fly over any terrain in any weather and under varying tactical conditions without having ever to look at the ground from take-off to landing.[28] The A-6 proved its worth in Vietnam from July 1965 onwards. Of course, these systems required space within the aircraft, cost money and were subject to ECM.

Aircraft Weapons: Air-to-Air – Guns/Cannon

Machine guns and cannon have traditionally been the primary weapons of the aerial dog fight; they were used decisively, for example, in the great air battles of the Second World War, like those fought by RAF Fighter Command over Southern England in 1940. Machine-guns mounted in turrets provided some defence for the slow-moving American bombers as they flew over Germany in daylight. After the war it was envisaged that for as long as could be foreseen, guns and cannon would provide the main armament for interceptor aircraft in their role of protecting the homeland and air/naval bases overseas.

As we have seen, the main threat at that time was expected to come from fast, high-flying bombers, possibly but not necessarily, without escort. As they might be carrying nuclear bombs it was vital that the interceptors should be equipped with weapons with a high kill probability rate. The protagonists of guided missiles, as these developed, believed that the air-to-air missile (AAM) would eventually replace rapid-firing machine guns and cannon as the primary air-to-air weapon. Consequently, a number of interceptor aircraft in the Western and Soviet air forces were not equipped with cannon because the missiles they carried had greater range and were believed to be more effective against jinking targets.

For the time being, however, the time required for the development of the AAMs required that guns and cannon should be the main armament until the mid-1950s. Subsequently, in the Middle East and Vietnam wars, pilots discovered that the older forms of weapon were often much more handy in close quarter air combat, where the ability to fire at close range, at low altitude and against elusive targets, gave them the edge over missiles. They could also deal with non-jinking missiles. Furthermore, most guns had an ammunition capacity allowing for more kill opportunities than the limited number of missiles which a fighter could expend. Cannon were relatively inexpensive to produce and fire and were not subject to interference from ECM. But they were limited to a tactical range of only a few thousand feet. Two outstanding guns in our period were the ADEN gun used by the RAF and the M61 VULCAN gun used by the USAF.[29] After the Second World War the bogey of the British Air Staff was the possibility of losing an air-to-air combat. It was decided to enlarge the German 30 millimetre Mauser aircraft gun to 40 mm in order to make it a more dangerous weapon against Soviet bombers and their escorts – this was the ADEN gun. Similarly, most American and Soviet cannon had calibres of 30 millimetres, though the 20 millimetre projectile fired by the American VULCAN had a shorter time of flight and slightly greater range and lower bullet dispersion than its French and Soviet equivalents. The latter, being more powerful, were, however, more likely to inflict casualties, provided the target had been hit. Greater rates of fire, as compared with wartime weapons, now became possible. The ideal range for firing cannon was between 1000 and 3000 feet. Engaging targets at greater ranges than this introduced an excessive lead angle, while the factor of reduced visibility and the possibility that the shell would hit the target with insufficient energy to cause the impact fuse to detonate, all reduced the probability of a kill.

The Americans even brought up to date the multi-barrelled automatic GATLING gun first used in the American Civil War. In its airborne form, it was a 20 millimetre gun driven by an electric motor, with the shells fired electrically. Whereas in Korea the F-86 SABRE fired an average 1000 rounds from its 12.7 millimetre guns to destroy a *MiG15* in the air, a PHANTOM firing a GATLING over Vietnam expended an average of only 500 rounds to shoot down a *MiG21*.

Pilots using these weapons relied on their fire control equipment to detect and attack a target. At the beginning of the period, this was achieved at night by a combination of airborne radars for detecting other aircraft and ground targets while, in daylight, an effective gunsight on its own was used. Guns had been revolutionised in the latter part of the war by the lead-computing gyroscopic gunsight that gave the pilot a continuously up-dated indication of the proper point at which to fire in order to hit a turning aircraft. SPITFIRE squadrons of the 2nd Tactical Air Force were equipped with the new sight in time for the Normandy landings. But the new sight never had a chance to show its superiority over the old reflector gunsight, as most air actions were fought at short range and there were no encounters with German jet fighters. Although initially not well received, pilots eventually found that they could fire more accurately at high deflection angles or at long range with the gyroscopic gunsight.[30]

In the early 1980s, gyroscopic gunsights and fire control systems for missiles were vastly improved.[31] Earlier models required constant readjustment to the size of the target. The new gunsights, such as the Ferranti ISIS F-195 R-3 had three range settings and both air-to-air and air-to-ground targets could be attacked.

Aircraft Interception Radar Development

The next step was to modernise the technique which enabled the all-weather fighter (with or without a radar officer in addition to the pilot) to detect *unseen* enemy aircraft by day or by night at ranges of up to 15 miles, and then to manoeuvre into a favourable position for launching an attack with gun or cannon at a range of 1,200 yards. The anticipated targets were likely to be small, fast jet bombers carrying a 8,000 pound bomb load. The need for good search characteristics was even more important for the British than for the Americans, as the former would have to face 'heavier attacks and more complex air situations than in the USA.'[32]

An operational requirement for an RAF/Royal Navy Mark 18 AI radar was made in 1954, following a complete reassessment of the original demand, made six years earlier, and development now began at the GEC laboratory at Stanmore. Three factors had to be taken into account; first, the equipment would be installed in the first generation of supersonic fighters and the scanner, in particular, would not only have to withstand the stresses of high speed flight but also be able to locate and hold twisting and turning targets. Second, the set would be required for use in conjunction with AAMs instead of with guns. Third, the wavelength of the radar was shortened from 10 to 3 centimetres when it was discovered that the Americans were using the shorter wavelength because of its superior range (15 miles for search and 4000 yards for tracking, as opposed to 10 miles search and 200 yards for tracking with the 10 centimetre set). This improvement hinged on the use of a combined search and lock-on scanner. Production of the new AI set had been scheduled to start in 1957 but, because of the changes made in design, had to be postponed until 1959–60.

Evolution of Air-to-Air Missiles

Meanwhile work was proceeding in the United States, United Kingdom, France and the Soviet Union on the development of AAMs which, it was anticipated, would sooner or later supersede guns and cannon as aircraft armament. In their early stages, these missiles, like the guns and cannon, were primarily designed to defeat bomber attacks and were intended to increase the range from which projectiles could be launched. They could not, however, be used in dog fights or at very short ranges.

AAMs were divided into three groups: short range, but beyond the range of enemy aircraft guns (2 to 6 miles); medium range (11 to 60 miles); and, by the end of the period, long range (100 miles and more). Guidance systems were based on radar or infra-red. The latter were useful for short range purposes such as aerial combat; they pursued the target from astern, homing onto the heat of the jet engine. To begin with, they were relatively simple weapons, consisting of a tubular air frame with control fins at the front and stabilisation wings at the rear. Contact or proximity fuses, warhead and solid fuel rocket motor were fitted behind the guidance section. Infra-red energy has the drawback of being absorbed or diffused by atmospheric carbon dioxide, water vapour, rain or clouds. The sun, or the sun's glint off snow or water or hot spots on the ground can create false targets that will deceive the missile's seeker. Infra-red guided missiles were most effective when employed in fair weather, preferably at medium or high altitudes, where the missiles were less likely to be attracted to heat sources on the ground.

Examples of early infra-red-guided short range AAMs were the American SIDEWINDER and the British BLUE JAY which was the prototype for FIRE-STREAK. SIDEWINDER was developed for naval aircraft by a team under William Maclean at the US Naval Ordnance experimental establishment at Inyokern in the Mojave Desert, starting in 1951.[33] The new missile, which was intended to counter the faster Soviet fighters, was expected to become operational after the Korean war. Maclean's aim was to produce a simple, easy-to-make missile requiring the minimum equipment on the parent aircraft and using the simplest possible components to make the manufacture straightforward and economical. A series of seven versions of SIDEWINDER were produced over the period of 1956–79 and they eventually attained a range of 11 miles. They were used in Vietnam in SABRE fighters from February 1965 to March 1968 and a total of 175 SIDEWINDERS were responsible for destroying 28 Vietnamese aircraft (a success rate of 16 per cent).[34] The Soviet equivalent of SIDEWINDER known as *ATOLL* (four miles range) was installed in the *MiG21* and was also used in Vietnam, being rather more successful than the American missile, as the parent aircraft was controlled from the ground.

SIDEWINDER was issued to all NATO air forces at one time or another. The RAF/Royal Navy were provided with the AIM-9L version which had an argon-cooled indium antimonide detector and scanning head. SEA HARRI-ERS were equipped with this weapon for the Falklands war and because of the Mach 2.5 speed of the missiles were able to were able to intercept and destroy several of the much faster Argentine *MIRAGES*, even on collision course.

Development of BLUE JAY was undertaken by a team from de Havilland Propellers led by George Hough. They worked closely with TRE which undertook the fundamental research (incidentally, a German infra-red device for long range guns was used as a guide). BLUE JAY/FIRESTREAK was originally intended to be mounted in the all-weather supersonic fighters of the 1970s to intercept enemy bombers at heights of 50,000 feet, though the Air Staff was apprehensive about its performance if an attack was mounted in cloud; in that case, interceptions would be dependent on fighters with guns and AI radar.[35] Lacking a radar-guided AAM, the RAF had to rely on FIRESTREAK (in service in 1958) followed by the faster RED TOP, which had a speed of Mach 3 and was installed in the LIGHTNING in 1964. FIRESTREAK was intended for use by the RAF and Royal Navy, its lethality compensating for reductions in the number of interceptor aircraft.

Radar-guided AAMs tended to be larger, more complex and more expensive than infra-red guided missiles. Unlike the latter, which homed independently onto the target, radar-guided missiles travelled along a radar beam from the launching aircraft. This procedure did not allow pilots to engage a second target until after the attempt on the first had been completed. Semi-active radar did not require the target to be illuminated as it received the latter's reflections of radiation; it was able to attack a target in all-weather conditions and from all aspects and at very long ranges (60–129 miles). Although more flexible than an infra-red missile, it had to lock on to the target until the missile struck home. Once the lock was broken, the missile behaved like any other ballistic projectile. The major disadvantage of radar-guided missiles lay in their susceptibility to ECM as well as to ground clutter, which made their performance at low altitudes somewhat unreliable. They could also be evaded by a skilful pilot turning hard at the right moment as the missile approached him.

The British radar-guided missile programme was handicapped by lack of finance and the drastic reduction of their fighter programme by the 1957 cuts. It had been intended that RED DEAN, mounted in the thin wing JAVELIN, specially adapted for all-weather performance, should come into service in the 1960s.[36] But the project died after the cancellation of this aircraft in the summer of 1956. However, in its place, BLUE SKY, developed by Fairey Aviation, was given top priority by the DRPC, though in the event it was only issued to a limited number of squadrons. Its successor, FIREFLASH and the second generation semi-active AAM SKYFLASH, which came into service in the 1970s, were given a wider circulation. SKYFLASH was developed during a period of severe financial stringency and more attention was given to trying to achieve the required performance and too little to reliability with the result that numerous modifications had to be made. However, in the long run, it was accepted as being an outstanding AAM in NATO's armoury.

The Americans, perhaps less harassed by cancellations, produced two useful radar-guided AAMs in the 1960s and 1970s, namely SPARROW and PHOENIX. The former (a medium range missile) was in service from 1956 to 1977; it had a maximum range of 62 miles and was widely employed by NATO air forces. In that time, it underwent five major modifications.

Plate 31a PHOENIX: US air-to-air missile guided by digitally-controlled, multi-sensor radar (AWG-9). This was the first radar to track and search targets simultaneously. (*Hughes Missile Systems Group*)

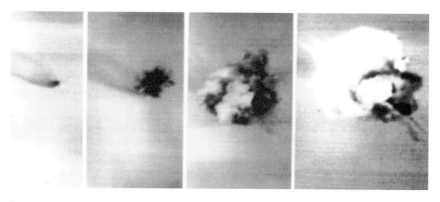

Plate 31b PHOENIX destroys a target. (*Hughes Missile Systems Group*)

PHOENIX (in service from 1970 onwards) was installed in the F-14 TOMCAT fighter which provided the US Navy with cover against cruise missile-carrying aircraft and cruise missiles travelling on their own.

SPARROW and PHOENIX were guided by the remarkable digitally-controlled multi-sensor fire control system known as AWG-9 which was able to intercept multiple targets at long range in any kind of weather. At the heart of this system was the radar which used both simple pulse and pulse Doppler modes to detect targets at greater range than any other radar mounted in a fighter. The radar noted the presence of large aircraft up to 200 miles away and fighter-sized targets more than 100 miles away. The AWG-9 was the first radar able to track and search for targets simultaneously.[37] The pilot or radar officer could launch a PHOENIX or SPARROW missile and track up to 24 other targets at the same time. In November 1973, a TOMCAT launched six PHOENIX missiles in just over 30 seconds against six individual targets. Four of the missiles scored direct hits. In addition to USAF aircraft, pulse Doppler radar and missile systems were fitted in British, French and Soviet aircraft.

At the end of the period, the advanced medium range air-to-air missile (AMRAAM) was just going into pilot production for the USAF, US Navy, US Marine Corps, the RAF and the German Air Force. This weapon was an important advance on previous AAMs because it eliminated the need for the launching aircraft to keep flying towards the enemy while illuminating the target with its radar. It was to fly on inertial guidance until close to the target when it would activate its own miniature guidance radar. The TORNADO F-2 and the American F-15 (EAGLE) fighters were destined to be equipped with this formidable weapon.

French and Soviet Air-to-Air Missiles

Before turning to air-to-ground weapons, the French and Soviet achievements in AAMs should be recognised. The French were, in fact, the first to put an AAM into an aircraft; this was the AA-20, equipped with a radio command guidance system; it had a range of 2 miles and went into service in 1956.[38] Two years later, it was followed by the R-511, a semi-active radar-controlled missile and then by the R-530, intended for the *MIRAGE IIIC*, which could be guided either by infra-red or by radar. The SUPER 530 (13 miles range) was designed for the *MIRAGE F-1C* and *MIRAGE 2000* which entered service in 1978; finally there was the MAGIC R-550 (one mile range) which was guided by infra-red and used for close-quarter fighting.

About the Soviet AAMs there is very little hard information. The Russians did produce a series of semi-active/infra-red guided AAMs from the mid-1950s onwards and there is no reason to suppose that they were inferior to their equivalents in the West. It is worth mentioning the following: the *ALKALI* which had a speed of Mach 1.2 was installed in the *MiGs* 17 and 19; *ATOLL*, as we have seen went into the *MiG 21*; the *MiG 25* was equipped with *APEX* and the Su 11 with *ANAB*. In the Yom Kippur War, *ALKALI* and *ATOLL* were both fired by Arab pilots.

Air-to-Surface Weapons

For about 20 years after the end of the Second World War free fall, or 'iron' bombs and rockets, were the main weapons used in air-to-ground attack. Bombs ranged in weight from 250 to 3000 pounds; the bomb most commonly used was the 1000 pound weapon. Cluster bombs, still in a primitive stage of development, were used for certain specialised tasks such as the attack on concrete runways. With the introduction of improved types of aircraft like the CANBERRA, highly manoeuvrable and with greater powers of endurance than the wartime piston-engined medium bombers, the distinction between 'bomber' and 'fighter' became increasingly blurred. Apart from the long range strategic bombers like the British V bombers and the American B-36s and B-52s, able to fly to targets 3,500 miles from base, which were entering service towards the end of the 1950s, the most likely targets in a limited or conventional war were to be found at around 300–400 miles from forward air-fields. The fighter bomber or strike aircraft, as it was usually called, became the principal air offensive weapon, not least in the interdiction role, and had become especially effective, thanks to the new technological aids described above. It is illuminating to compare the effort needed to destroy the target at Peenemunde in the well-known Bomber Command raid in the Second World War, which involved some 560 heavy bombers, with the capability of a modern strike force. Now, just over 40 years after Peenemunde, the same task could be accomplished by 12 TORNADOS carrying 24 aircrew (the force multiplier again).

Radar controlled anti-aircraft defences had, however, robbed the new aircraft of some of their effectiveness. In the Korean War, jet fighter bombers suffered heavy losses in close support missions. This led to a demand for air-to-ground guided weapons which could be launched beyond the light anti-aircraft gun zone. The Americans and the French (after experience in Indo-China) were the first to devise air-to-surface missiles called BULLPUP and AS-30 respectively. The former, propelled by a solid fuel rocket, was launched by the pilot who guided it to the intended target (bunkers or caves) using a joystick radar control. Later BULLPUP was propelled by a liquid fuel rocket and a 1000 pound HE warhead replaced the earlier 250 pound version.

The early British air-to-surface missiles were more ambitious in scope, but were less successful than the early American efforts. In the early 1950s, the British Air Staff defined the bombing tasks in the event of war as:

1 reduction of the Soviet long range air force and the attack of strategic objectives; and

2 the reduction of the Soviet tactical air force and the direct and indirect support of the land and sea battle in the NATO area of operations.

Much fruitless effort was expended in the early 1950s on two weapons – BLUE BOAR, an air-delivered TV-guided bomb and RED RAPIER, a ground-launched missile similar to the German V-1. BLUE BOAR was planned to come into service in 1957.[39] It was designed by the Vickers Special Projects Division and intended primarily to put airfields out of action. After being discharged by the aircraft, the missile was to glide to cloud base and be guided to the target with the aid of a TV set in the nose of the bomb. What does not appear to have been foreseen was the likelihood of unfavourable weather conditions over the Soviet Union where, for two days out of three, the cloud level is usually less than 10,000 feet rendering TV homing useless. Another disadvantage was that at night the target would have to be illuminated by a 5000 pound flare, revealing the proposed target to the enemy air defences. In October 1953, BLUE BOAR was abandoned. Some of its components were later incorporated in GREEN CHEESE – an anti-ship weapon.

At that time, some senior RAF officers, noting developments across the Atlantic were attracted to the idea of supplanting, or at least supplementing, tactical bombing attacks with easily-constructed unmanned aircraft like the German V-1s. (The USAF had begun to deploy ground-launched MATADOR cruise missiles in Europe in 1955.) The case for RED RAPIER by the Vice Chief of Air Staff, Air Chief Marshal Sir Ralph Cochrane, was that a subsonic expendable bomber (as it was then called) could be manufactured cheaply and in bulk and then stock-piled ready for use when the Soviet Army launched its massive attack towards the Rhine and beyond. Moreover, as another senior RAF officer put it, 'the most expensive item in the manned bomber is the man himself. It takes 21 years to produce this particular piece of equipment.'[40] Air Vice Marshal Tuttle, the Deputy Chief of Air Staff, on the other hand, argued that an expendable bomber was merely an extension of field artillery without the flexibility provided by direct support aircraft. 'Targets are often fleeting,' Tuttle continued, 'dispersed, camouflaged or hidden from ground observation in such a way that they can only be attacked as opportunity targets by ground attack aircraft. We do not visualise that ground-launched guided weapons can cover the role of direct support.'[41]

Nevertheless RED RAPIER, for a short while, was a serious contestant for adoption by the RAF in 1952–53; it was even seen as a possible successor to the CANBERRA, for which at that time no replacement seemed to be forthcoming. RED RAPIER would have had a 500 pound HE warhead and, after being catapulted into the air, would have flown 460 miles to its target, guided by radar. This would have been a more sophisticated version of the wartime GEE, providing enhanced security against enemy ECM. It was to have had a CEP of 100 yards. However, the probability of the British acquiring a ballistic missile in the shape of CORPORAL made the argument for RED RAPIER less convincing, even though longer-ranged than the former. The clinching factors for abandoning this weapon were the growing expense of the electronic components and the large size of the air frame, which made the missile very vulnerable. On 11 November 1954, RED RAPIER was cancelled on the recommendation of the DRPC.[42]

Air-launched Cruise Missiles

In the meantime, until effective ballistic missiles became available, the USAF continued to deploy cruise missiles like MATADOR, RIGEL and MACE on the Central Front. When the USAF appreciated that the Soviet defences 'will have advanced to such a point as to make the use of high altitude subsonic cruise missiles impractical by 1957,' strenuous efforts were made to provide MACE with a self-contained guidance system enabling it to fly at low altitudes. But cruise missiles like MACE were too heavy and unwieldy and lacked the accuracy and range to make them strategic nuclear delivery systems.[43]

By the late 1960s, however, the cruise missile was being transformed by the electronic revolution. Small turbofan engines and high energy fuels provided efficient propulsion at both low and high altitudes. The range of the cruise missile was increased to at least 600 miles. On-board computers improved the missile's guidance system. As the cruise missile could now be built much smaller, so decreasing the size of its radar cross section, its chances of survival and ability to penetrate air defences were greatly improved. Inertial guidance systems were now supplemented by a terrain contour-matching system (TER-COM) which corrected any inertial guidance error by taking periodic fixes on the terrain features over which the missile was passing. TERCOM permitted the cruise missile to attain an accuracy of within a few hundred feet of the target over ranges of up to 1,400 miles.[44] Cruise missiles could also be carried in multiple numbers under the wings of aircraft and they could be launched from submarines. Such assets enhanced the operational flexibility of the cruise missile concept. They could carry conventional or chemical warheads instead of nuclear ones and were cheaper and more versatile than ballistic missiles.

In the early 1980s, the elderly B-52s were fitted with air-launched cruise missiles (AGM-86B). Each aircraft carried 12. The purpose of this was to maintain an adequate airbreathing strategic nuclear delivery system until the advanced technology (STEALTH) bomber became operational in the early 1990s.

In 1984, the Soviet Union began to deploy a long range land attack cruise missile (AS-15) aboard its intercontinental bombers. It was comparable in many ways to the air-launched cruise missile carried by the B-52.

Introduction of Terminally-Guided Bombs for Strike Aircraft

The importance attached to cutting communications targets in North Vietnam in the mid-1960s led the USAF and US Navy to concentrate on the development of guided, as opposed to free fall, bombs. On account of the powerful air defences (SAMs), targets had to be attacked from a distance in order to avoid casualties. And accuracy was needed both for pin point targets and to satisfy the political requirement to minimise collateral damage to civilians and non-military buildings. The US Navy specialised in TV-guided weapons and in 1967 introduced the 1,100 lb WALLEYE TV-guided bomb.[45] Carried by SKYHAWKS operating from carriers in the Gulf of Tonkin, WALLEYE was directed against bridges, buildings and other important targets. The USAF TV-guided bomb was called the Homing Optical Bombing System (HOBOS). It was similar in calibre and manner of operation to WALLEYE. HOBOS and WALLEYES were used extensively in Vietnam and were claimed to have destroyed or severely damaged between 70 and 80 per cent of all targets attacked. The Israeli Air Force used WALLEYE successfully in the Yom Kippur war.

The appearance of the first laser-guided bomb, known as PAVEWAY, was described on page 47. This weapon found its target through a semi-active homing technique. The target could be illuminated by a soldier on the ground, by the launcher aircraft, or by an escort aircraft. The laser seeker near the nose of the bomb passively homed on to the laser beam reflected from the target. Another laser-guided system developed by the Americans about this time was called PAVE TACK.[46] It was designed for the F-111 E/F and F-4E fighter-bomber for day and night employment of laser and FLIR systems; it could also be used by day for the employment of TV-guided and all free-fall weapons. (It was effectively used in the Gulf War in 1991.) Following the success of laser techniques in Vietnam, both France and the Soviet Union exploited lasers for the same purpose. But because of the restricted conditions in which both laser-guided and TV-guided bombs had to be launched, and as guided bombs were usually dropped from medium height and in good weather, it was inevitable that bombers and their escorts or guides became vulnerable to SAMs and anti-aircraft artillery. Air superiority became a prerequisite as well as suppression of ground defences. Nevertheless, the use of the laser beam demonstrated that this PGM was a feasible weapon of war.

Free fall, unguided bombs underwent further changes in the 1970s and 1980s. Special attention was paid to the improvement of the cluster bomb such as the US Navy's ROCKEYE.[47] Cluster bombs were an attempt to overcome inaccuracies by saturating the target area with large numbers of bomblets usually discharged from a cannister. After the canister had been ejected from the aircraft flying at a low level, a nose fuse split it open, dispensing the bomblets over the target. The advantage of this type of weapon was that the pilot did not have to expose himself to enemy fire by flying directly over the target, but could loft* his weapon – though with reduced accuracy.

Attempts were made in the 1970s to increase the accuracy of cluster bombs. ROCKEYE, for instance, was fitted with a laser guidance seeker and a proximity fuse to initiate release of the bomblets when the cannister neared the target. Laser-guided cluster bombs were developed by the USAF for use against armour and troops. The West Germans, too, produced a large (10,000 pound) captive dispenser containing a suite of anti-armour, anti-material munitions and anti-personnel mines and runway and shelter penetrators designed specifically for use on their TORNADO aircraft. In addition to instantaneous anti-personnel or anti-tank warheads, a cluster bomb dispenser could release delayed action bomblets or special mines to destroy transport, armour or personnel over a period of hours.

At about the same time, Britain and France developed respectively the BL755 and BELUGY cluster bombs dispensing anti-armour or anti-personnel bomblets. They were released from aircraft at low altitudes and were able to saturate a large area.

Fuel Air Explosives

Another form of air-to-ground attack originating in the Vietnam war were fuel air explosives sometimes referred to as 'concussion bombs.' They operate by dispersing fuel into the air and then detonating the dispersed fuel cloud. This creates a near uniform overpressure under the cloud. The pressure falls off with range outside the cloud in a manner somewhat similar to standard high explosives.[48] Late in the Vietnam War, the US Navy and the Marine Corps used fuel explosives (designated CBU-55B) for clearing minefields, preparing helicopter zones, and for damaging targets of low to moderate hardness. Fuel air explosives could also prepare the way for PGMs by eliminating camouflage or foliage.

Anti-runway Bombs

An admirable example of the strategy of eliminating an enemy air force with a pre-emptive strike on his air bases was the Israeli Air Force's operation

---

*A loft-delivered bomb was released by the aircraft during a steady climb but *not* under a 'g' pull. A toss-delivered bomb *was* delivered under a 'g' pull. To obtain maximum range for a toss attack, the bomb had to be released at the 45° point.

against the Egyptian Air Force's base in 1967. No doubt after studying the well known surprise attack by the *Luftwaffe* on Allied airfields on New Year's Day 1945, General Ezer Weizman, the Israeli Air Force commander, planned the destruction of the Egyptian Air Force in a similar manner. Two low level attacks in rapid succession were made by small formations of fighter bombers, mainly using their 30 millimetre cannon and a few blasting bombs (not ASMs as was assumed at the time. Cratering bombs were not then available). In the second phase of the operation, Israeli aircraft were diverted in mid-air to attack two airfields in Jordan. All these attacks were completely successful.

Following this spectacular *coup*, aircraft of the Warsaw Pact began to be installed in hardened concrete aircraft shelters. NATO followed suit some-what tardily from 1970 onwards. Attention was now given to the development of special weapons to crater runways, prolong repair periods and destroy aircraft in shelters and key maintenance facilities. The prevention of aircraft from taking off was a high priority. Hitherto, attacks on runways had been made with ordinary bombs dropped at medium altitude and level flight, or from a high angle to penetrate and seriously damage the concrete surface. Such attacks were dangerous because of anti-aircraft fire. Low level attacks using retarded (high drag) weapons were safer, but the low impact speed of retarded bombs limited their capability to penetrate concrete or protective structures.

In 1975, the British, with American financial support, began to develop an anti-runway bomb designated JP-233 which could be used by TORNADO and other NATO low-level strike aircraft. Development was carried out by a team under Geoffrey Williams of Hunting Engineering.[49] Contained within the dispenser were sub-munitions attached to a parachute. When the dispenser was released by the pilot, thirty bomblets coded SG-357 exploded on impact, cratering the runway immediately; 215 other area-denial weapons coded HB-876 were turned upright by a system of spring legs, so turning them into small mines. This ingenious weapon was air-tested in 1980 by an aircraft flying at 500 knots at a level of 200 feet. Also intended for delivery by high speed low level flight was the *Matra*-designed *DURANDAL* anti-runway bomb. A parachute retarded its opening after release to prevent damage to the aircraft. Several seconds later, the parachute was loosed and a booster rocket was ignited to drive the bomb downwards and thus increase its impact velocity. A wide deep crater was caused by the bomb. A rather less sophisticated bomb called BRFA was made by the Spanish firm *Construcciones Aeronaauticas*, also penetrating the runway surface before explosion. Of the two *DURANDAL* had a greater effective damage radius.

Experience in the Gulf war indicated that aircraft concrete runways are now strengthened against the effects of the sub-munitions just described and that air forces may well revert to the traditional free fall 'iron' bomb in a future conflict. The JP-233s were also dangerous to deliver at the required low level altitudes, exposing the TORNADOS to anti-aircraft fire, compared with the American glide-bombs launched from higher altitudes or from stand-off positions.

Increasing Accuracy of Air-to-Surface Missiles

Complementary to the efforts to improve the accuracy of free fall bombs were more efficient ASMs. One of the most notable was the USAF's 462 pound MAVERICK which had a range of 15 miles, providing a much greater stand-off capability than guided bombs. Its guidance system was similar to the HOBOS bomb just mentioned. It was used in Vietnam. In the Yom Kippur War, Israeli aircraft fired 69 MAVERICKS against Arab tanks and bunkers with a high rate of success. Later MAVERICK was modified so as to be able to be fired in both day, night and in adverse weather conditions. Operating as a TV camera, sensitive to infra-red wavelengths, the missile's seeker could detect and lock on to targets such as tanks, aircraft, or ships, all of which are warmer than the surrounding land or seascape.[50]

In the 1970s, the expense and sophistication of air-launched missiles made cooperative development between the Western Allies ever more essential. MARTEL, an Anglo-French product, was designed for two roles: an anti-radiation version (discussed later) or an electro-optical version used by the French against land targets and by the British in maritime patrol aircraft. MARTEL detected the target with its TV sensor before it was launched, but the pilot or weapons system officer had to guide the missile to the target via a data link that sent continuously updated commands to correct its trajectory.

Indispensability of the Electromagnetic Spectrum in Air Warfare

Radar had first shown its value in the Battle of Britain in 1940. Then it was used in a defensive role, but when two years later the air war was carried into Germany, the enemy's radar system had to be neutralised and methods for protecting Allied aircraft against enemy radar detection had to be devised. After the Cold War began, it was appreciated that if the enemy was denied the effective use of his radars, the West obtained a

strategic and tactical advantage because [it denied] him the eyes and ears of his offense and defence. Conversley, the existence of electronic-resistant military radars has become a *sine qua non* of military power.

By the beginning of the 1970s, the West appreciated that the Soviet Union had embraced the new maxim that he who controls the electromagnetic spectrum controls the outcome of any war conflict in modern war or global politics. They understand and appreciate the essential role radar plays in fulfilling this dictum.[51]

The following section deals with the defensive and offensive aspects of radar.

Changes in Ground Early Warning Systems

Before the introduction of semi- and fully-computerised air defence systems (PLAN AHEAD/LINESMAN) described in Chapter 2, there was an urgent need to modernise the wartime early warning radars to provide warning of hostile jet bombers flying across the North Sea at altitudes of around 40,000 feet. In June 1950, the Air Council approved the ROTOR scheme which was designed to provide early warning and control of fighter aircraft along the coastline from Aberdeen to Portland Bill and to a lesser degree other high priority targets in the UK. [52]

After a month, TRE submitted a design for a high power centrimetric radar which was intended to come fully into operation in 1957. This set would increase the range of existing early warning radars from around 150 to 240 miles, thus allowing fighters to be scrambled in time to intercept high performance bombers before they reached the English coast. A prototype of what was to be the TYPE 80 set was first tested in an air defence exercise in October 1951 and before the end of that year orders were given for 12 sets to be made.

In the meantime, the air defence of the United Kingdom was based on the TYPE 14 search radar which had a limited range and was dependent on the TYPE 13 set to provide height. Control was obtained from the TYPE 7 radar which suffered from poor discrimination and was susceptible to jamming. At that time, the number of fighter squadrons was in process of being reduced from 57 to 32 (a total of 736 aircraft).

Production of the new TYPE 80 sets had been planned to begin at the rate of one a month in 1954. But this did not satisfy Air Marshal Sir Basil Embry, Commander-in-Chief Fighter Command, who in a letter of complaint to the Vice Chief of Air Staff, Air Chief Marshal Sir Ralph Cochrane, on 24 April 1952, quoted a conversation of his Chief Signals Officer with Dr Eric Eastwood, then Deputy Director of the Marconi Laboratories.[53] When told of the difference the new equipment would make to the efficiency of the air defences, Eastwood replied 'Then why does not someone in authority put us in the picture?' Embry suggested a meeting of the heads of the leading radio companies to

'make them understand their responsibilities . . . I believe that once we have achieved that, we could expect to see this equipment within a time scale

Plate 32 TYPE 82 three dimensional radar developed for the RAF and used for the air defence of the UK. (*GEC Marconi Ltd*)

which will give us a chance of survival in the holocaust which grows perceptibly and inevitably nearer month by month.'

In reply, Cochrane said that even with hand-made sets 'there was not the slightest chance of getting them as quickly as you suggest.' The TRE prototypes were not strong enough to stand up to service conditions and needed further modifications. As the naval three dimensional set (TYPE 984) was unlikely to come into service in the near future, it might be necessary to depend on the ORANGE YEOMAN (TYPE 82) fire control system (mentioned on page 33) as a stop gap.

In the event, in August 1952 the Air Council gave approval for 29 TRE centimetric radars to be installed at early warning stations under a comprehensive production scheme known as ROTOR. This system stood in to provide long-range radar surveillance until the installation of the TYPE 80 radars. They were followed in turn by the first three dimensional ground surveillance radar (TYPE 82) which came into operation in the late 1950s and early 1960s. When LINESMAN was planned, its backbone was formed by the TYPE 85 set (developed from the RRDE prototype BLUE YEOMAN – an advance on ORANGE YEOMAN which had weak anti-jamming facilities). The TYPE 85 was a high-powered, multi-frequency set with a range of signal processing facilities; it had a good anti-jamming capability, high accuracy in the clear and was especially suited for high-speed fighter control. It was supported by an extremely sophisticated passive detection system (WINKLE) produced by Marconi and which operated on a base line drawn between Patrington north of the Humber and the Marconi test site near Chelmsford. LINESMAN was not fully in service, as noted earlier, until the late 1970s.

While the Air Staff was encouraging the development of ground surveillance radars, it was equally concerned about 'a serious gap in the radar defences' which might be penetrated by low level aircraft flying at altitudes of 500–5000 feet. Warning of their approach was needed while they were at least 100 miles away from the coast line. In the days before over-the-horizon radar, the answer seemed to lie either in radars suspended from balloons flying at a great height or in radars mounted in small ram jet helicopters. At least the latter were cheap and could carry a 200 pound scanner. The Americans were working on the same problem and both Jerome Wiesner and George Valley, at that time involved in the SAGE project, were called upon for advice. Their answer then was the development of very high powered ground radar transmitters with ranges up to 130 miles.

In the end, balloon-supported radars seemed to be the more acceptable proposal.[54] A radar at 5000 feet would give a horizon range of 84 miles. BLUE JOKER, as the scheme was called, would give sufficient time for the V bombers to scramble and for BLUE STREAK (the British ballistic missile) to be counted down to 30 seconds readiness. But before BLUE JOKER could be realised in the late 1950s, the threat of low level air attack had diminished – for the time being – for the threat was now more likely to come from the long range ballistic missile, warning of which could not then be given by any known radar system.

Before long, the situation was to change. Instead of the V bombers, the Royal Navy became responsible, with its POLARIS submarines, for delivering the nuclear deterrent. The need to protect the V bomber bases diminished. Then came the policy of 'flexible response' with an emphasis on conventional warfare which called for a reappraisal, not only of the British, but the entire NATO air defence system to take into account the advent of new Soviet bombers like the BEAR as well as cruise missiles, backed up by much more highly sophisticated electronic support and counter-measures. In 1960, the NATO powers agreed to build a radar chain extending from Northern Norway to Eastern Turkey called the NATO Air Defence Ground Environment (NADGE). The system was constructed by 14 nations (the United States itself contributed 31.83 per cent of the cost) and comprised some 47 radars and 37 computer centres which were capable, in seconds, of locating and displaying aircraft tracks and unambiguously labelling them as friendly or hostile. It was originally capable of detecting air intruders to a height of 100,000 ft but was vulnerable to out-flanking and to low altitude penetration. In due course, the separate British and Spanish systems were linked to it. The French, with a data processing system called *STRIDA II* contributed to the all-round NATO air defence coverage. Further modernisation took place and by 1975 NADGE provided a satisfactory early warning system; trajectory, height, speed and the future position of every target could now be fed into the NADGE computers. Another series of improvements was made to NADGE in the early 1980s under the Air Defence Ground Environment Integration Segment which included the addition of three dimensional radars providing plot, track and target information in digital format. As we shall see, provision was also made for airborne early warning.

Airborne Early Warning

This was, in effect, a long step forward from the balloon and helicopter-supported radars just discussed. It became known as the airborne early warning and control system (AWACS). Equipped with long range radar and communications systems, an aircraft operating over wide areas of sea and land could see, interrogate and classify all targets and pass on the appropriate information (in real time) to surface control agencies, at the same time instructing fighter aircraft to intercept hostile aircraft before coming within striking distance of their targets.

The need for airborne early warning (AEW) had arisen in the Second World War in the war at sea as aircraft carriers began to replace battleships and greatly increased the air threat to surface vessels. Naval actions were now taking place without vessels firing at each other, the casualties being inflicted by carrier-operated or land-based aircraft operating several hundred miles from their enemy. Although radar picket ships could give warning, they themselves were vulnerable to attack. There was an urgent need for an AEW system to locate enemy aircraft emerging over the horizon. Mounted in an aircraft flying at 25,000 feet the radar horizon would be extended to 200 miles. The naval operations supporting the recapture of Okinawa in April 1945 strikingly illustrated the need for this new requirement.[55] In that month alone, 13 radar picket ships or destroyers were sunk or damaged after being attacked by Japanese suicide (*Kamikase*) aircraft.* Although too late for the Japanese war, airborne radar equipment made by Philco Radio Corporation, capable of making up to four interceptions at a time, was hastily installed in CONSTELLATION and FORTRESS heavy bombers.[56]

After the war, exploiting their burgeoning electronics industry, the Americans had already installed AEW equipment in 54 aircraft by 1949, putting, as British naval officers visiting the States enviously reported, 'our own miniature efforts with a MARK 13 radar in one obsolete aircraft in the shade'.[57] At that time, the principal American AEW aircraft was the Douglas SKYRAIDER, fitted with a AN/APS20 radar. Subsequently, other aircraft were developed for the same role including the CONSTELLATION, and two aircraft from the Grumman Company – the TRACER and the E-2C HAWKEYE. In the late 1960s, the Boeing Aircraft Company won a contract from the USAF to build the first AWAC aircraft, using one of its 707s. It was intended to provide warning of air attack by Soviet bombers against targets in North America.

The British were also interested in AEW, at first less for detecting aircraft than for long range spotting of exposed *Schnorkel* submarines, described on page 13, which the Germans had belatedly used in British coastal waters in 1944/45, and which, in the service of the Soviet Navy, again posed a threat to seaborne communications. A perceptive naval operational research study made at the end of 1945 forecast that AEW could

provide all ships of the fleet with a continuous and automatic picture of the 'surface' to a radius of 200 miles and of the air to a lesser distance. The physical limits of air-surface range have not yet been reached and even when this should occur, warning can still be extended to any distance by the use of radar links . . . [AEW] should eliminate the element of surprise in surface

*In the 80 day battle, 36 ships were sunk and 368 damaged by *Kamikase* and other suicide weapons.

232

warfare and reduce considerably the number of craft required for reconnaissance.[58]

However, the idea of an AEW aircraft did not meet with much enthusiasm despite a demonstration by two American FORTRESSES equipped with AEW radar over the United Kingdom in 1949. But at that time the radar was confused by sea clutter and was unable to judge heights properly or to plot overland. Concern over the lack of AEW for the United Kingdom continued however. In the early 1950s, trials were made with a specially-equipped NEPTUNE maritime patrol aircraft fitted with an American AN/APS20 radar operating in conjunction with a parent CHAIN HOME EXTRA LOW station (intended to give warning of low-flying sneak bombers) with VHF/RT communication. The NEPTUNE was able to detect and track three or four targets simultaneously and this information was immediately fed into the static control and reporting system. The airborne radar extended the range of the CHAIN HOME station by at least 70 miles, depending on the size of the target, though it was subject to clutter when operating in the vicinity of the coastline. In November 1952, four of these NEPTUNES,[59] known as the Vanguard Flight, were seconded from Coastal to Fighter Command and NATO for AEW duties until the arrival of the SHACKLETON (another maritime patrol aircraft) in 1971 equipped with a huge radome under the nose. But the SHACKLETON had to be content with the now ageing American radar which was limited to a range of 100 miles while the SHACKLETON's own range did not exceed 3,045 miles.

AEW for the Fleet meanwhile had been provided by 16 US Douglas SKYRAIDERS also equipped with the APS20 set from 1953 until 1960 when they were succeeded by Fairey GANNETS operating off aircraft carriers.[60] British electronics firms had been endeavouring to design a more up to date alternative to the APS20 to be installed in the successor to the GANNET, but this project was cancelled in the defence cuts of 1966, which envisaged the phasing out of Fleet carriers.

The AEW SHACKLETON had to soldier on into the 1980s because of the long time taken to find a suitable successor and then through the failure of that aircraft to come up to expectation.[61] In 1972, Hawker Siddeley and Marconi Avionics were funded by the Ministry of Defence to consider the best means of replacing the SHACKLETONs. At the same time, strong competition for alternative AEW aircraft was provided by the Grumman E-2C HAWKEYE and the larger Boeing E-3A AWAC aircraft already ordered by the US Navy and USAF. At last, in December 1974, the Ministry of Defence decided to select the Hawker Siddeley-Marconi design called NIMROD, an AEW version of the maritime patrol aircraft – essentially on the grounds of its low cost. Unlike the other proposals, its radar had a higher frequency and worked through antennae mounted fore and aft on the fuselage to see clearly when looking downwards.

Meanwhile, NATO had become interested in acquiring the Boeing E-3A as an AEW aircraft to augment NADGE. The British approved this investigation with the intention of taking part in a NATO purchase, provided that the system was suitable and funds forthcoming. They therefore funded the AEW NIMROD as a fall back in case the E-3A was unsuitable or the NATO commitment did not materialise. Two companies prepared plans for the development of the aircraft and its radar. However, in March 1977, NATO failed to agree on the purchase of the AWACS and the Ministry of Defence decided to go ahead with AEW NIMROD to meet the British air defence requirement.

Two years later, NATO changed its mind and decided after all to employ the E-3A in the revised NADGE programme already mentioned. Joint programmes would enable individual states to buy their own aircraft. Britain meanwhile would continue to develop AEW NIMROD. By mid-1986 18 AWACS aircraft were in service or being fitted out for completion. Unfortunately, the British programme was falling far behind and becoming very expensive (more than £900 million had been spent and another £600 million was needed to complete the programme). After an evaluation of AEW NIMROD over 20 flights, in which only three were able to provide suitable

Plate 33 Boeing E-3A AWACS aircraft, able to track 400 targets simultaneously. Provides cover against low-flying aircraft and sea-skimming missiles. Can also be used as a mobile command post for the control of air/land operations. (*Royal Aeronautical Society*)

information, the aircraft was scrapped in favour of the E-3A or SENTRY. The latter was, in fact, superior to NIMROD with an effective range of 287 miles and it was able to track 400 targets simultaneously. Seven AWAC aircraft were ordered to provide air cover of the UK from low-flying aircraft and wave-hopping missiles.*

Nevertheless the E-3 type with its electronic equipment was likely to be exceedingly vulnerable in the vicinity of the battle area. It was in effect '150 tons of slowly orbiting metal only of value when its telling everyone it is there' on account of its active radar emissions which could only too easily be homed on to by enemy missiles. Though the AWAC aircraft could, of course, be protected by chaff dispensers, infra-red decoys and projective jammers (of which more later), they would have to operate at least 100 miles away from the scene of any fighting. On the other hand, the smaller E-2C HAWKEYE could just as well perform an AWACS role. It was used successfully by the Israeli Air Force supporting the invasion of the Lebanon in June 1982. Contemporary accounts of the operation indicate that over the relatively small belt east of Beirut, HAWKEYE could perform nearly 100 per cent of the required AWAC mission just as well as the more expensive SENTRY.[62] For even more limited conflicts, two British SEA KING helicopters were fitted out with a Thorn EMI SEARCHWATER radar from the NIMROD. It was able to give cover at ranges of over 100 miles from an operating height of 10,000 feet and was capable of locating a large number of targets. Its development was in direct response to the lack of an AEW system for naval operations which very nearly affected the outcome of the Falklands War. The main snag to this development was the helicopter's lack of endurance.

Electronic Countermeasures

It was the Germans who first began to exploit the electromagnetic spectrum deliberately for offensive purposes when, on 12 February 1942, their two battleships, *Scharnhorst* and *Gneisenau* escaped from Brest and slipped through the Channel into the North Sea. The jamming of the British radar system was very effective, mainly because it was unexpected, but at least it provoked Allied airmen and scientists into thinking seriously about the potentialities of radio countermeasures.

In the first place radio countermeasures, later called electronic countermeasures, were developed with the object of assisting the bomber offensive against Germany. Rudimentary electronic warfare was waged by British night bomber crews as early as 1941 when they discovered that by switching on their IFF sets they could upset German searchlight control. (This move was soon

---

*The Soviet *TUPOLEV* 126 was an AWAC aircraft (*MOSS*) in service by this time.

countered by the Germans to their own advantage.) Jamming and deception on a much more organised scale became widespread in the latter years of the war. Radio countermeasures could be either passive or active. In the former case warning devices were designed to alert the air crew to enemy interception; in the latter case WINDOW (Chaff) was dropped to dislocate enemy radar/radio wave lengths. Even a pulse radio navigational aid like GEE provided a countermeasure as it improved time keeping and made concentrated bomber attacks over the target area possible and thereby reduced the effectiveness of both the German ground-controlled night-fighter interceptions and predicted anti-aircraft fire.

When the Cold War began, it soon became clear that ECM would assume even greater importance than it had done at the end of World War Two.[63] Britain was in the front line against the Soviet Air Force, a specialist ECM headquarters was set up in March 1951 under Air Vice Marshal E B Addison, the signals expert who had done so much to organise the jamming and deception operations in the night bomber offensive against Germany. Intelligence in the West had by then appreciated that the Soviet Union, taking advantage of the knowledge of German scientists and technicians available to them, and of the latest American radar equipment like the SCR 584, would be a formidable adversary in the new medium of electronic warfare either on the Central Front in Europe or in air attacks on the British Isles.

Electronic warfare had been sadly neglected in that critical five year period following the end of the war. The essential warning and jamming equipment did not appear to be forthcoming to enable a smooth passage of the V bombers to their targets. Electronic protection for the Royal Navy was equally essential. Yet during an air-naval exercise held in the summer of 1950 'the entire Western Approaches radar system of the Fleet was completely jammed for a considerable time. Ship/air communications were interrupted and an RAF LANCASTER shadowed the Fleet by radio search from a distance of 200 miles.'[64] Supply of equipment was in arrears and nothing in the way of, for example, airborne homing equipment, was to be received by the RAF until the end of 1953.

Equipment of Aircraft with Radar Homing and Warning Devices

In the Second World War, as we have seen, ECM equipment was carried by individual aircraft (usually bombers) or by aircraft which supported them by dropping chaff or carrying out deception measures. Tail warning devices were also carried by bombers to give warning of trailing interceptors. These practices were continued after the war but were dependent on improved valves incorporating magnetrons and carcinotrons (backward wave oscillators which made a noise, described on page 240), reducing weight and increasing power.

But when American combat aircraft began to operate over Vietnam, they met with unexpected opposition from the radar-controlled SAMs and anti-aircraft artillery supplied by the Russians. Special crash programmes devised by electronic warfare specialists trained at Stanford University, had to be launched to equip all aircraft in the combat zone with radar homing and warning (RHAW) receivers, flare and chaff dispensers (see page 238) to counter the Vietnamese radar and infra-red systems.

The essentials of a RHAW system were a number of receiving antennae, a signal processor and a cockpit display.[65] The latter indicated the bearing and type of radar signal being reflected off the pilot's own aircraft by an enemy radar. He became aware that he had been detected by radar when he heard an audio tone in his head set. RHAW systems were able eventually to identify threats from a number of directions, assign a priority to each and display them all, simultaneously controlling the release of chaff or flares. By the end of the period, computers built into the aircraft automatically identified the type of threatening radar whether it was a search radar, an anti-aircraft artillery fire control radar, a missile radar, an AI receiver, or even an unknown type. The pilot was also informed of its position and range.

The British followed suit by developing their own RHAW systems. The Marconi ZEUS, for example, incorporated an RHAW receiver with an automated jamming suite designed to counter SAM tracking and guidance. In addition to activating the ZEUS jammer, the radar-warning receiver could trigger the release of chaff, flares and decoys. Other European electronic firms developed comparable systems.

ECM equipment was either carried internally in an aircraft or in a pod under its wing. Pods were cheaper and more adaptable than external systems, even though they took up space and made the aircraft less manoeuvrable. Internal systems weighed less and had no aerodynamic penalty, but they were more expensive and more difficult to modify to meet changing threats.

Special aircraft, with the task of disrupting hostile surveillance early warning systems and communications emissions, were fitted with their own brand of equipment. Much more powerful jammers and more sensitive receivers than the self-protection equipment carried by a tactical fighter were needed to detect the threat radiation at maximum range, and the associated signal processing had to cover a very wide band at very high speed. It was not unusual for a converted civilian aircraft to be used for these support or stand-off duties. In the Bekaa Valley action in June 1982 already mentioned, Syrian fighter controllers were jammed by stand-off equipment probably mounted in converted Boeing 707s crewed by the Israelis. The Americans converted the F-111 into a specialist ECM support aircraft called RAVEN.[66] The crew of two, using computers and miniaturised equipment, were able to jam communications over a wide range of fire control radars. RAVEN fulfilled three roles: first, as a stand-off aircraft it could operate outside enemy air space and protect AWACS aircraft by jamming long range surveillance radars. Secondly, it could move in close to the battle area and jam the acquisition radars of the enemy ground forces; and thirdly, it could escort long range interdiction aircraft to their target areas, jamming all the electronic elements of the enemy's air defence system and reducing the likelihood of successful hostile missile attacks.

Defence Suppression

Once equipped with an RHAW system, strike aircraft could penetrate well-defended areas and actually attack the radars. These specialised aircraft were called WILD WEASELS or IRON HAND and operated first in Vietnam against the Soviet-designed *FANSONG* fire control radars.[67] At first F-100 SUPER SABRE two seat fighters, followed by the F-105G THUNDERCHIEF, were used. The radar officer used his RHAW equipment to take precise bearings on the selected radar and directed the pilot towards it. In the spring of 1966, anti-radiation missiles (ARMS) called STANDARD were used for attacking hostile radars. STANDARD was replaced by SHRIKE with a 23 mile range. WILD WEASELS were modified to carry SHRIKES which were still being used at the end of the period. In the autumn of 1966, WEASELS were fitted with pods carrying chaff enabling them to operate without supporting aircraft. This 'winkling out' of enemy fire control radars became known as defence suppression.[68]

An assessment of the effect of airborne ECM equipment used in Vietnam revealed that American naval aircraft losses from attack by SAMs were reduced by a factor of five. Between 1966 and November 1972, United States naval aircraft destroyed by enemy SA-2s amounted to 85, but the installation of RHAW equipment prevented the further loss of some 340 aircraft to SAMs. It is probable that support and self-protection jamming prevented a further loss of approximately 200 naval aircraft to radar-directed anti-aircraft artillery.

The first ARMs could only operate on one frequency and so were unable to cope with the countermeasure of frequency hopping. Nor were they able to store information and this made their success rate limited. Hence a second generation of ARMs had to be produced in the 1970s which were faster, smaller and cheaper, but which had larger warheads and could be fired over longer distances They could now engage their targets before the enemy radar could be switched off, so making the weapon impotent and unable to retaliate. The American High Speed Anti-Radiation Missile (HARM) was characteristic of the new generation. A variant of HARM was used by the Israeli Air Force in the Bekaa action of June 1982.

The British, on the other hand, preferred to develop a missile which could operate over a number of modes, using one which was most appropriate to the aircraft's mission. This was the Air Launched Anti-Radar Missile (ALARM) produced by the British Aircraft Corporation (later British Aerospace) in response to an invitation from the Ministry of Defence in 1976 to submit studies to reduce the threat of air defence encountered by attacking aircraft. At first the favourite scheme was based on a high-flying missile-carrying drone, but this was later converted to an air-launched missile from TORNADO. The project hung fire for some years but interest was revived in 1982 when the RAF's need for an air defence suppression weapon became more urgent and HARM was seen as a serious contender to ALARM. A contract for the RAF was placed with British Aerospace in 1983.

ALARM could be used by most military aircraft. It was usually pre-programmed on the ground and had the benefit of memory circuits It was most effective in a situation in which the preferred target had not been found. In that event, the missile deployed a parachute which enabled the missile to loiter over the area until the enemy switched on the radar again. The missile then dived on to the target and delivered a lethal warhead containing armour-piercing metal pellets.

Spurious Reflectors and Jamming

The object of chaff, or WINDOW as it was called by the British in the Second World War, was to confuse the enemy's ground and airborne radars. It was made of a combination of aluminium and paper strips, a few hundred of which were sufficient to reflect as much energy as a heavy bomber. However, the decision to use WINDOW was not taken without a great deal of agonising in case it should provoke the Germans to retaliate against the British air defences. It proved to be an instant success and many Allied aircraft were saved thereby. Chaff became an important weapon in every air force's armoury.[69] Today it is made of fine wire or glass fibre as well as aluminium foil, cut to one half of the enemy's radar wave length. When released into the slipstream of the discharging aircraft, chaff quickly billows into a cloud that reflects a return signal to the enemy radar, thus preventing the aircraft's true position from being detected; it can also break the radar lock-on of an AAM or SAM and may even prematurely detonate the proximity fuse of a warhead.

Chaff has some disadvantages. When carried in small quantities by a fighter, it is insufficient to screen the presence of other aircraft. More seriously, within a few seconds of release, chaff comes to rest in the air and begins to dissipate. Consequently, radars with moving target indicators or pulse Doppler filters are able to sift stationary or slow moving chaff clouds from the true target. However, the initial velocity of the chaff can momentarily confuse even pulse Doppler and continuous wave fire control systems.

Methods also had to be devised to confuse infra-red detectors including the use of flare decoys. A source of heat was required and high temperatures proved to be the most promising countermeasure because most infra-red sensors were incapable of differentiating between a flare and the jet exhaust of an aircraft. But in order to be effective, the flare had to be ejected at the proper time and on a trajectory that would divert the threatening missile from the aircraft. Flare decoys could be placed in the same dispensers used for chaff and thus could provide fighters with protection against both radar-guided and infra-red threats.

Jamming countermeasures were more complicated on account of the enemy's ability to distort or use them for his own ends. Jamming usually took three forms. First, noise jamming, technically known as point or spot jamming. This involved transmitting a strong radar signal on the same frequency as the hostile radar. If the exact frequency of the radar was known, continuous noise transmitted on the same frequency prevented the operator from receiving an accurate radar echo. But the ability of modern surveillance and fire control radars to make frequency hops (already discussed in relation to radio communications) tended to frustrate this technique.

Hence the second form of jamming, known as barrage jamming, had to be introduced. This involved transmitting noise on all frequencies of a radar's operating band width. Barrage jamming required far greater power than spot jamming, thus decreasing the power transmitted on each individual frequency. The third form was called sweep jamming. This combined the high power of spot jamming with the wide coverage of barrage jamming.

Furthermore, the ability of the latest magnetrons in the early 1950s to retune to different frequencies enabled the band width of a radar to be shifted. Airborne jammers were consequently forced to carry an operator and a radio receiver either to monitor the radar frequency continuously or to resort to barrage jamming across a broad band and thereby dilute available energy. Added to this was the more or less simultaneous invention of the backward wave oscillator or the carcinotron by scientists in the *Compagnie de Télégraphie Sans Fil* and by Rudolf Kompfner, a German refugee who had left SERL and joined BTL where he had more scope to work on microwaves, and where he invented the travelling wave tube.[70] The carcinotron could be used either in ground or airborne radars and enabled the jammer to tune more rapidly to a new radar frequency or to sweep the noise jamming signal across the known operating band. Missile guidance systems as well as ground and airborne radars could be jammed.

Electronic Counter Countermeasures

To remind the reader, electronic counter countermeasures (ECCM) may conveniently be defined as 'actions taken to ensure the friendly use of the eletromagnetic spectrum against electronic warfare.' It should also be remembered that '*any radar* or communications system can be jammed and *any ECM* can be jammed, depending on the resources to which either side is willing to commit.' In air operations, ECCM began as early as the summer of 1944 when RAF Bomber Command suspected that the Germans had introduced a new AI radar operating on a frequency of 160–170 megacycles per second (Mc/s) necessitating a change of policy for the jamming aircraft. But no firm information about the new radar was forthcoming until it was discovered that the German AI was operating at 90Mc/s. The Germans also rapidly adapted themselves to the British WINDOW screens and other forms of deception and, it was believed, intentionally delayed broadcasting plots of bomber aircraft to their night fighters in order to deceive the British that their countermeasures were delaying the response of the German fighter controllers.

With rapidly-developing semiconductor circuits, a host of ECCM have been developed. They rely, mainly, on good filters and low sidelobe-level antennae to pass the signals of interest and attenuate interfering signals; the latter use spectral allocations of bearings which differ from the desired transmissions. Many established signal processing techniques can be applied to ECCM. For instance, radar moving target indicator filtering can be used to separate slow-moving chaff from a fast-moving target. Similarly constant false alarm rate (CFAR) techniques alter the display threshold to stop it becoming obliterated with high level jamming. CFAR receivers, which are widely employed, are based on a number of different signal detection techniques, for example, logarithmic amplifiers with adaptive threshold automatic gain control circuits. Alternatively, a limiting amplifier followed by a matched filter like the Dicke Fix* receiver may be used. The latter is principally used against fast-sweeping jamming, like that generated by the carcinotron. All these sophisticated techniques support the statement that the 'electro-magnetic spectrum will increasingly become a crucial battleground where the margin between victory and defeat may be narrow but very conclusive.'

Stealth

So far we have seen how aircraft can be protected in penetrating hostile air space by extraneous measures such as dispensing chaff, flares, or employing electromagnetic means for disrupting an enemy's radar system. Yet there is another method of rendering an aircraft 'invisible to probing radar beams; that is to make the structure of the aircraft itself impervious to detection.

Attempts to render aircraft inconspicuous, apart from camouflaging them, were made from the First World War onwards.[71] As early as 1917, a few

---

* So named after a radio astronomer who, long before the Second World War, was experiencing radio interference from nearby car ignitions.

German combat aircraft were covered with heavy cellophane skins to make them less visible to air defences; these experiments were not a success. Later, the ability to fly at speeds and heights undetectable to the human eye made electronic methods of detection essential. The first aircraft to undergo anti-radar treatment was the U-2 reconnaissance plane, to be followed by the RPVs; it was essential that these clandestine flights made in peace time should not be detected. Stealth techniques were then adopted for offensive missions; tiny pilotless aircraft which gave radar returns similar to those of the one hundred times larger B-52 bombers were employed to confuse enemy defences.

It was, once again, the extensive use of defensive electronic equipment in the Vietnam war that led the USAF to investigate more seriously the notion of a 'stealth' aircraft. As already described on page 91, the most important factor in stealth is the reduction of radio reflectivity, i.e. the reduction of the RCS. For example, the frontal RCS of a modern fighter may be 100 square metres while a B-52 might exceed 1000 square metres. Yet using a stealth design the frontal RCS aspect could be as low as 0.01 square metres (equivalent to a flat plate one centimetre square). This is approximately equivalent to the RCS of a medium-sized bird. An RCS is increased by weapons and other equipment carried in pods outside the aircraft and by cavities such as engine inlets, cockpits and vertical or near vertical plane surfaces. In order to overcome these tell-tale features, some stealth designs are virtually flying wings. Certain materials, such as carbon fibres, are radar absorbent.

A stealth designer must also make his plane proof against infra-red detection. He has to suppress the heat emitted from engines and exhausts. Acoustic and optical signatures also need careful attention. Noise can be reduced by a long, baffled engine inlet and by the installation of a medium by-pass engine and a mixed exhaust. The principal means of avoiding detection by the naked eye or tracking by electro-optical systems is to operate at night whenever practicable. Aircraft may be made less conspicuous by reducing their side and head-on profiles.

Stealth aircraft and their modes of operation were, and still are, shrouded in secrecy. In the early 1970s and 1980s the Americans developed both fighters and bomber versions of stealth aircraft. This was in response to the increasing effectiveness of the Soviet air defences. The design of the Rockwell B bomber (cancelled by President Carter) was based on stealth. Following its demise some attention was given to making the F-117A fighter impervious to radar. The great expense of constructing such highly specialised aircraft at that time restricted them to tasks like electronic reconnaissance. However, in the Gulf War a handful of F117As were used to attack high priority targets. Their performance proved them to be excellent force multipliers, more than justifying their cost and, at the same time, confirming the value of 'low observation technology' as stealth was now officially called.

Identification Systems

There are, however, occasions when combat aircraft *need* to be recognisable. This need, acknowledged from the start of the Second World War, led to the production of a British device called IDENTIFICATION FRIEND OR FOE (IFF) based on separating the original function of radar – locating a target – and that of identification.

A special band of wave lengths was set aside exclusively for identification purposes and all aircraft, ships, and vehicles which might have to identify themselves were fitted with this equipment, which responded automatically to interrogation on this band. All radars on the ground, or on ships, as well as many aircraft had to be fitted with equipment for interrogating IFF. An alternative form of recognition was provided by beacons whereby an aircraft would interrogate a radar on the ground instead of the IFF procedure of the ground-based radar identifying the aircraft.

IFF or, as the Americans call it, SELF IDENTIFICATION FEATURE (SIF) meaning the ability to transmit, receive and display selected coded replies is, of course, vulnerable to ECM either by jamming or deception. IFF continues to be of the greatest importance, particularly when friendly aircraft returning from a mission have to inform friendly ground defences of their identity. Automated techniques for IFF were introduced during the course of the period but details must perforce remain secret. In the 1980s, a NATO Identification System was developed, the intention being to equip all ground attack aircraft with it.[72] One of the greatest difficulties in the fast-moving, high technology of our times is what is known as 'control of the airspace' – that is to say, the ability to identify incoming and outgoing aircraft over the battle area. The introduction of IFF is only part of the solution to the problem but without it that problem is insoluble.

Conclusion

It has been impossible to provide more than a broad outline of the development of military aircraft and their armament in the 40 years following the Second World War. But at least enough has been said to sum up briefly: first, the policy which provided guide lines; secondly, improvements in the performance of aircraft; and, thirdly, to assess the performance of aircraft armament in war.

The policy for deciding on the type of aircraft needed by nations of the Western Alliance was determined in the first place by experience of the Korean war. Further changes were made when the policy of mutual assured destruction was abandoned, while technical changes in the armament of aircraft became necessary following the outcome of the Vietnam war and the 1973 War in the Middle East. These latter wars happened to coincide with the so-called 'emerging technologies' which, as we have seen, affected the performance of so many weapons.

Government policy also affected the long term development programmes of the British and the Americans. The British programme for combat aircraft was delayed (quite apart from the lengthening period of research and development) not only by restricted aeronautical research facilities, but also by the decision taken after the Second World War not to award contracts until most of the basic research (in guided missiles) had been done. Had contracts been placed earlier, the 'long and difficult task of building up teams of scientists and engineers in the firms concerned and educating them would have been completed much sooner and weapons developed much earlier'.[73] Though the Americans suffered rather less from restraints on research and development, the Defense Department became preoccupied with ballistic missile development, so much so that the services failed to learn the lessons of Korea and so were unprepared for the task of fighting a limited war in Vietnam.

Operational requirements from the 1950s onwards became more and more technically demanding, especially when the aircraft had to perform equally well at 300 ft and at 60,000 ft. The solution of these problems could only be achieved by the closest cooperation between scientists, engineers and air staffs. There is little doubt that cooperation had greatly improved as a result of experience in the Second World War. Yet occasions continued to arise when the operational requirements staff (both in Britain and the US) did not pay enough attention to what the scientists and engineers told them. Oddly enough, whereas in Britain there was a good understanding between, for example, aircraft designers like George Edwards, and Government officials, American equivalents responsible for aeronautical research and development were, more often than not, out of touch with the aircraft industry.

Some attempts were made by the British in the early 1970s to rationalise demands for new equipment. For example, the General Operational Requirement was replaced by the Air Staff Target and the Feasibility Study. But most designs tended to be the subject of controversy between the Royal Air Force and the other two services, both of whom would often have rather different requirements to be met by the same aircraft (for example, the HARRIER). And these reforms did not save the RAF from making the error of not commissioning an AWACS aircraft – with unfortunate results in the Falklands.

Finally, in this brief summary of policy must be mentioned the ever-looming threat of cuts in defence expenditure which probably affected aircraft more than any other weapons system.

The major technical developments of transonic/supersonic flight, variable geometry and VTOL/STOL were enhanced by new avionic systems which enabled aircraft to operate in any kind of weather, day or night, and to fly low and find the target, as well as being provided with electronic equipment to penetrate highly sophisticated defences without coming to harm. VTOL aircraft while (as yet) incapable of supersonic speeds were able to decelerate in combat quickly thus robbing a pursuing fighter of its advantage of superior speed.

Flexibility, endurance and fire power were the principal characteristics of the strike/air superiority aircraft of the 1970s and 1980s. The F-111 and the TORNADO were able to function in either a defensive or offensive role because of the advantages conferred by variable geometry. The combat radius of these planes extended to at least 600 miles, but greater distances could be covered with mid-air refuelling by tanker aircraft. They were able to deliver a four ton bomb load – as much as a Second World War long-range bomber.

The evolution of interceptor aircraft and their fire control and weapon systems advanced at a similar pace. The HUNTER had neither missile capability nor search radar, nor computer with which to navigate. The HUNTER's successors like the LIGHTNING and the US PHANTOM had first generation missiles with a maximum range of four miles; they, in turn, gave way to the fighter version of the TORNADO able to detect a target at 30 miles and over. The AMRAAM would have the ability to engage several targets simultaneously. Nevertheless, operational experience in the 1970s indicated that the traditional machine gun and cannon were still favoured by pilots as close quarter weapons even as late as the war in the Lebanon in 1982. Yet the main shift towards technically-dominated aerial combat occurred between the 1973 Arab-Israeli War and the Falklands War in 1982, in which AAMs and the associated avionics of strike aircraft were decisive factors. This trend seemed to favour the AAM. (It is worth remembering that in Vietnam air combats were relatively few in number.) A further important factor for success was the need for pilots and ground crew, who either flew, controlled, or communicated with sophisticated aircraft in a hostile environment, to undergo intensive technical training. Actual combat served to emphasise this requirement.

In offensive operations, unguided free-fall bombs continued to be used until the arrival of TV or laser-guided munitions. Yet despite the introduction of these aids, they often failed to make the impact on the ground battles of the 1970s and 1980s that had been anticipated. It has been suggested that this may be attributed to inadequate target acquisition, C^3I, training and poor design of munitions. Past experience also suggested that air forces tended to ignore the lessons of past operations. Thus the actions of the Israeli Air Force in the Lebanon in 1982 showed no improvement or its failings exposed in the operations of 1973. On the other hand, this Force's suppression of the enemy's SAM systems in the Bekaa Valley in June 1982 has become a text book example of drawing upon all technological assets to achieve a decisive victory. Such assets involved new radar tracking systems, AWACS aircraft and RPVs supplying near real time information to command centres.

Despite the importance ascribed to them by defence staffs, interdiction and long-range bombing have only played a prominent or decisive role in two wars during the period. The decision to carry out Second World War scale bombing against Hanoi towards the end of the Vietnam War undoubtedly hastened that end. Until then, political restraint had prevented the USAF from carrying out such attacks, although the effectiveness of the North Vietnamese air defences was a deterrent until new ECM and PGM became available. In 1973, the heroic attacks of the Israeli Air Force against the Syrian armoured formations advancing on the Golan Heights undoubtedly saved the day, though at great cost in lives and aircraft. The effectiveness of modern air defences in both these wars showed how hazardous long range strike and interdiction operations would have been, had war broken out on the Central Front in Europe and how great an effort would have been required.

The evidence of recent limited wars suggests that more accurate targetting systems and weapons need to be developed. Despite the considerable technical achievement of launching the VULCAN attack against the airfield at Stanley, in the Falklands, the results were by no means commensurate with the effort involved. Similarly, Soviet bombers were notably unsuccessful in the carpet bombing campaign in Afghanistan. Whilst skilled flying and considerable courage brought the Argentinians more spectacular results in their attacks against British naval targets in the Falklands, had they not been let down by the failure of their bombs to detonate on several occasions, those results might have well been nearly decisive. A significant lesson which has emerged is that for all the wonders of modern technology and the force multiplication that it can provide, the lack of one important capability can virtually cancel out the advantages gained – the whole offensive and defensive package must be as complete as ingenuity and skill can devise.

Although IFF techniques were being improved by automation, control of the air space remained a serious problem, although some sort of solution had evidently been worked out by the time of the Gulf War. For the time being aircraft needed to operate in their own air space rather than leaving it, for example, on a strike mission and risk being shot down by SAMs on their return.

The purpose of this chapter was to show that in spite of competition from missiles and their improved guidance systems, the manned aircraft has survived. But this will only continue as long as the ever more formidable air defences and their ECMs can be suppressed or deceived. If not, strike aircraft will have to depend on deploying stand-off weapons which require their own propulsion and guidance systems to accomplish their objectives.

. 8 .

THE SEA WAR IN THREE DIMENSIONS

The necessity of wielding air power over the ocean as well as over the land was one of the most important lessons to emerge from the Second World War. The winning of the Battle of the Atlantic was crucial to the sustenance of the United Kingdom and to the success of the liberation of North-West Europe. Yet the naval forces could not have won it without the support of *land-based* aircraft operating against U-boats passing through transit areas from French ports to attack convoys in the open sea. From 1941–44, land-based aircraft destroyed 50 U-boats and damaged another 56 in this way. Surface vessels and carrier-borne aircraft between them destroyed 42½* U-boats in the course of protecting convoys. Another 18½ were destroyed in offensive operations beyond the convoy area.[1] The successful tactic of the close support of convoys, backed up by air support and reconnaissance, was the keystone of post-war Western naval strategy; it continued to be so until the arrival of the hunter-killer submarine.

Changes in the Exercise of Sea Power

Air power also led ultimately to the demise of the capital ship, as was so dramatically shown in the Allied or enemy attacks on warships at Taranto, Pearl Harbor and off the Malayan coast. Even so, the battleship managed to survive, though not without criticism. As late as 1954, in one of the interminable reviews of the future of the Royal Navy in the nuclear age, the Second Sea Lord, Admiral Sir Guy Russell, told his superior how unhappy he felt 'at the C. in C. Home Fleet floating around in *Vanguard* [the last British capital ship] with gummed up guns. *Tyne* [a 15-year old destroyer depot ship serving as a

---

*The half refers to a sinking shared between aircraft and surface escorts.

247

flagship] will be even more ridiculous.'[2] *Vanguard*, after being laid up and then resuscitated, was at last sent to the scrapyard in 1960. Only the Americans could afford to retain two battleships, festooned with early warning radar and laden with air defences, eventually becoming platforms for cruise missiles, though still able, when required, to fire their main armament.

Meanwhile, the carrier had assumed enormous importance, as the great sea battles in the Pacific – notably at Midway – had demonstrated. After that war, the carrier replaced the battleship as the core of any naval task force. Fleet and light carriers with complements of 50 and 30 aircraft respectively presented a formidable fire unit with a range of about 400 miles. However jet-propelled aircraft, with their heavy weight, required a boost for take-off while their high approach speed led them to land much farther up-deck than their predecessors. The British were the first to find solutions to these problems.[3] The steam cat-apult was the answer to the first, using energy derived from the ship's boilers, while the angled deck was the answer to the second; the flight deck being off-set about 8 degrees to the centreline of the ship. Aircraft could now land with the help of an arrester-wire without hazarding other aircraft parked on the deck; and take-off and landing could take place simultaneously by day or night. A third British invention was the mirror landing system (rediscovering a Japanese experiment of the 1920s) which dispensed with the deck officer and left the pilot to judge his own approach to landing.

The first angled deck was built into HMS *Triumph*, a light carrier, in 1951–52, while the US Navy used it as a model to build the USS *Antietam*. HMS *Perseus* demonstrated the steam catapult to the Americans late in 1951. In due course, British fleet carriers like the *Ark Royal* and *Eagle* incorporated these improvements.

But carriers were immensely expensive; only the Americans were able to deploy them in force around the world, though the Russians eventually built a small number. Even so, by the end of our period, the carrier as a powerful fire unit had not yet been superseded, as had been forecast, by 'broad-based sys-tems of surveillance and strike power built up from a complex of vessels large and small.'[4] Mainly on account of reductions in expenditure, the Royal Navy was forced to abandon its fleet carriers, to which it had tenaciously clung, though retaining its smaller and less vulnerable anti-submarine warfare (ASW) carriers supplemented by frigates, able to put in the air their complement of ASW weapon-carrying helicopters and SEA HARRIERS.

The second major change was the advent of the true submersible. This was the fast (upward of 30 knots), *schnorkel*-equipped submarine which presented a tiny target to radar when surfaced and rendered inadequate overnight the equipment and tactics developed against current submarines. By the early 1970s, active sonar, in the unpredictable conditions of the underwater world through which sound pulses were transmitted, had reached its limits for the time being, its performance being inadequate against the true submersible. Passive sonar working at lower frequencies therefore became the principal means of detection (it also had the advantage of being less susceptible to hostile countermeasures).

An even more significant step in the growing importance of underwater warfare was the introduction of the first American nuclear-powered submarine, USS *Nautilus*, in 1954, closely followed by nuclear submarines in the British and Soviet Fleets. By 1970, the latter was operating regular nuclear-powered patrols off the east coast of North America. Eventually, equipped with conventionally-armed cruise missiles or thermonuclear ballistic missiles, the nuclear-powered submarine became one of the most powerful – and elusive – weapons in any nation's armoury.

Furthermore, continuous development in other fields became imperative with the transformation of the Soviet Navy under Admiral Sergei Gorshkov into a great naval force. It was Gorshkov who, learning from the Second World War, taught his colleagues not to rely on a submarine force on its own to win a maritime war. Surface ships and submarines had to complement each other and, in due course, fast, well-armed cruisers and carriers were added to the Soviet Fleet.

The sea thus continued to be an area of potential conflict. Ships were still needed to carry troops and heavy equipment which could not be carried by air. For most of our period, NATO naval strategy was based on the close protection of transatlantic convoys. In the mid-1970s, the AirLand battle strategy already described did not permit the methodical build-up previously anticipated. Reinforcements had to be moved rapidly to support the thrust of an Allied counter-stroke. Ships had to cross the Atlantic independently rather than sail in slow-moving convoys. Anti-submarine defence had to be readapted, emphasis being placed on static underwater barriers blocking the entrances to the North Atlantic; on long range maritime patrol aircraft equipped with submarine detection devices; and on ASW carriers equipped with VTOL aircraft and helicopters to protect the transit lanes through which shipping would pass.

Throughout the period, naval forces played a significant role both in minor wars like Korea and Vietnam and in 'policing' operations such as the enforcement of sanctions against Rhodesia or the Beira patrol. In the former, their purpose was to provide an additional 'front' from which aircraft power could be projected inland. It is significant that most of the conflicts that have occurred since 1945 have taken place within 180 miles of the sea. Even so, the Falklands war was the only occasion when sea power was a vital element. But it did demonstrate very clearly how the hunter-killer submarine had altered the whole balance between surface and submarine vessels. The mere presence of one or two hunter-killers had a marked effect on the Argentine Navy after the sinking of the *Belgrano*. Not only were hunter-killers the most effective weapon for dealing with enemy submarines, but as was seen later in the Gulf war, they performed a variety of tasks such as providing a warning screen for carrier groups, collecting intelligence, supporting special operations forces, and launching land-attack cruise missiles.

In addition to providing the means to project fire power inland. the sea has assumed increased importance with the exploitation of its depths and bed for oil and minerals, again offering a cause for maritime conflict, while the increase of illicit activities such as drug or arms smuggling has required the provision of larger coastguard or seaborne security forces equipped with aircraft and suitable weapons.

The purpose of this chapter, however, will be to emphasise the three dimensional nature of sea warfare; it will deal, first, with naval air defence and its concomitant ECMs; secondly, the airborne and seaborne methods of detection of submarines and the evolution of weapons to destroy them; and, finally, the transformation of the traditional sea mine into a potent weapon capable of immobilising shipping in ports or narrow waters and which could also be used as an effective anti-submarine weapon.

Defence of Ships against Aircraft and Missiles

Next to torpedoes, bombs were responsible for more ship sinkings than any other weapon in the Second World War. By the end of that war, improvements in weapon radar enabled accurate blind attacks to be made. It was quickly appreciated that the development of radar early warning systems was the 'factor most likely to revolutionise the employment of weapons.' The need for new shipborne early warning radars became an urgent priority. For large ships like carriers, centimetric radars seemed appropriate. The British TYPE 984 was one of the first three dimensional radars giving simultaneous height and plan position indication (PPI) on all targets.[5] It had a range of 175 miles. This was the first set able to control high speed jet fighters but because of its great weight was unsuitable for small ships.

For British frigates and destroyers, radars operating on metric wavebands continued to be used. Typical of these was the TYPE 965 which became the standard long range air search set for all classes of ship of the frigate type and upwards. The TYPE 965 was also used in guided missile destroyers to indicate the target to the TYPE 901 radar controlling the first SAM (called SEASLUG) which will be described below. An additional (centimetric) target indication radar was used between the TYPES 965 and 901 to indicate targets to the latter. Similar developments took place in the US Navy but on a more lavish scale. Three dimensional sets were fitted in the guided missile ships from 1960 onwards. More advanced radars such as the SPS 32 and SPS 33 were installed in the nuclear-propelled carriers and in a guided missile cruiser. They,

Plate 34 TYPE 984 three dimensional radar, the first to be installed in large ships of the Royal Navy. It had a range of 175 miles. (*Public Record Office ADM220/796. Crown Copyright. Reproduced with the permission of Her Majesty's Stationery Office*)

too, operated on a short wavelength and were able to scan over a range of more than 300 miles.

Enough has been said already on the British requirement for an airborne early warning system in Chapter 7. Suffice it to recall that the Royal Navy's need for such a set was appreciated almost before the end of the war: a charge of failing to keep abreast of lessons learned in the Pacific war cannot be laid against it.

In 1951, the British began to develop their first naval SAMs. A weapon was required to engage targets flying between 5000 to 50,000 feet. The anticipated threat was torpedo bombers flying at high altitudes and the aim was to intercept them at a distance of about eight miles.[6] The missiles and their projectors would have to be mounted on specially-adapted destroyers or frigates. Until the new weapons were ready, ships would continue to be protected by anti-aircraft guns and carrier-launched interceptor fighters. SEASLUG, as we have seen, was the name given to the naval SAM. Unlike those destined for the other services, the somewhat inelegant name of this prototype had to be retained, apparently on account of an admiral's 'post-prandial indiscretion.' The method of control was beam riding, the warhead being exploded either by a proximity fuse or direct action. SEASLUG had a range of 27–36 miles. Testing took place during 1954. The store ship *Girdle Ness* was fitted with a launcher and the first seaborne missile was fired on 17 February 1956.[7] Further development was slow as *Girdle Ness* was only allowed to fire 25 missiles a year for reasons of economy. Meanwhile, guided missile ships had to be prepared for convoy and fleet protection. The first convoy guided missile ship came into service in 1961 and seven years later eight County class super-destroyers* had been fitted with missiles.

Development and production of American naval SAMs was much faster, in spite of encountering similar difficulties in trials. Early development took place with the BUMBLEBEE, leading on to the rocket-propelled TERRIER (range 11 miles) and TALOS, propelled by a ram jet making it possible for carriers, with armoured flight decks, to operate against land-based air forces. TERRIER became operational in 1953 and TALOS (range 74 miles) was ready for service in 1958. A suggestion made in Washington, that the British should buy TERRIER on account of the slow development of SEASLUG was not taken up.

The next generation of Western naval SAMs included the US Navy's TARTAR (range ten miles). TARTAR was succeeded by STANDARD guided by a semi-active radar and with a range of 19 miles; it became operational in 1966. STANDARD II replaced TERRIER in 1978 with a range of 75 miles.

---

* The ships were really cruisers but had to be called destroyers to get them through the Estimates.

Plate 35 SEASLUG: the Royal Navy's first surface-to-air guided missile. It is being fired from HMS *Girdle Ness*. (*Royal Aeronautical Society*)

The British SEA DART in the meantime had entered service in 1967. It had a range of over 50 miles, semi-active radar guidance and ram jet propulsion; it was fitted into the Type 42 class destroyer and could be used to engage targets attacking other ships in the area. The French appeared on the scene in 1960 with *MASURCA* (range 30 miles) using either radio command guidance or semi-active homing. It was fitted into two cruisers.

Short range missiles were also required, both for point defence of ships without the advantage of long range missiles and in order to meet the threat from low level attack which, in the absence of airborne early warning, was invariably sudden, as radar could not detect low flying aircraft because of interference from sea reflections. Hence the adoption of missiles like the British SEA CAT, the American SEA SPARROW and the French *CROTALE* (adapted from the Army SAM) all with ranges of around five miles. It also became necessary to meet the threat of sea-skimming missiles launched from ships, submarines, or aircraft which descended from their initial high point to fly at wave level top level towards their target. The British SEA WOLF was introduced to counter these threats; it had Doppler radar to give a fully auto-matic anti-missile capability and a three mile range.

Several of the missiles just described went into action. Probably the first was TALOS, installed in the US Navy guided missile cruiser *Long Beach*, which was responsible for downing two *MiG* fighters 65 miles away. The Falklands war provided the most extensive opportunity for British ship-borne missiles to show their paces. All the types described above were employed. SEASLUG was the least successful though it may have been used for bombarding shore targets. SEA DART was credited with the destruction of eight Argentine aircraft. It was handicapped by lack of Identification Friend or Foe (IFF) and therefore depended on a manual decision for firing. SEA WOLF, despite its primary role of intercepting sea skimmers, brought down five enemy aircraft. SEA CAT, with its old fashioned radio command guidance, definitely brought down eight with two 'possibles' unconfirmed.[8]

The missiles engaged in the Falklands war could only provide point defence for individual ships; they were unable to provide area defence. The Americans attempted to solve this problem with a highly sophisticated fire control system called AEGIS (after the magic shield that protected Zeus). They intended this system to be fitted into the latest guided missile destroyers and certain nuclear-powered cruisers of the 1980s. The aim was to achieve an integrated three dimensional combat system to cope with both air and surface and sub-surface threats. At the core of the system was a new phased array radar called AN/SPY -1A (see page 33), capable of detecting of detecting the target, providing accurate tracking information for the fire control of the missiles, and, finally, transmitting mid-course guidance commands to them while in flight.[9] Development of this radar was one of two technological advance that made the three functions possible. The second was the improvement of the STANDARD II missile. STANDARD I's target was illuminated by radar throughout its flight, but for STANDARD II, whilst guidance was provided throughout its flight, illumination was only needed before striking the target. The ANY/SPY-1A radar could simultaneously provide mid-course guidance to a number of missiles and the semi-active radars could be programmed when the moment was ripe for terminal guidance. Thus the number of simultaneous engagements was not limited to the number of radar illuminators and it was possible to engage many more targets over a given period of time.

AEGIS was intended to be used in full scale naval actions in collaboration with AWACS aircraft and radar picket ships and its use was therefore reserved for the moment when the outer defences had been penetrated. It was unfortunate that its capabilities were first tested in a 'policing' operation in the Mediterranean and Persian Gulf. In 1983, AEGIS failed to spot a Cessna light aircraft flying towards American ships off the Lebanon even though the aircraft could be sighted from the deck and from a nearby destroyer.[10] In trials held at about the same time with USS *Ticonderoga*, the first cruiser to be fitted with AEGIS, only four out of 16 missiles aimed at the ship were 'hit' – not a reassuring result should Soviet missiles ever be launched at AEGIS-equipped vessels as they certainly might have been.

A more notorious incident receiving widespread publicity occurred during the Iran-Iraq war when the American cruiser *Vincennes* was protecting neutral shipping in the Persian Gulf three years after the end of our period. On 3 July 1988, while investigating what were believed to be hostile intentions of Iranian gunboats towards a merchant ship, an aircraft approaching the *Vincennes* was picked up by the AEGIS radar. As it was believed to be an Iranian F-14 fighter, the Commanding Officer of the *Vincennes* gave the order to fire. The aircraft was in fact a civil airliner – Iran Flight 655 – and 240 lives were lost. It had just taken off from the same airfield that was being used by military aircraft. The digital radar of the AEGIS was unable to distinguish between a large and a small aircraft. The subsequent enquiry completely exonerated AEGIS from blame.[11] All its functions had been in order and the report explained that the system was designed to deal with complex air threats in a combat environment and not to detect or identify civilian aircraft.

To conclude this section, it should be noted that the Soviet Navy developed SAMs a little later than the NATO powers. In the 1970s the latest classes of cruiser named *KARA* and *KRESTA* were equipped with the SA-N-3 (GOBLET); two guided missile helicopter ships were built also carrying the SA-N-3. As we shall see, the Russians gave more attention to SSMs.

Need of Guns for Close Air Defence

The likelihood of an outer screen being penetrated by hostile missiles encouraged the designers of naval guns to take advantage of advances in technology to improve these weapons as 'close-in weapon systems' against incoming radar-controlled missiles.[12] Gunnery experts appreciated that small calibre rapid fire guns could be used to hit and explode the warhead of an attacking missile during the last thousand feet of its trajectory. Guns would be automated and the controlling sensors contained within one system. All that was required was a power supply to operate the gun. Such a weapon can carry out a search, detect a target and track it, declaring the target a threat if it fits certain criteria such as range and velocity of hostile weaponry in the area. Guns may be fired manually or automatically without human intervention.

The mechanical elements of naval guns have also been improved. Gun barrel stability, rate of fire, internal ballistics, servo technology, ammunition handling and improvements to the external ballistics of the shell have reduced the dispersion of shot and make the gun a more certain killer. A good example of a modern naval gun is the American PHALANX made by General Dynamics. It is able to spray 200 millimetre shells at incoming missiles at a rate of 50 rounds per second. The integrated search and targeting radars of PHALANX can detect sea-skimming missiles and apparently have successfully intercepted EXOCET missiles in trials. The British and Italians have recently developed the 76 millimetre MELARA; the former are currently developing course-corrected and guided shells.

Anti-Ship Weapons

The development of missiles to be directed against ships and launched from airborne or sea platforms were considered after the successful employment of airborne missiles by the Germans in the latter stages of the Second World War. In the West, several projects were put in hand by the Americans and British which could be used against cruisers, destroyers or merchant vessels from about 1948 onwards. The Americans developed a series of 'flying torpedoes', or plunge bombs (known as KINGFISHER), intended to be aimed at surface ships and were intended for service in the early 1950s. Later came a maritime version of BULLPUP to be used by NATO forces. In 1953, the British Naval Staff, concerned about the havoc among merchant shipping that might be caused by the 12 gun Soviet Navy *Sverdlov* cruisers asked for a 'weapon that could be launched outside the effective range of anti-aircraft fire, by day and night, yet having a high probability of hitting and damaging a ship of cruiser size'.[13] It was necessary to cause damage equivalent to that of a 21 inch torpedo or a 2000 pound bomb. The missile had to be able to home on to a vessel underway or stationary on the surface of the open sea. Nothing came of this project called GREEN CHEESE adapted from the rejected RAF weapon BLUE BOAR. (See also page 222).

On 31 July 1953, a prescient Director of Torpedoes and Anti-Submarine Warfare in the Admiralty, comparing the merits of torpedoes and missiles, suggested that by 1965–70 'the era of guided missiles will be upon us. Warships within radar range of one another will be able to despatch a guided weapon and probably hit an opponent before a torpedo would have completed a quarter of its travel.[14] Notwithstanding the conflict in the interval, it took 14 years for the first ship to be sunk by a homing missile. It occurred in October 1967 four months after the end of the 1967 Arab-Israeli war when the Israeli (British-built) destroyer *Eilat* cruising off the Egyptian coast, was sunk by a Soviet-built short range ship to ship missile SS-N-2 (*STYX*) fired from a small Egyptian fast patrol boat.

The disparity in the size of the two vessels encouraged the belief that small navies like those of Israel and Italy could counterbalance their deficiencies by installing shipborne guided missiles. This hope was only partially fulfilled as it eventually became apparent that small ships had no hope of inflicting damage on a naval task force with ample air cover. On the other hand, the performance of the *STYX* jolted western naval experts who had complacently put their faith in tactical nuclear bombs and had failed to notice that the Soviet Navy had taken the lead in ship to ship missiles – mainly because of their lack of carriers from which aircraft could attack surface vessels at that time.

Although the Eilat incident compelled western navies to modify their SAMs, so that they could also be launched against ships, the development of new anti-ship missiles proceeded tardily. In the mid-1970s, the only United States air-to-surface weapon which could be delivered outside hostile air defences was the weather-limited CONDOR which had no more than a 40 mile range; this project was cancelled by the United States Congress. At the end of the 1970s, HARPOON became operational with a range of 68 miles; it was fitted into ships and aircraft but was still no match for the Soviet SS-N-9 and SS-NX-12 fitted in cruisers and corvettes, with respective ranges of 150 and 170 miles. At that time the United States preoccupied with tactical aircraft able to carry nuclear weapons, had given little thought to target acquisition for long range SSMs. An American admiral commenting on this state of affairs concluded that the 'Soviet notion of tactical independence among ships, submarines and landbased aircraft – each acquiring targets for the other – has only been weakly developed in the USA.'[15] A revival of interest in the cruise missile, neglected since the late 1940s, was shortly to rectify this situation. The TOMAHAWK, in particular, was to prove a success. It had an anti-ship range of 275 miles and was able to home onto a target with great accuracy and could be set to explode on impact or after penetration.

In Europe, the French and the Italians were the most prominent SSM makers. The French produced four versions of the *EXOCET* for ships and aircraft from 1972 onwards. *EXOCET* was an inertially-guided missile with a range of about 30 miles; it was guided by radar on the terminal stage to the target. It was an *EXOCET*, launched from an Argentine aircraft at 23 miles range, that failed to explode but nevertheless caused a fire leading to the sinking of the British cruiser *Sheffield* in the Falklands war. Five years later, the USS *Stark*, a frigate, was struck and disabled by two Iraqi *EXOCETS* in the Persian Gulf. In 1969, the French company *Engins Matra* collaborated with the Italian firm *Oto Melara* to develop the *OTOMAT* with a range of 62 miles. The Italians went on to produce the radar-guided SEA KILLER. Meanwhile, the Israelis had not been slow in learning the lesson of the *Eilat* and were able to retaliate against small Syrian patrol boats in the 1973 Yom Kippur war with their *GABRIEL* (25 miles range).

Ship-to-ship missiles with ranges of over 80 miles found another role – that of coastal defence. Mobile batteries could be deployed near the coastline and fired against enemy vessels over the horizon. In limited sea areas, like parts of the Mediterranean or the Persian Gulf, these missiles could be used as interdiction weapons against merchant or military sea traffic.

Effect of Armaments on Ship Design

The siting of sensors, missiles and guns and their mountings on upper decks and the provision of magazines below for stores and munitions in ships where there was little enough space for the crew, all of these needs dominated by the necessity to keep expenditure as low as possible, provided many headaches for warship designers. In fact, the most expensive item in a ship was the sailor himself. In the late 1980s, the British Ministry of Defence estimated that the saving of one man over the life of a ship was £3m taking into account his whole training and back-up. Replenishment of fuel and ammunition at sea was another demanding and expensive operation, taking the ship off station for a long period and requiring the escort and protection of the replenishment vessels. Various solutions were proposed, such as the use of containers for equipment and weapons which could quickly be exchanged and eliminated the need for deep magazines, permitting the hull volume of a ship to be reduced. The length of a vessel was another important consideration in siting sensors and weapons so as to obtain the maximum all-round coverage.

Electronic Warfare in Naval Air Defence

The expansion of anti-ship missiles in the 1970s inevitably gave rise to a search for suitable ECM and electronic warfare support measures (ESM) to thwart their incoming path. As we have seen, large numbers of warships could no longer cruise with impunity unless accompanied by carriers, even when engaged on policing duties, due to the purchasing of missiles by small developing states. Such missiles were then installed in small, speedy vessels.

Essentially, countermeasures took two forms: detection, followed by jamming of anti-ship missiles and electronic decoys. Characteristic of the various systems developed in the late 1970s was the American firm Raytheon's AN/SLQ-32 intended for the US Navy. It was able to pick up electronic transmissions from weapons and navigation systems of aircraft, ships and missiles. The characteristics of a given emission (ie. its signature) enabled it to be identified as friendly or hostile and to be assigned a distinctive signal on the SLQ-32 display, The SLQ-32 software classified radar emitters into eight 'threat levels'. Three of them were highly threatening in descending order: the launching of a missile; a high probability that a missile had been launched; or an indication by an emitter that a missile might have been launched.[16]

A system which was rather different to the SLQ-32 was the British CUTLASS ESM developed by the firms Racal/Decca from 1976 to operate in dense signal environments.[17] It was appreciated that current equipment was unable to cope with the new generation of surface weapons particularly in the vital parameter of reaction time. Three variants of CUTLASS were designed.

The first two covered a number of frequency wavebands and were backed up by a software library of 2000 signatures to enable any kind of hostile missile to be checked. The third system was intended for smaller warships where price, overall weight, and size considerations were all-important. A choice of overall frequency coverage could be obtained, but frequency measurements were less accurate and presented simpler solutions for analysis. Another British firm, Mullard, developed the SUSIE ESM system which could either fire chaff for passive ECM or operate with an active jammer like the Dutch SCIMITAR system. American and British naval ECM systems came under criticism as a result of performance in the Persian Gulf and the Falklands. The US frigate *Stark*'s SLQ-32 failed to identify the approach of the Iraqi *EXOCETS* in May 1987. According to an official US Navy investigation, 'the audible signal had been shut off and the radar operator was distracted from the visual signal.[18] A representative of Raytheon, makers of the equipment, suggested that the operator might have confused the radar signal of the missile with the targeting radar of the Iraqi aircraft. Whatever the reason* the incident drew attention to possible limitations in the equipment or in its operators in the heat of action. In the case of the *Sheffield*, at the moment when the *EXOCET* missile was approaching, the ship's radar/ESM had been switched off to enable satellite information to be received. If the gear had been operating, SEA DART missiles or chaff could have been brought into play.

Apart from radar, the launching of chaff to confuse radar guidance became the most popular shipborne form of protection against missile attack. It had the advantage over weapons of being cheap and non-threatening in the event of an ambiguous target turning out to have no hostile intent. Naval chaff is usually launched by rockets, either manually or the right moment can be left to the computer's judgement. The decision to launch chaff may be taken by an officer on the bridge who, unlike the radar operator, can see nearby threats directly. Once launched, chaff will form a cloud of metallic strips just as it does when discharged from aircraft. It reaches its maximum 'bloom' in about 10 seconds. A favourite tactic in using chaff is to move clouds progressively away from the target to provide immunity from attack. Chaff will force the enemy radar operator to switch from automatic to manual tracking in an attempt to separate the fast moving target from the stationary chaff.

Jamming or deception may also be used to assist offensive operations. In a multiple attack, for example, each missile is provided with enough power to distract the tracker from the target ship. More than two or three missiles launched at the target would make tracking almost impossible. Moreover, the

---

* A more recent explanation of the incident suggests that the *Stark* may have been covertly supporting an Iraqi offensive operation and the fighter may have accidentally homed on the ship's radar beam.

Plate 36 SHIELD: a fully automatic decoy system designed to protect Royal Navy ships from attack by anti-ship missiles. (*Marconi Underwater Systems*)

use of a turbojet (the current method of propelling missiles) enables the thrust modulation to be controlled, making it possible for a missile to arrive at a given point at a pre-set time. Thus missiles from several quarters can arrive near the target almost simultaneously, making individual tracking of them very difficult.

Hunting the True Submersible

The application of underwater acoustics for detecting submarines began in the early years of the 20th century and grew in importance as the submarine became a potential war-winning weapon. But progress in developing a reliable long range sonar was laborious compared with the spectacular development of radar beams transmitted through the air. Unlike the air, the sea is full of noises, sources of interfering sound and scattered or reflected energy from the sea surface and sea bottom. Severe refraction and consequent bending of sound ray paths and the creation of shadow zones are commonplace. Sound waves are attenuated to an extent dependent on water conditions and frequency and are continually varying.

While information from a radar transmission is obtained almost simultaneously, an echo from a sonar target may take many seconds to return because of the low velocity at which sound is propagated in the sea. Although the speeds of submarines are much lower than those of an aircraft – perhaps 20 to 30 times – this is greatly outweighed by the disparity in signal transmission times, typically between 10^5 to 10^6 times greater for sonar. This slow rate of acoustic propagation not only limits the rate of data acquisition but can cause other complications.[19]

The backbone of echo detection (sonar) is the electro-acoustic transducer which converts an electrical into an acoustical signal and vice-versa. Thus the same device can be used for transmission and reception. There are two types of sonar – active and passive. Active sonar transmits a short pulse of sound and then listens for an echo. Passive sonar listens for sounds created either by ships internal machinery, propeller cavitation (bubbles) and sometimes from the water flowing past the hull of an submarine. Sonar provides the means for detecting, classifying and estimating the location and motion of vessels (enemy or otherwise) at sea.

Shipborne Sonars

For most of the Second World War, mechanically-operated 'searchlight' sonars were used. But in 1942, the first attempt at an integrated weapon system was made in the form of the British TYPE 144 set which could be used to direct mortars or 'ahead-throwing weapons' as they were called.[20] By the end of the war, a start had been made on all-round detection sets called 'scanning sonars' which became operational in the late 1940s. They employed much more sophisticated transducers. The maximum range of these sets was 2,500 yards, an advance on the average detection range of 1,300 yards during the war.

After the war, the problem was to bridge the gap between the maximum range at which a submarine could accurately launch a torpedo at a target (about 10,000 yards) and the maximum range of sonar. The need to improve sonar was urgent. Using the formidable German TYPE XXI as a model, by the early 1950s the Soviet Navy was able to deploy probably three times the number of submarines that the German Navy had at its disposal in 1939. These submarines were able to travel underwater at about 25 knots for short periods and, of course, were equipped with *schnorkels*. British naval scientists at the Underwater Detection Establishment at Portland, in company with their counterparts at the US Navy Underwater Sound Laboratory at New London, had a wealth of fundamental research at their fingertips and had already begun work on post-war sets. Apart from range, priority was given to increasing the area of all-round search. The British began by adapting the radar split beam, which had been so valuable in aircraft detection, to sonar.[21] This evolved into the 'four square' sonar in which the measurements could be combined by means of a transducer with four equal parts: the horizontal ones for bearing and the vertical ones for depth. This obviated the need to sweep across the target in a series of steps.

Much of the preliminary work was done by two Norwegian scientists, F Möller and H Notvedt who had escaped from German-occupied Norway during the war. When it was decided to introduce a new ahead-thrown weapon called LIMBO (described below), the new TYPE 170 set incorporating this innovation provided the range, bearing and depth of the target. At the same time, the directing gear was housed in a new high speed dome under the ship increasing operating speeds to 25 knots. TYPE 170 was introduced in 1952 for frigates and destroyers. Of all the anti-submarine weapons, such as torpedoes and ahead-thrown weapons of the period, the TYPE 170 operating in conjunction with LIMBO was the most effective.

In the meantime, automation was improving. In 1956, the TYPE 177 was introduced into Royal Navy frigates. It was a low frequency, long range search sector scan and incorporated the fruits of post-war research. Like the TYPE 170, it was complementary to the use of ahead-thrown weapons. It could provide detection in the widest range of sea conditions and ships' movements. In 1963–64 TYPE 177 was followed by TYPE 184, which had an all-round capability both for echo ranging and passive listening. It was originally designed to protect battleships and give warning of torpedoes, but was adopted for smaller ships when it was found that, on balance, it was operationally preferable to the sector-scanning TYPE 177, although the latter, in principle at least, had a somewhat greater range. Meanwhile, the Americans had been concentrating on omni-directional scanning sonars since the end of the war.

A tactic introduced by U-boats marauding around the English coast at the end of the war was to lurk on the sea bed to avoid detection. In response, naval scientists developed a 'bottom contact' set in which a fixed narrow beam swept across the target (as the detecting ship was sailing ahead) in such a way that the absence of echoes produced a silhouette of the submarine on the range recorder.[22] The set had a second role of being able to differentiate between a submarine on the sea bed and a wreck; one of its first true tests was a tragic one when it detected the wreck of H M Submarine *Affray* lost with all hands in the English Channel in 1951.

Shipborne sonars, however, were limited in three ways. Sets could not perform effectively in bad weather because of the beam being masked, or 'quenched' because of the turbulence of the water; they were adversely affected by the diurnal warming of the surface layers of the oceans; and by conditions caused by the high speeds of the ships carrying them. Each of these conditions had 'the effect of reducing to near zero efficiency all of our present and future sonar equipment.' A practical alternative was to immerse the transducer well into the body of the sea away from the detrimental effects of the ship. This led to the development of 'towed' and 'dunking' sonars.

Variable Depth Sonars

Experiments with towed sonars were begun by a group of Canadian naval scientists. In the last year of the war, they discovered that sonar ranges were seriously affected in eastern Canadian waters by a strong negative temperature gradient under a shallow isothermal layer caused by the Labrador current. It appeared that the only way to overcome this was to place the sonar beneath this current. At the same time, advantage could be taken of the long range sound channels. Such was the beginning of variable depth sonar (VDS).[23] The Canadians passed on details of their research to the Americans and, by the mid-1950s, the Americans and the British, as well as the Canadians, were working on towed VDS projects. The British built their version round the TYPE 177 set while the Americans concentrated on an omni-directional scanning VDS. But both sets, which were active sonars, proved to be over-ambitious and only the Canadian set, based on the British TYPE 170 and housed in a towed dome, went into production. While the Americans continued to experiment with increasingly sophisticated types of VDS, the British, after spending some time grappling in vain with a cumbersome concrete construction containing the sonar decided, in 1960, to abandon it in favour of the lighter Canadian VDS which was designated the TYPE 199. VDS equipments were later installed on most destroyers, but their advantages only became apparent in certain sea conditions.

Dunking sonars found an admirable vehicle for immersing them – the helicopter.

Helicopters and Sonar

Both the Americans and the British had been alerted to the potential of the helicopter as a ASW weapon well before the end of the war; and British pilots had learned to fly the early Sikorsky models. In November 1946, the Captain of HMS *Osprey*, the Anti-Submarine School at Portland, outlined the advantages of the helicopter, its 'extreme mobility and flexibility compared with anti-submarine vessels' and immunity from weapons like homing torpedoes.[24] Helicopters could fly from the upper deck of an escort vessel and could be fitted with sonar to enable them to maintain continuous contact with an enemy submarine. Other naval officers drew attention to the use of a helicopter as a strike weapon carrying a suitable homing torpedo.

The Admiralty agreed to the formation of a Helicopter Development Unit at Portland working in collaboration with the Anti-Submarine School and using for the purpose a flight of Sikorsky helicopters. At about the same time, an American company (the EDO Corporation) had completed a helicopter dipping or 'dunking' sonar, the AQS-1. They had also developed a sonar to be towed by naval airships, but the latter were found to be too slow and fragile to keep track of a fast modern submarine. Helicopters, on the other hand, were developing rapidly (the Bell HSL-1 followed by the Sikorsky HSS-1) and had greater speed and were able to winch down a sonar into the sea. These experiments were observed by British naval officers who appreciated that 'water conditions' were the deciding factor in sonar ranges, but who believed nevertheless that helicopters should become a naval requirement.[25]

As we have seen, the British helicopter industry was slow in getting underway and, for the time being, the Royal Navy had to rely on Sikorsky 55s, a few of which had arrived in the United Kingdom in 1955 under the MWDP arrangement. It was not long before the young Westland Company obtained a licence from Sikorsky to build S-55s. This helicopter equipped with a TYPE 174 sonar based on the American AQS-1 went into service in the Navy in the early 1950s – around the same time as the US Navy counterparts. At first, the helicopter could hardly cope with the instrumentation that it had to carry. In time, the transistor enabled weight to be reduced and the equipment to become more sophisticated. By the end of that decade, the British had evolved a low frequency multi-beam directional version with electronics derived from the TYPE 177 set.

As helicopters grew in size, they became able to strike as well as to detect; bomb bays were added to accommodate torpedoes. By the early 1980s, every frigate and destroyer had its own helicopter to project its power. Fitted with

Plate 37 CORMORANT: a light weight dipping sonar providing a low-frequency active and passive acoustic sonar for use against submarines. Fitted in RN ships. (*Marconi Underwater Systems*)

radar and carrying air-launched torpedoes, air-to-air surface missiles and sonar, the helicopter is able to extend the offensive capability of its mother ship, since the systems within the helicopter are integrated into the operational systems within the ship.

The accommodation of helicopters and flight decks on board vessels already, as we have seen, cramped for space faced ship designers with another problem. Helicopters had to be protected from the elements and hangers had to be built (a SEA KING, for example, required a space 72 feet long and 53 feet wide). Doors had to be fitted not only for protection but to enable maintenance to be done on board. A proposal for telescopic hangars to be extended over the machine was unacceptable because of the possibility of jamming.

Submarine Sonars

Very soon after the war, naval staffs realised that with the advent of the true submersible, hunting submarines with surface ships might well become difficult. The use of a 'fighter' or 'hunter-killer' submarine was seen as a possible answer to the Soviet threat.[26] It had a number of advantages over surface escorts. The submarine was less likely to be detected by a hostile submarine; its sonar would be operating deeper and under more favourable conditions; the submarine's speed was unaffected by weather (a modern submarine was able to act as a convoy escort and keep station for at least eight hours totally submerged). There remained the problem of identifying an escort submarine. But this was not believed to be insoluble as submarines had proved themselves to be effective anti-submarine vessels in both world wars. On the other hand, whether 'surface escorts, submarines and aircraft could ever operate together with efficiency and full mutual confidence could only be resolved by sea trials.'

As the British had had to concentrate on anti-submarine rather than pro-submarine sonar during the war, the latter had inevitably been neglected. American research in the 1950s, however, indicated that passive hydrophone arrays were the most practical form of detection. The fruits of this research and information gleaned from examining the German *Gruppenhorchgerät* (group listening apparatus) used on battle cruisers and TYPE XXI U-boats combined to produce the '*knout*' or TYPE 186 set.[27] Further intensive development on advanced hydrophones was made by the Americans. All the hydrophones had to be perfectly matched, demanding a very high degree of quality in their manufacture. New signal processing techniques had to be devised before these complex arrays could be used effectively. By 1955, about 20 United States submarines, including *Nautilus*, had been supplied with passive arrays, and the mechanically-trained array had lost its supremacy. The British were working in the same direction. A new generation of conformal arrays (the TYPE 2000 series) was introduced with HMS *Dreadnought*, their first nuclear submarine. These sets could be used both actively and passively though active transmissions were used with caution.

Sonobuoys

Before turning to deal with the detection measures that had to be introduced to cope with long range nuclear-powered submarines, one other ASW device that originated at the end of the Second World War – the radio sonobuoy – must be described. Sonobuoys were small receiving and transmitting sets with a hydrophone to catch the noise of a submarine dropped by parachute from an aircraft into the sea. The original intention was to use them in conjunction with an acoustic mine, the sonobuoy providing evidence of the mine's explosion on the target. After the war two types of sonobuoys were developed: the non-directional sonobuoy and the directional sonobuoy.[28] The former was small, cheap, expendable and passive. It had an endurance of four hours, a reception range of 2000–2,500 yards in calm seas, but was less effective when there was a surface wind of over 16 knots. The directional sonobuoy was intended to detect, track and fix the position of a submarine moving above cavitation speed. It had an endurance of only one hour.

In 1951, the British and the Americans agreed to develop an omni-directional sonobuoy with a combined echo-ranging listening unit and an associated aircraft receiver. It would be no more than six and a half inches in diameter. In a calm sea, it could give a bearing at a range of 2000–2,500 yards on a submarine that had either previously been contacted by other means or was attempting to break through the sonobuoy barrier. It could also investigate doubtful contacts such as a disappearing radar contact and oil slicks. British sonobuoys were to be fitted in the RAF SHACKLETON maritime patrol aircraft and it was anticipated that they would be able to pick up the Soviet Intermediate Type submarine. However the 'accuracy of all passive sonobuoys whether directional or not was bound to decrease as the target became more quiet for any reason; and all passive sonobuoys could be completely defeated by silence.'[29]

By the 1970s, active directional sonobuoys with a life of about ten hours had been developed with ranges of as much as 17–23 miles. Larger sonobuoys dropped in conjunction with towed arrays and fixed passive systems (to be described below) could search very large areas. At a distance of 55 miles, a submarine could be detected in about one minute. However, by this time, submarines had indeed become much quieter and there seemed to be 'no prospect of a practical acoustic system which will guarantee acquiring all submarines entering its normal area of search.'[30]

Limit of Active Sonar Reached

By around that same time it looked as if active sonar had reached its practical limit. It was quite effective at holding a contact at close range but inadequate at making reliable first detections over the increased ranges necessary for defence against modern submarines.[31] In certain instances, long range detections were possible when underwater conditions were favourable, e.g. when propagations caused energy to focus at one or other of the convergent zones about 40 or 80 miles from the sonar-carrying vessel, or when refraction conditions were right. Better results were achieved by using VDS – though, as just observed, that had its own limitations. Nevertheless efforts to improve active sonar had to continue.

Fortunately, significant advances were made in improving passive detection in place of active techniques. This became possible through the use of lower frequencies which have better propagation but require ever larger apertures to maintain directivity and gain, preferably greater than can be accommodated within the body of a ship or submarine. Hydrophones which were relatively light and remote from any vehicle background noise were to provide a means of detecting modern submarines.

Detection of Nuclear-powered Submarines: Passive Sonar

Hitherto, protection against submarines had been confined to the perimeters of the area defence of convoys or task forces. Now the great range of nuclear-powered submarines compelled a revision of strategy. The answer, implementation of which lay mainly in the hands of the Americans, was to establish extensive underwater barriers, at the outset to protect the United States Atlantic and Pacific seaboards, and later, at the entrances through which Soviet submarines would debouch into the North Atlantic and Pacific Oceans. These were off the coasts of Norway, Greenland and Iceland in the case of the former, and the Aleutian Islands in the case of the latter. Development of these passive underwater surveillance systems by the US Navy began in the 1950s. The first was the Sound Surveillance System (SOSUS).[32] (Actually it was on the agenda of Project Hartwell that gave rise to the spread spectrum concept.) SOSUS consisted of hydrophones moored on the sea bed which were connected by cable to shore stations for signal processing. The information gathered by SOSUS was fed into computers, enabling an acoustic picture or 'signature' of enemy submarines to be scrutinised. The information thus received would be passed on to attack-submarines and carrier-based aircraft. The first SOSUS was laid in 1954. However, because it was fixed and restricted to specific areas, SOSUS became vulnerable to enemy countermeasures (it could easily be cut). It was also costly and time-consuming to lay.

In the early 1960s, therefore, the SOSUSs were complemented by the

Surveillance Towed Array Sensor System (SURTASS) in which surface vessels towed sensors embedded in a cable hundreds of feet long and with capabilities similar to the SOSUS arrays. The information received was likewise relayed to shore stations for processing. At the end of our period, the Rapidly Deployable Surveillance System (RDSS) was being developed. It was a static acoustic surveillance buoy dropped by aircraft either in shallow or deep water. The data collected could either be transmitted to base immediately or stored for later transmission.

Passive towed arrays were adopted by escort vessels from 1977 onwards. The growing emphasis on passive detection of course stimulated a battle of measure and countermeasure. Systematic and elaborate programmes to reduce the many sources of submarine noise were matched by increasingly sophisticated signal analysis in the sonar, made possible by the enormous increase in the processing power of modern computers. One development of acoustic detection in support of the US Fleet should be mentioned. This was the Light Airborne Multi-Purpose System (LAMPS), carried by helicopters, which were able to transmit sonar signals back to a surface vessel. In 1985, eight US Navy helicopter squadrons were equipped with this device.

Non-acoustic Methods of Detection

There were other means of detecting the presence of submerged or surfaced submarines from aircraft. Even before the Second World War, the possibility of detecting the magnetic field of a submerged submarine had been discussed by the Tizard Committee and some experiments were carried out at RAE before the idea was passed on to the Americans. They developed the Magnetic Anomaly Detector (MAD) to locate submarines which had submerged after sighting and for patrols covering transit areas like the Straits of Gibraltar. MAD was unaffected by weather but was handicapped by a range of only 800–1,200 feet despite strenuous efforts to improve it. The development of long range maritime patrol aircraft like the US P-2 ORION in the mid-1960s, with an endurance of 12 hours and a range of 3,450 miles and the RAF NIMROD (range over 5,000 miles) led to a revival of interest in MAD.[33] In the case of the RAF, it was intended to be a stand-in for the active directional sonobuoy, as it was the only equipment capable of locating a submerged silent submarine. But even with an increased range, it was not very effective against fast submarines because of the period of delay between the reception of a MAD signal and the release of an anti-submarine weapon.

A British airborne system for detecting surfaced submarines was called AUTOLYCUS (after the Rogue in Shakespeare's 'The Winter's Tale': 'a good nose is requisite also, to smell out work for the other senses'). A favourite of Lord Cherwell, who continued to dabble in scientific warfare after Churchill returned for his second premiership in 1951, it was intended to detect the exhaust gases of a submarine's diesel engines; like MAD and radar it was unaffected by rough seas and was relatively inexpensive.[34] It was, however, unable to distinguish between the exhausts of submarines and surface vessels. Yet, installed in the RAF SHACKLETON at the end of the 1960s, it was the only equipment, apart from radar, able to locate a submerged submarine at long range.

But apart from all these detection devices it was radar – air or ship-borne – that continued to be the principal method of submarine detection and every effort was made to improve its performance against the fast submersibles coming into service. In the early 1950s, the Royal Navy needed a ship-borne radar able to detect submarine periscopes and to be able to track their supporting aircraft to a distance of 30 miles. This was intended to supersede the 277Q set used for submarine detection and the TYPE 974 intended to detect periscopes. High frequencies were needed for this purpose and several radars working on the 3 centimetre band proved to be quite adequate for the purpose.

The post-war RAF set – the ASV15 intended for the SHACKLETON was also useful; at a height of 2000 feet it could pick up a *schnorkel* in calm seas at a distance of 11 miles and a surfaced submarine at 22 miles.[35] The ASV15 developed for naval aircraft had a comparable performance to the RAF set. Even so, the American naval search radar AN/APS20, originally developed as an AEW equipment and fitted into the Douglas SKYRAIDER proved to be superior to contemporary British sensors. This could pick up *schnorkels* at ranges well beyond those just mentioned. It was also used for 'strike direction'; positioning itself to obtain echoes of its parent carrier and the enemy target at the same time; it could thus direct attacking aircraft to their target. In due course, a British radar (SEARCHWATER) with superior performance was introduced into the RAF NIMROD.

Anti-Submarine Weapons: Torpedoes

Since their invention in 1866, torpedoes had hardly kept pace with the rapid development of other weapons. It was German ingenuity that was responsible for introducing the first homing torpedo in 1943 and thereby compelling the Western Allies hurriedly to seek various (mainly noise-making) countermeasures. Nevertheless, the torpedo was a formidable weapon and in the Second World War (as well as in the First World War) had been responsible for causing the largest number of sinkings of all types of vessel (in the Second World War the figure was 57 per cent). Yet on 29 August 1947, two years after the end of that war, the Director of Underwater Weapons at the Admiralty complained that 'no work is being done on any homing torpedo' and listed three requirements for the Royal Navy which he believed to be necessary:

1 an electrically-propelled homing torpedo;
2 an interim torpedo for submarines and possibly surface vessels to be used against submarines and other targets; and
3 a new anti-submarine and other targets torpedo to be launched from submarines.[36]

How were torpedoes classified in the post-war period? Basically there were two types: the light weight torpedo, launched from aircraft and ships primarily against submarines and the heavy weight torpedo, launched from submarines against other submarines and ships. Modern torpedoes could achieve speeds of 30–50 knots and could reach a target 20 miles away and further, depending on the sensors with which they were equipped. They could be carried by helicopters as well as by fixed wing aircraft.

Torpedoes were now virtually underwater guided missiles and were just as sophisticated as missiles launched through the air, except that the sea is a much more difficult medium through which to travel. Torpedoes may have to descend from the surface to depths of over 3000 feet, a change of over 100 atmospheres or a pressure on the hull of nearly three quarters of a ton per square inch. Consequently, in contrast to an airborne guided weapon with a skin a few millimetres thick and representing only about one or two per cent of the weight of the missile, the hull of a torpedo is massive. In general, it requires some 20 per cent of the total weight of the torpedo. Thus special alloys were required to give sufficient strength whilst of minimum mass. Torpedoes also have to withstand immersion in sea water over a long period of time; because of corrosion, great care has to be taken in the choice of materials.

The propulsion of torpedoes is another source of difficulty. As they must travel underwater for long distances, very high energy density fuels are needed and an oxidant has to be carried as well. These fuels are usually highly volatile and require stringent safety measures in handling. Finally, the torpedo's sensor has to cope with the same underwater problems of noise and changes in temperature as a sonar set.

It is hardly surprising that post-war torpedo development was both arduous and slow. The need to find a safe and efficient oxidant was especially important. The Germans had been using high test peroxide (HTP) combined with diesel fuel and experiments with this volatile mixture were made by the Americans, British and Swedes. The British built a number of experimental torpedoes using HTP under the code name FERRY.[37] They were intended to provide protection against the large Soviet cruisers then under construction and were to have a range of 1,500 yards and a speed of 35 knots. The tests had to be abandoned after an explosion led to the sinking of HM Submarine *Sidon* on 16 June 1955 with loss of life. It took another decade before the Americans began to use the more reliable Otto fuel to power their MARK 46 light weight and MARK 48 heavy weight torpedoes. Meanwhile, the European navies continued to use electrically-powered torpedoes, though the increasing speed of modern submarines made the adoption of new types inevitable.

Light Weight Torpedoes

The early British post-war light weight torpedoes were none too successful. The first was called DEALER – a passive acoustic type. But it was too heavy (670 pounds) to be carried by current helicopters or fixed wing aircraft and there appeared to be 'no prospect of a light weight version in the UK for some years. The US MARK 43 is therefore the only anti-submarine weapon available for these aircraft.'[38] However, when the GANNET entered service, work on DEALER B was continued. It was developed as 'an entirely new weapon and was so superior to the American interim counterparts as to be in an entirely different class without costing so much.' In 1954 DEALER B entered service as the Royal Navy's MARK 30 torpedo and indeed proved to be better than the American version.

Another acoustic light weight torpedo called PENTANE was an improvement on DEALER, though heavier (2000 pounds). In contrast, the Americans were developing homing anti-submarine torpedoes using the simplest available active homing system; ie. those with a narrow beam. PENTANE was an active homer and, like DEALER, could be carried by the GANNET. Nevertheless, development flagged for lack of a suitable launching aircraft and the project was cancelled in 1953. The possibility of this happening drew from the Superintendent of Torpedo Experiment and Design the indignant retort:

> 'To crab the weapon because there are not suitable carriers savours to me of insanity, when already in two wars we have so nearly lost the anti-submarine campaign.'[39]

The Royal Navy and RAF had meanwhile set out their common requirements for a joint anti-submarine light weight torpedo which could be fired from ships, helicopters and fixed wing aircraft.[40] This was known as the STING-RAY project and was the first of a new era of underwater weapons entering service in 1983. STINGRAY was produced by Marconi and contained the most advanced control and homing techniques and the provision of very compact and powerful digital computing hardware and software within the weapon. Before being launched, the weapon was pre-set with all the necessary information about the target and water depth. After launch, its trajectory was controlled by a parachute. On entering the water, the torpedo pulled out to avoid hitting the sea bed. It then searched for and homed on to its target. On

Plate 38a STINGRAY: Royal Navy light weight torpedo. It can be deployed from fixed or rotary winged aircraft and a wide variety of surface ships. The warhead can drill a hole through the hull of a submarine. (*Marconi Underwater Systems*)

Plate 38b KINGFISHER: containerised light launch system for STINGRAY. (*Marconi Underwater Systems*)

detonation, its warhead produced a molten jet of copper which literally drilled a hole through the submarine's pressure hull.

STING RAY was one of a breed that included the US MARK 50, the French MURENNE and the Italian A290S; all had warheads similar to that of STING RAY. For this, of course, accuracy was a prerequisite. For the immediate future, greater speed, operating depth and better acoustic performance were required of light weight torpedoes.

Heavy Weight Torpedoes

In the heavy weight field, the British began to work on a wire-guided torpedo (MACKLE), casting an eye back on German wartime developments.[41] The advantages of wire-guided systems were:

1 the ability to fire shortly after contact had been made with the target;
2 chances of success were believed to be superior to any known or projected type of torpedo;
3 the control system was simple requiring less training than in other systems;
4 the chances of a kill meant expending fewer weapons for a given effect; and
5 a human initiator might help to defeat decoys.

Although reluctant to allow MACKLE to prejudice the development of the DEALER B and PENTANE, the Naval Staff approved its development by Vickers. But it proved to be too complicated and was replaced by GROG based on the earlier MARK 20 torpedo. GROG came into service as the MARK 23 in 1966 but was not fully operational until 1971.

Heavy weight torpedoes developed in the 1970s were primarily a hunter-killer submarine's weapon*. The successor to the British MARK 23 was the wire-guided MARK 24 (ONGAR) eventually known as TIGERFISH, which had greatly improved guidance and homing, both active and passive. TIGERFISH marked the watershed between earlier generations of torpedo, principally products of mechanical and electrical engineering produced in a Government factory, and underwater guided weapons with a much more enhanced electronics content in which overall responsibility for design as well as production came to be undertaken by industry. A long and difficult development stage had to be followed by a 'get well' programme in industry, for which Marconi was selected as the prime contractor. TIGERFISH entered service in 1980.

---

* This meant that, until an anti-surface capability could be added, submarines had to rely on the wartime series of MARK 8 torpedo for attacking surface ships.

Plate 39a TIGERFISH: Royal Navy submarine-launched heavy torpedo. The principal weapon for the hunter-killer submarine . Its electronics are greatly improved in comparison with those of its predecessors. (*Marconi Underwater Systems*)

Plate 39b A Mark 24 TIGERFISH hits HMS *Devonshire*. (*Marconi Underwater Systems*)

Experience with TIGERFISH enabled Marconi to develop STINGRAY and some of the advanced technology was later incorporated in SPEARFISH, an exceptionally fast, deep-diving, quiet heavy-weight torpedo with a range of 11–15 miles which succeeded TIGERFISH.

Stand-Off Weapons

Appreciating that there was a limit to the range of a torpedo, an attempt was made by Western navies in the 1960s and '70s to provide the homing torpedo with additional reaching power by combining it with a rocket or depth charge. This type of weapon had its antecedents in the mortars or ahead-thrown projectors developed by the Allies in the Second World War. Instead of dropping depth charges from the stern of a ship, the mortar would fire bombs which were intended to detonate in a pattern around the presumed position of the enemy submarine.

After the war, these mortars (the British HEDGEHOG/SQUID) were further developed to operate with the TYPE 170 sonar. An improved version of SQUID called LIMBO was tried out in 1951 in a Fleet exercise and apparently 'proved to have a greater percentage claim of success against fast submarines than depth charges.'[42] In 1953 LIMBO was shown off to the Americans who were then working on a similar weapon to be used in conjunction with a scanning sonar. LIMBO could fire bombs up to 1000 yds and, according to the Underwater Detection Establishment officer accompanying it, covered a pattern, was lighter, could be installed more easily, was more reliable and, most important, cheaper than its American counterpart.[43]

Western naval staffs were soon faced with the likelihood of submarines travelling faster than torpedoes and attention was given to using missiles for anti-submarine warfare. In 1955, the Americans began to develop an underwater-launched rocket (SUBROC).[44] After leaving the torpedo tube, SUBROC travelled several hundred yards underwater, then, using rocket propulsion to leave the surface of the sea, it adopted an air trajectory, approached its target in a controlled glide and released a depth charge which sank to a pre-determined depth and exploded. Such a complex weapon took eight years to evolve. SUBROC was deployed operationally in 1965 and was further improved to meet the threat of Soviet nuclear-powered submarines in 1977–78. Later it became obsolete.

A companion anti-submarine rocket was evolved for surface vessels called ASROC. It became virtually a rocket booster to the American MARK 40 torpedo. After a vertical launch, it could hit a target at 20 miles distance.

Outside the States, the Australians and the French developed missile-carrying torpedoes. The former produced IKARA which was fitted in ASW frigates (after the removal of their 4.5 inch guns) in the early 1970s. It was equipped with an advanced combat data computer system which converted information received by sonar.[45] Compared with a helicopter-launched torpedo, IKARA reacted more quickly to the presence of a target but lacked the flexibility of the helicopter to perform other tasks. Unlike ASROC, it was radio-controlled. Later, the British Leander frigates were equipped with *EXOCET* missiles in a forward position, an ASW helicopter, ASW torpedoes, and the latest automation equipment. IKARA had a minimum range of 12 miles and maximum range of 57 miles. The French weapon was called *MALAFON*, also automated and with a comparable range.

In the 1970s and early 1980s, exploiting automation techniques, the Americans had developed the first torpedo mine. This was CAPTOR, primarily for use against submarines in deep water. It encapsulated a MARK 46 light weight torpedo in an outer hull[46] which was moored to the sea bed; the torpedo was released in response to the mine's target selection and attack programme. When a sound signature had been recognised at a range of about 3000 feet, the torpedo was released, homing on to the target. The mechanism of the sensor disregarded the noise of surface traffic. When Soviet submarine hulls were coated with special materials to reduce a sonar signature, CAPTOR was upgraded to restore its homing capability. Its flexibility was enhanced by forming a load, when needed, of a B-52 bomber. CAPTOR initiated a new breed of mobile mines for use in ASW.

Countermeasures against Sonar and Other Detection Devices

Countermeasures and the cultivation of stealth techniques were applicable to underwater warfare just as much as they were to the war in the air. The German use of acoustic torpedoes in the Second World War forced the Allies to retaliate, either reducing the speed of a ship likely to be attacked or by towing noise makers to divert an acoustic torpedo away from its intended target. Most of the strategems, hurriedly produced, were rather rudimentary but nevertheless impelled the Germans to make their U-boats' machinery quieter. Their endeavours to muffle the noise of ships' propellers were no more successful than those of the British. The Germans did, however, make an important advance by using sound-absorbing (or anechoic) coatings for the hulls of their latest submarines. One in particular named *ALBERICH* (after the dwarf in German legend who wore a helmet which made the wearer invisible) consisted of a layer of synthetic rubber which entrapped air bubbles.[47] Sound reflected from submarines coated with this substance was reduced by between 60 and 85 per cent, depending on depth and other factors. It had several disadvantages, one being that air began to leak, making it less efficient; more seriously, it tended to tear away from the hull at high, submerged speeds.

After the war, much more research went into improving anechoic coatings and they were adapted by both the Western and the Soviet navies for their submarines. All the other wartime measures to make submarines less vulnerable were continued. The increased speed of modern submarines made them noisier and great pains were taken to make engines and propellers quieter.[48] Writing to the Engineer-in-Chief at the Admiralty in June 1953, the Director of Aeronautical and Engineering Research noted, in submitting a proposal for an insulated combustion chamber, that in 'view of the outstanding importance of developing a quiet diesel engine for submarine propulsion, it appears that any novel suggestions . . . should be looked into.' [49]

Both the new conventional and nuclear submarines were initially noisy when running at speed, but by the late 1950s, the noise of conventional types running at medium speed on batteries had already been reduced to a level low enough to prejudice the performance of the new passive surveillance systems. The first nuclear submarines were much noisier because priority had, quite rightly, been given to achieving a high speed vessel with almost indefinite submerged endurance, as quickly as possible. During the next two decades, a great effort was made, first by the Americans and later by the Soviet Union in reducing noise by a very considerable amount. While some measures could be introduced retrospectively, others had to await a new design of a submarine. A high building rate was clearly advantageous.

We have seen that electromagnetic methods of detecting submarines were less effective than sonar, but no acoustic indicators could be used when a submarine or a portion of it broached the surface. In order to counter MAD devices, thought was given to the partial demagnetisation of submarine surfaces. Alternatively, materials with a low magnetic value such as titanium were used as in the Soviet *AKULA* class submarines.[50] More importantly, titanium increased the maximum operating depth which was a revolutionary feature of the modern submarine. Here was yet another area where measure was succeeded by countermeasure.

In all, by the end of the period, the submarine was still an extremely elusive weapon. Even if active sonar was improved, it could still betray itself to the enemy while, according to an experienced Royal Navy submarine officer, passive sonar

'has been grotesquely exaggerated. On some days, you can detect a moving submarine because you are looking in the right direction and the acoustic path is a good one. On other days, you can't because there are too many acoustic barriers. It is true the Russians have produced quieter submarines more quickly than expected but that does not mean that they also have a greater capability of detecting submarines. Neither side is very good at detecting the other. Ballistic missile-carrying submarines in the West are virtually undetectable. As for the Soviet equivalents, detection may be made on an occasional basis. On any one day, though, no one in the West can say where they all are.'[51]

Mine Warfare

At several points in the maritime war of 1939–45, the Germans were within reach of gaining an ascendancy by deploying non-contact mines; their attempt to block shipping lanes around the British coast in 1939 with magnetic mines and the sowing of pressure mines in the Channel during the Battle of Normandy are examples. Prompt countermeasures devised by naval scientists and luck (in the case of pressure mines the sea swell was an effective sweeper) robbed this weapon of its power. During the war, nevertheless, the sea mine ranked second to the torpedo in the total sinking of ships.

Three types of non-contact mine were used in the war: magnetic, acoustic and pressure; they are still extant today. Compared with the contact mine, they extend the danger radius of an individual mine, and they make the task of the minesweeper much more difficult. Moreover minesweeping could be made even more hazardous by, for instance, using combinations of magnetic and pressure mines, as was done infrequently in the latter stages of the war.

The Soviet Navy and its predecessors had always been mine-conscious and mines were a cheap device for denying the use of sea lanes to a belligerent. In the early days of the Cold War, Western naval officers appreciated how easily ports and estuaries could be blocked and cross-Channel communication cut by submarine-laid mines. Sir Henry Tizard, while chairman of the DRPC, was especially concerned about the latter; he was supported by a member of the Admiralty who warned that

> mining by submarine and aircraft offers a most dangerous method of attack on this country's sea communications. No work is in hand on this aspect of defence . . . compared with the expenditure being contemplated on super-sonic flight.[52]

The somewhat primitive pressure mines that were considered to be 'unsweep-able' in the 1950s were activated by the suction effect caused by a passing ship. Electro-mechanical circuits caused the mine to detonate. In order to ensure that the mines were only activated against a target vessel, it was valu-able to know the amplitude and frequency of the swell in the area where the mines had been sown. Western naval officers responsible for countermeasures against mines were therefore curious to know the extent of research on hydrometeorology and hydrodynamics currently in progress which might be of value to an enemy.[53]

Plate 40 STONEFISH: a micro-processor controlled ground mine able to select its target and reject enemy countermeasures. Used by the Royal Navy, it can be deployed from a variety of surface ships, submarines and aircraft. (*Marconi Underwater Systems*)

The advent of microprocessors and the microminiaturisation of electronic circuits made it possible to modernise basic mine designs and make their target selections systems more flexible.[54] The wartime combinations just mentioned could now be controlled by software programmes. By controlling the point of detonation, the ship could be damaged at the point at which it was most vulnerable.

Although the computer greatly increased the flexibility of mines and enhanced their resistance to sweeping, their lethal range had not been increased. Consequently research began on mobile mines which had the ability to move for short distances under their own power or even to undertake limited pursuit of a target. The former are known as positioning mines and are launched, usually from a torpedo tube, several miles away from their final resting place on the sea bed. But the guidance and control facilities are very complicated. Programming has to take account of tides and currents and undulating sea bed features. The propulsion system must be quiet but sufficiently powerful to retain stability in flight of a weapon which is negatively buoyant. All these features must be inserted within a limited space and also make room for the mine's explosive. It is hardly surprising that development programmes are extremely costly.

The pursuit mine is intended to penetrate the inner skin of a submarine by placing the explosive in the mine in a closer proximity to the submarine. A secondary advantage is that, if it is secured to the sea bed by a very short tether, it is very difficult to sweep. There are two forms of pursuit mine, unpowered and powered. The unpowered type is simple in operation and relatively cheap to develop. In its simple form, it rises by buoyancy until it is in the vicinity of the target usually directly overhead; control surfaces have been fitted to provide limited manoeuvring. Its radius of action, however, depends on the depth of the target; this is considerably reduced against submarines which have dived and are operating close to the sea bed. Unpowered pursuit mines need either a prediction system to follow a ballistic trajectory or some form of homing device. The target-seeking systems, like the control surfaces, must be powered by stored energy.

Powered pursuit mines are able to track and follow submarines both in azimuth and in depth. It is, in fact, debatable whether the powered pursuit mine should be designated as an advanced sea mine or as an autonomous torpedo. The first example was the CAPTOR mine, already described. Again, its development was very costly and was of the order of £75 million during the 1970s to the early 1980s. The unit cost of each CAPTOR mine is about £300,000 in spite of using a torpedo which was at that time already in service. Regardless of the cost, it seems probable that pursuit mines will continue to be developed in order to deny submarines unrestricted access to sea space and, secondly, to defeat sonar minehunting operations.

Minesweeping

In the early post-war years, accurate detection of mines by sonar was impossible and much painstaking effort was expended on developing various kinds of sweep (principally against pressure mines). It appeared then that the most effective form was to tow an old merchant vessel which was 'either indestructible or which, if destroyed, will not block a channel' by filling it with oil drums or wood. The British experimented in the early 1950s with a semi-rigid displacement sweep – an envelope of rubber enmeshed with two sets of wire rope laid inside the rubber in a series of helices.[55] It was also planned to provide propulsion for these sweeps with turbojet engines.

For some years, minesweepers had been constructed principally of wood, to reduce their magnetic content. On 14 July 1974, the British put into service the world's first glass reinforced plastic (GRP) Minesweeper/Minehunter, HMS

Wilton. Cast in an enormous mould, it was the first of a string of similar vessels to be made by this unique process which reduced a ship's magnetic signature to a minimum.

Helicopters were later pressed into service as airborne mine-sweepers and spotters. In the Korean War, they flew ahead of minesweeping flotillas and passed back information about the position of mines.[56] When sea conditions were favourable, outstanding results were obtained. With the ability of helicopters to carry heavier loads minesweeping apparatus was developed. Two methods were brought into use. In the first, the helicopter dragged a V-shaped device with explosive wirecutters to break the mine's cable and let it rise to the surface (similar to the paravane). In the second method the helicopter towed a sled along the surface of the sea while it generated a strong electromagnetic current to detonate magnetic mines. Acoustic mines were detonated by simulating the noise of a ship's propeller with a cavitating disc in a venturi tube. These helicopters were used in the Vietnam War to sweep mines from the harbour of Haiphong, but apparently only one mine was found; the remainder were rendered harmless by internal timing devices.

A hydrofoil sled was devised for the US Navy which had a twin electrode magnetic tail which created a magnetic field similar to that of a ship. At the same time, it could be combined with the acoustic sweep. This type was employed with some success in minesweeping operations in the Gulf of Suez in 1984.

When sonar became more effective, it was used for the purpose of mine hunting as distinct from mine sweeping. The Americans used their wartime Q1A frequency-modulated sector-scanning sonar (it was later fitted to submarines navigating under the arctic ice). The British evolved the TYPE 192 in the early 1960s; this was a high definition multibeam set which was extensively fitted in the Royal Navy for many years.[57] Mine hunting became a principal shipborne mine countermeasure. Moreover, a mine hunting sonar was useless without some means of neutralising or destroying the mines it has found. A manned inflatable dinghy was used in conjunction with the TYPE 193 sonar in which divers could approach the mine, inspect it if necessary, and then place a charge sufficiently near to neutralise the mine when detonated.

In general, the US Navy appeared to be content to allow its European allies to formulate minesweeping techniques. But this policy had to be hastily revised when the unanticipated laying of mines by unfriendly Arab states in the Middle East made naval security operations not only hazardous, but minesweeping a slow, laborious and dangerous business. During operations in the Red Sea in 1982, a British minesweeper took six days to identify, disarm and neutralise a complicated 1,500 pound mine. The British were by then using a more sophisticated remotely-controlled vehicle (ROV) for mine hunting equipped with cameras and sonar which had originally been devised by the

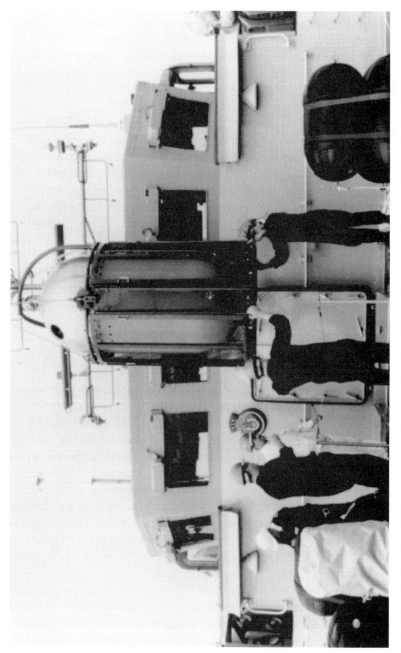

Plate 41 Variable depth multi-function sonar for mine hunting. Used with success in the Gulf War by Royal Navy mine counter-measure ships. (*Marconi Underwater Systems*)

French.[58] ROVs were, however, at least ten times more expensive than a mine; no more than two ROVs were carried per ship and had to be used with a good deal of caution. But it had become obvious that visual inspection systems were essential to determine the exact nature of a mine and small remotely-guided surface craft and submarines were designed to carry cameras and sonars. These 'robotic' systems provided a way of dealing with mines at minimum risk to personnel and ships.

Countermeasures in Mines

All these mine-hunting techniques were bound to stimulate mine designers into making mines less susceptible to sonar detection. In the first place, the minelayer had to be given fuller information about the sea bed in order to hide mines from sonar observation. Secondly, mines had to be fitted with counter countermeasures. Information about these devices is naturally hard to obtain. All that can be said is that the measure and countermeasure battle between mine hunting ROVs and mines is only at its outset. Mine designers believe that they have the initiative because the ROV gives the mine the information that tells it that it has been detected. By the mid-1980s, it looked as if counter-measures in mines had nearly brought to an end 'the honeymoon of the sonar-fitted minehunter's advantage over the mine.'[59]

Conclusion

Space does not permit more than a glance at the changes in the propulsion of surface ships whereby they could remain at sea for much longer periods than in the Second World War because of new design concepts for boilers and tur-bines, leading to higher steam pressure and more miles per ton. In 1945, for example, American vessels were able to remain at sea for 90 days whereas the limit of Royal Navy ships was no more than eight days, later increased to twenty. This small revolution was essential for surface ships which were required in all the conflicts from Korea onwards and not least in the Iran-Iraq war, when about 500 neutral merchant vessels were subjected to attack. The presence of mines in the Persian Gulf and in other waters in the Middle East required the deployment of mine countermeasure forces out of all proportion to the small numbers of these lethal weapons laid.

Fortunately, the best way of protecting transatlantic convoys (either by close escort or by concentrating on the destruction of submarines) never had to be put to the test, but the need for long range aircraft for patrolling choke points and for helicopters to act as close protection of surface vessels contin-ued to be (for lack of anything better) essential.

Technologically, the threat to surface naval forces was provided by aircraft, cruise missiles and the real submarine (by the end of the period the nuclear-powered, cruise missile carrying submarine). Whereas underwater craft continued to benefit from new stealth techniques, surface vessels remained highly vulnerable and conspicuous both to air and underwater attack. Not only was better air defence needed but a never ceasing concentration too on the development of ECM, ECCM and ESM.

By 1985, the state of anti-submarine warfare had hardly changed from that described nine years earlier by an experienced naval operational research officer who wrote: 'anti-submarine surface ships have lost ground in relation to the submarine [though] their anti-aircraft armament can be used as a final defence against anti-ship missiles. But the hunter-killer submarine, especially the nuclear version, with its ability to remain submerged for very long periods, has now emerged as the most powerful weapon system in any modern fleet – the classic example of a force multiplier. Its ability to remain quiet and let its enemy come to it means that it is probably better employed on barrier patrol than on convoy escort tasks. The long-range maritime patrol aircraft is obviously essential for escorting convoys, but it could also provide the distant attack capability which may be the only weakness of submarines forming a transit barrier . . . There is no single "solution" on the horizon to tactical anti-submarine warfare. The only effective method will be a combination of the different systems, since many of the weaknesses of one are offset by the strengths of others. A power or an alliance ill-equipped and unprepared for anti-submarine warfare could find itself driven off the oceans.'[60]

CONCLUSIONS

In this book, we have considered the impact of technology upon the whole span of conventional warfare between 1945 and 1985 – effectively the years of the Cold War between East and West and the years of unprecedented investment in research and development for defence and, despite the cost, of unparalleled scientific advancement.

The six years of the Second World War had inevitably seen huge advances in military technology, including the first tentative steps into the missile age and the emergence of the jet engine. However, of far greater significance than either of these were the introduction of radar, the birth of the computer and the widespread development of all forms of communications and information handling. It was these that would form the basis of what we have called 'The Silent Revolution', spurred on by the grim threat of nuclear war which underpinned the Cold War years.

As the atomic and then the thermonuclear threat developed, the whole broad canvas of defence was affected as the Western Allies and their Soviet opponents rearmed themselves to face the unthinkable, establishing vast programmes of research and development designed to enable each to keep one step ahead in the never-ending game of measure and counter-measure.

Only one constant remained – man and his inventive genius and his powers of decision. Yet so great were the technological advances in weaponry that even man began to find that, if new threats were to be countered in time, some measure of decision-making would have to be delegated to the machine. Therein lay the greatest danger for, in the extreme, man now ran the risk of losing absolute control of his weapon of last resort – the strategic nuclear strike. Nevertheless, only man had control of the resources needed not only to make war but to preserve peace.

Electronics: the Key

It was the invention in America of the transistor in 1947, followed by the invention of the integrated circuit and the laser beam which really drove the revolution in the means of making and controlling conventional warfare. The departure of the bulky and fragile thermionic valve, the arrival of solid state electronic circuitry and the wonder of microminiaturisation now made not only possible but even commonplace the achievement of what had hitherto been only a gleam in the scientist's eye. We now entered into a new age in terms of man's ability to assimilate, store and process data, much of which would derive from the breakthrough in the field of computing – a quantum jump from the huge, valve-infested COLOSSUS built at Bletchley Park to tackle the mysteries of *ENIGMA*, to devices whose dimensions were now measured in inches or even fractions of an inch but whose capacities were astonishing. Miraculous as the developments in weapon technology were becoming, the most important of all the changes taking place was the revolution in the acquisition of political and military intelligence and the new-found power of the politician to assert minute-by-minute control over military operations taking place many hundreds of miles away. Even more important, a single man, by the touch of a switch, could pass a coded message that would automatically launch a nuclear strategic strike that could trigger the destruction of the civilised world. That such a holocaust could be set in train had only been made possible by massive increases in the range and accuracy of strategic weapon systems, targeted by information which will often have been derived though the use of communications and reconnaissance satellites, the by-product of man's conquest of space. At every turn, it had become the acquisition of data and the ability to use it that had become the underlying driving force of modern warfare.

The great Soviet architect of naval strategy, Admiral Gorshkov, is reported to have claimed that the side that wins the next war will be the one that makes best use of the electronic spectrum. Yet Sir Richard Norman, a former Chief Scientific Adviser to the British Ministry of Defence, commented, that in spite of modern technology

'The human is still the best image processor for picking out targets . . . and still by far the best for making strategic decisions. Wars will be fought by humans, if they have to be fought, for a long time to come. To return to Admiral Gorshkov, the electro-magnetic spectrum is still subservient to man'.[1]

287

War on Land

It was inevitable that the Soviet Union would sooner or later acquire a nuclear capability to rival or even outstrip that of the United States and, as surely as night follows day, that both East and West would then seek to produce a whole range of nuclear weapons to meet the requirements of every situation from the strategic to the tactical. As they did so, new tactical philosophies and doctrine emerged. Protection and dispersion became the order of the day, tanks and armoured vehicles of all sorts overshadowed all else and costs soared. An immediate consequence was that some conventional capabilities began to be seriously reduced, the chief of which being artillery. Once cut, conventional capabilities are hard and costly to replace, as both sides would find when they realised that a policy of Mutual Assured Destruction was the purest folly and that should war break out, it was vital to be able to fight a conventional phase in the hope that the point of releasing any nuclear weapons, with the inevitable risk of escalation, could be avoided. Meanwhile, minor wars around the world were keeping alive many of the soldier's conventional skills but the burden of maintaining the ability to conduct such operations, many miles away from the home base, in addition to the cost of the highly sophisticated, heavily armed formations needed in Central Europe was crippling and, indeed, as we have recently seen, would bring about the ultimate downfall of the Warsaw Pact and its mentor, the Soviet Union. The great American war in Vietnam saw enormous strides in conventional warfare – the helicopter came into its own, not only as a load carrier but as a very effective close-support aircraft, whilst also adding dramatically to battlefield mobility. The first precision guided munitions made their appearance and the SAM had a telling effect upon the vulnerability of aircraft of all types operating in support of ground forces or in the interdiction role.

Throughout the world, new levels of capacity and efficiency in strategic and tactical communications, combined with the mass of technically gathered intelligence and other data now pouring in to headquarters, gave rise to a new term, C^3I (command and control, communications and intelligence), a term that encapsulated the new significance of information handling and processing to perfection. Whether that information or data was in the form of a textual message or an instruction to some part of a weapon system, it was this new-found ability to pass information in so many forms and for so many purposes that now made information the principal element in the whole spectrum of defence technology.[2]

In the field of hardware, the improvement in the performance of the tank owed less to electronics than to steady advances in the manufacture of guns and armour and the development of engines and transmissions. Only in the field of fire control equipment, where the laser and computer made possible far greater accuracy in rangefinding and the engagement of moving targets did electronics play an important role, although just outside the period we have considered satellite assisted navigation would prove of immense value in the desert warfare of the Gulf. Essentially, the tank and its associated armour within the battlegroup, was simply a much improved version of its forebear. Its role was little changed.

The realisation that the possibility of being able to fight 'round the clock' was fast becoming reality led to increasing pressure being put on the scientist to produce robust and reliable night vision equipment. The short sharp contests of Yom Kippur in 1973 and the Falklands in 1982 were ideal proving grounds and showed that the well-trained soldier could indeed operate very effectively during the hours of darkness, given this essential aid.

Finally, the need in a nuclear setting to be able to bring heavy concentrations of fire down at short notice led to the production of the multiple-launched rocket system – effectively a sophisticated version of the Soviet 'Stalin Organ' of the Second World War. This at least helped to restore the balance so badly upset when field artillery had been reduced during the early days of atomic fever. As the new emphasis upon the conventional phase of General War grew, so did enthusiasm for the use of the helicopter in all its forms and the concept of airmobility, nurtured in Vietnam, become all the cry in Europe, exemplified by the American doctrine of the AirLand Battle. But helicopters are immensely expensive – and so are tanks and infantry fighting vehicles. With the threat from the East now so radically changed, it may well be that equally radical changes will follow amongst the armies of NATO.

Manned Aircraft

Great though the technological advances on land may have been, they pale almost into insignificance against those in the air. The Germans' work on missiles and the experience of the *V-2* in its use against cities, made it inevitable that extensive research would go into the development of long range rocket missiles, an inevitability boosted by growing interest in the possibilities of outer space, both for scientific and military uses. As progress was made, suggestions were bound to be raised that the day of the manned aircraft was nearing its close. Meanwhile the development of the jet engine was leading to the design of faster and faster aircraft, each bringing with it new problems of handling and control, problems that the electronic scientist was rapidly overcoming by dint of a new complex of electronic aids soon to be known as the aircraft's avionics. In such an exciting area of development, it was perhaps hardly surprising that there was a tendency to rush into new projects without the potential problems or the full implications being thought through properly. The first twenty or thirty years after the Second World

War would be characterised by an appalling waste of precious funding and bitter inter-Service wrangling between the RAF and the Royal Navy, each fighting its own corner for funds and even for survival.

The switch of responsibility for the national deterrent from the specialist V-bomber force to the submarine made relations no easier, nor did the bitterness of the conflict over the demise of the fleet carrier and so of the Navy's fixed wing capability at sea. This was closely followed by an even fiercer battle over the adaptation of the HARRIER to a naval role in order to restore the position by using its VTOL capability on board the new ASW cruisers in conjunction with their planned compliment of SEA KING helicopters. The astonishing success of the SEA HARRIER in the Falklands would more than justify the Navy's case, which they had won in committee by the skin of their teeth.

Despite the ever-increasing importance of the role played by air power during the six years leading up to our period, the performance of military aircraft, their speed, armament and ability to navigate and bomb with accuracy were all rudimentary by modern standards, although the advent of the jet aircraft in 1945 was an early foretaste of things to come. Even in the latter days of the war when new bombing and navigational aids, based upon the use of radar, brought marked improvements, the maintenance of a major bombing campaign was not only immensely costly in terms of effort but also in the lives of trained aircrews. Crews tended to be large and aircraft to be very vulnerable to air defences. For the fighter pilot, target acquisition and engagement were still matters almost entirely within the sphere of his own skill and competence. Close quarter fighting and hence manoeuvrability and skill, combined with high morale and great courage, were the prime requirements. On the ground, radar had already done much to enhance the capabilities of the air defences, both as a means of early warning and of providing air defence fighters with some target orientation. Indeed, it had transformed the task of the air defence commander, both by providing early warning and, later, as an aid to the anti-aircraft gunners in fire prediction.

The substantial progress made post-war in every aspect of the performance and control of strike and air defence aircraft outshone all the changes that were taking place on land or at sea. The early assertion of air superiority, with local air supremacy where this was essential, became a first requirement for any commander-in chief and an essential prelude to successful land operations. The power, flexibility and accuracy of the air arm was yearly becoming more awesome. Electronics provided a new range of aids and controls affecting every aspect of the pilot's task – so great was the speed at which strike aircraft now operated in their nap-of-the-earth mode that such aids as terrain-following radar and flight control and weapons delivery computers became essential ingredients of the avionics of the strike aircraft. Similar advances in air defence systems, which were increasingly being based upon SAMs, and the growth of electronic warfare, forced new tactics on strike missions. Either they must fly under the enemy radars – and hence use the nap-of-the-earth mode – or they must fly at height, escorted by specialist ECCM aircraft designed to break through the 'electronic fence' of the defence. The winning of the war in the air had become a matter of absolute priority. As early proof of this, it is only necessary to look back to 1967 and the Six Days' War, won, effectively, by the brilliant preemptive strike mounted by the Israeli Air Force against the Egyptian airfields, rendering their air force ineffective in a matter of minutes. Much more recently, the overwhelming success of the Coalition air forces in the Gulf, combined with the masterly selective use of cruise missiles from ships at sea, achieved a similar result at very small cost in human lives. Here, indeed, was the ultimate example of the power of a modern air force.

The size and strength of the Soviet air forces, which had quickly developed many of the special new skills of the West, meant that added attention must be paid to AEW, both at sea and over the land. The American project to provide command facilities and wide-ranging early warning across the Central Front in Europe as well as over the North Atlantic led to the creation of an electronic flying miracle, known now to all the world as AWACS. Earlier, the British had produced a maritime patrol aircraft, NIMROD, to provide reconnaissance cover against marauding nuclear submarines and long-range aircraft such as the Soviet BEAR. The introduction of flight-refuelling gave this aircraft an extended patrol time, as it did, of course, to air defence fighters.

The cost of these remarkable advances, on top of the rest of the huge bill for R & D in other areas, was crippling and made no lighter by the sad story of order and counter order described in Chapter 7. The point was soon reached at which it became clear that any new aircraft projects would have to set up as international cooperative developments. Whilst this would inevitably involve delays in in-service dates and added costs, the spreading of those costs over several defence budgets would represent worthwhile savings to individual countries. The inability of the Soviet Union to enter into such agreements must have greatly added to the strain on the national economy of their defence procurement budget and even contributed to the final downfall of the Warsaw Pact.

At the beginning of the period, aircraft armament had tended to embrace cannon, machine-guns, iron bombs and air-to-ground rockets. The changing characteristics of combat aircraft made it very clear that a major change in armaments policy was essential. Close-quarter fighting soon became a thing of the past, as air-to-air missiles of increasing range and accuracy appeared and the ground-based armoury of air defence became ever more menacing and effective. It was in Vietnam that what the Americans first called 'smart' bombs were used in war. At long last they had a PGM that would take out a difficult target like a bridge with minimum effort – a task that heretofore had involved many aircraft, often at great cost, and with doubtful success. The trend continued by the introduction of stand-off weapons that could even allow a pilot to make his attack from within the security of his own airspace or at least from a position in which he was least exposed to enemy ECM and ground fire from SAMs. The newfound accuracy, which gradually increased the range of a weapon's effectiveness, now affected the whole weapons inventory – a force multiplier if ever there was one. To meet the demands and stresses of the new air warfare, the avionics of all combat aircraft became increasingly complex so that the pilot and his navigator (where he had one) could compete with as little strain as could be contrived – thanks to radar, the computer, micro-miniaturisation and the whole field of solid state electronics – the modern strike aircraft or air superiority fighter provides its human controller with resources and capabilities that were undreamed of at the start of the period we have considered. Even as the period drew to a close, the concept of 'stealth' aircraft whose radar signature makes them almost invisible to enemy air defences became a reality – albeit at enormous cost. In spite of all that has been achieved in weapons systems development, the final arbiter in air combat is the man – and he is likely to remain so for years to come.

The War at Sea

The birth of the nuclear submarine, with its capacity to operate submerged for many weeks, thousands of miles from its base, brought substantial change to the whole concept of naval operations, switching much of the emphasis from surface to underwater fleets, an emphasis that was enhanced by the decision to transfer responsibility for the national deterrent force from the RAF to the Royal Navy. No longer would it be delivered by stand-off weapons from specialist aircraft but by submarine-launched ballistic missiles (SLBMs) – a method which represented a much higher degree of invulnerability. Furthermore, to keep the deterrent force on permanent alert was infinitely more cost effective by stationing one or two submarines on long patrols than keeping aircraft permanently airborne – as had been the case with USAF's Strike Command. That such a change could be made was largely due to the sweeping advances made in underwater communications, sonar and satellite communications for extreme navigational accuracy (an essential capability for any missile-firing vessel). Even as the deterrent force was being developed another powerful weapon system was beginning to feature as a naval force multiplier of immense importance – the hunter-killer submarine. So invulnerable were these vessels, so easily concealed in the vastness of the ocean, that the presence of only one or two boats, armed with new torpedoes of greatly increased effectiveness, was enough to enable a nation to impose domination upon a sea area through which enemy shipping of all sorts might pass. Twice the existence of such a presence was used to deter Argentinian naval activity. On the second occasion, the destruction of the *Belgrano* by a hunter-killer acting on real-time orders direct from the War Cabinet through the Commander-in-Chief's headquarters at Northwood, effectively confined the enemy fleet to its home ports for the rest of the campaign.

On the surface, the vulnerability of warships to air and submarine attack, particularly to sea-skimming and cruise missiles and stand-off air-launched weapons, led to a massive increase in the defensive weapons and communications fits of all vessels, adding enormously to their cost and creating a plethora of problems for the naval architect as missiles, air-defence guns and radars had all to be fitted into the slender hulls of frigates and destroyers, leaving less and less space for their human complement. At the same time, sonars and helicopters had also to be accommodated and the whole system for the control of the ship in action concentrated in a fall-out and gas-proof 'citadel', the heart of which was the ship's operations room from which it would be fought. An immediate penalty to be paid was the limited number of missiles of each type that could be carried, giving the ship a very limited combat endurance before replenishment became essential. For some years that replenishment could only be effected in port. Even when replenishment at sea became possible, the question of sustained battle effectiveness remained.

Thus it was that of the two parts of any fleet, the underwater element now possessed great powers of survivability and sustained combat effectiveness whilst the surface vessel became increasingly vulnerable in a major war situation. Nevertheless, the bulk of any navy's day-to-day tasks must be carried out by the surface fleet which, by its visible presence is a principal means of keeping national supply lines open in a peace situation and also of creating a political presence in times of potential unrest in distant parts of the world. It is the frigates, destroyers and minesweepers who must do the inevitable policing tasks, as they have in the Gulf for over 20 years – tasks which make heavy demands on an ever-shrinking number of warships. That those patrol tasks are carried out so effectively owes much to the by-products of the Silent Revolution.

Looking Ahead

Despite the emphasis that has been placed throughout this book upon the scientific and technological developments and the structural and philosophical changes which they have brought about to national defence policies and doctrines, it would be wrong to succumb to any form of 'technophilia'. Even as recently as 'Operation DESERT STORM', less than 10 per cent of all the weapons used were PGMs and the accuracy of those was reckoned to be nearer 75 than 100 per cent. More than 82,000 conventional iron bombs were used in the winning of the air war.[3] Similarly, in the ground battle, although new wonders like satellite navigation, night vision and radar played leading roles, the battle was fought on what were essentially traditional lines, apart from the massive use of helicopters in one AirLand Battle type operation, the first of its kind in the history of warfare. But conventional artillery fire and the free flight rockets of MLRS were the chief sources of close fire support. Whether he was launched into battle by Infantry Combat Vehicle or helicopter, the infantryman had still to dismount and seize his final objective on foot.

The collapse of the Warsaw Pact has thrown new emphasis upon the importance of conventional forces. Although the nuclear threat may seem almost to have disappeared, the world remains a very dangerous place in which potential needs for conventional forces exist on every side and in which there must still be due regard to the power of deterrence – but now the driving force behind that deterrence has to be the presence of highly trained, well-equipped and combat-ready conventional troops and naval and air forces. It is easy to postulate such a demand but it represents a requirement that is far from easy to fulfil. From now on, much of the research effort in defence needs to be concentrated upon the means of easing the problems which face the conventional fighting man in an intensely complex and stressful situation and of giving him the means of acquiring the essential skills he must have to operate his powerful and highly sophisticated equipment effectively at the drop of a hat – the days of breathing spaces during which reserves are mustered, resources gathered and defects in training are made good, are fast disappearing. It would be fatal to draw any conclusion from the six months reprieve of DESERT STORM that lead us to think otherwise.

SOURCES

The following abbreviations are used for the location and designation of documentary sources:

Public Records Office (PRO):

ADM   Admiralty
AIR   Air Ministry
AVIA   Ministry of Aviation
CAB   Cabinet Office
DEFE Ministry of Defence
T   Treasury

Introduction

1 CAB 122/354. German Scientists, DRPC mtg, 30 Nov 1948.
2 The Rand Corporation: *The First Fifteen Years* (Santa Monica, Calif., Nov 1963).
3 Kistiakowsky, G B Presidential Scientific Advising, *Science*, Vol 184, 5 Apr 1974.
4 Kolodziej, E A *Making and Marketing Arms. The French experience and its implications for the international system*, (Princeton Univ Press, 1987), pp 45–6.
5 Perry, R Comparisons of Soviet and US Technology, *Rand Rept* R-827, (Santa Monica, Calif., June 1973). Amann, R *et al. The Technological Level of Soviet Industry*, (Yale Univ Press, 1977), Chap. 9, pp 409–40.
6 Burt, R *Defence Budgeting. The British and American Cases*, IISS Adelphi Papers No 112, 1974/50; Cox, A and Kirby, S *Congress,*

Parliament and Defence, (London 1986); Broadbent E *The Military and Government*, (RUSI Defence Studies, 1988).

7   WO 163/209. Weapon Development Cttee, 31 Aug 1949.

8   Zuckerman, Lord, *Monkeys, Men and Missiles*, (London, 1988), pp 206–7.

9   Mathews, E (Ed). *The Parameters of War*, Kinnaird, D McNamara at the Pentagon, (Pergamon-Brassey's, 1987), pp 166–70.

10 Norman, Sir R Research and Development in Defence, Speech to Air League, (Royal Aero Soc, 22 Nov 1988), pp 13–14.

11 James, R R Standardisation and Common Production of Weapons in NATO. *Defence Technology and the Western Alliance, No 3*, (IISS, Jul 1967).

Chapter 1 A New Era in Warfare

1   AIR 14/361, HS and FX Bombs, Technical Information.

2   WO 32/15266, German Research and Development at the Time of the Armistice (sic), 1945.

3   *Ibid*; AIR 20/8774, German Guided Missile Research, 1945.

4   ADM1/22311 Research and Development on Guided Weapons, 1945. AVIA 48/1, Coordinating Committee on Guided and Propelled Missiles and Projectiles, 1945; AIR 20/4658, Weapons: Future Development 1944–46.

5   ADM1/22311, *op cit.*

6   Hall, R C (Ed) *History of Rocketry and and Astronautics*, Vol 7, Pt II, (AAS Publns, San Diego, 1986), pp 153–201.

7   *Ibid*. p 43.

8   Sir Charles Wright, Director of Scientific Research at the Admiralty.

9   WO 163/205, V T Fuses: Development and Production in UK) 15 Jan 1945; WO 32/11025 Radio Proximity Fuses. Future if jammed.

10 Postan M M *et al*, *Design and Development of Weapons*, Chap IX passim (HMSO 1963).

11 Lee, Asher, *Air Power*, Chap III Air Defence, London 1957, p 65.

12 *History of Rocketry and Astronautics*, *op cit*, F J Malina, US Army Air Corps Jet Propulsion Research Project, 1939–46.

13 WO 195/9842, Attack of Armour. Methods of attack of tank armour by gunfire. Present limitations and future possibilities, 1948.

14 Ellis, L F *et al Victory in the West*, Vol I, (HMSO, 1968), p 546.

15 WO 32/13039, Research on Armour, 1947; AVIA 44/84 Defence of AFVs in Attack by Hollow Charge Weapons.

16 WO 208/2183, Investigation into Tabun and Sarin Products and Anabasine, 1945.

17 Waddington, C H *Operational Research against the U-boat* Chap 2, (Elek Science, London, 1973).

18 Hackmann, W *Seek and Strike: Sonar, anti-submarine Warfare and the Royal Navy*, 1914–54, (HMSO, 1984), pp 270–4.

19 *Ibid.* p 311.

20 Lewis, Cdr D L USN, *The Fight for the Sea*, (New York, 1961), p 292.

21 Hodges, A *Alan Turing: The Enigma*, (London, 1983), pp 91–3 and p 107.

22 Randell, B, Alan Turing and the origins of Digital Computers. (Univ of Newcastle upon Tyne. Tech Dept), Series No 3, May 1972.

23 Hinsley, H *et al, British Intelligence in the Second World War*, Vol I, (HMSO, 1979). p 494.

24 Randell, B The Colossus. (Univ of Newcastle upon Tyne, Tech Dept), Series No 90, Jun 1976.

25 Stern, N *From ENIAC to UNIVAC* (Digital Press, 1981), *passim.*

26 Hodges, A *op cit*, p 299.

27 Hoelzer, Helmuth, The fully-electronic analog computer, *Annals of the History of Computing*, Vol 7, No 3, Jul 1985.

28 Larnder, H Quoted in Obit of E C Wiliams, *Jnl of the Operational Research Society*, Vol 31, No 7, Jul 1980.

29 WO 195/14070, Advsy Council on Scientific Research and Tech. Dev. 23 May 1957.

Chapter 2 The Electronic Revolution

1 Brooks, H, The military innovation system and the qualitative arms race, *Daedalus,* Summer 1985.

2 Valley, G E, How the SAGE development began; *Annals of the History of Computing*, Vol 7, No 3, Jul 1985.

3 Stern, *op cit.*

4 DSIR 10/385,. Development of ACE by John Womersley, Feb 1946.

5 DSIR 10/386,. ACE: Pilot Model, Womersley to D R Hartree, (Cavendish Laboratory, 26 Apr 1949).

6 DSIR 10/343. Research on ACE with the Min of Supp and Prof Williams, (Manchester Univ); Flamm, K *Creating the Computer: Government, Industry and High Technology*, (Brookings Instn, Washington, DC, 1988), pp 136–143.

7 Hodges, A *op cit*, p 392.

8 *Ibid*, p 393.

9 Hoddesden, L, The discovery of the point contact transistor, *Hist Studies in the Phys and Biol Sciences*, No 12, Pt I, 1982; Obit of Wiliam Shockley, *The Times*, 16 Aug 1989.

10 *The Times*, Obit of John Bardeen, 1 Feb 1991.
11 AVIA 65/518. Transistors: Construction and Materials, 16 Oct 1951.
12 *Ibid.* Memo by R A Smith on need for transistor research in the UK, 30 Oct 1951.
13 *Ibid.* F E Jones to T R Scott, STL, 18 Mar 1953.
14 Tomlin, D H letters to author, 5 and 30 Jan 1992.
15 AVIA 65/902. Establishment of transistor production in UK, 1956–57.
16 Tomlin, *op cit*, 5 Jan 1992.
17 Kilby, J S Invention of the Integrated Circuit, *IEEE Trans on Electron Devices*, Vol ED-23, No 7, Jul 1976, p 648.
18 *Ibid*, p 649.
19 Dummer, G W A, A History of Microelectronics Development at the Royal Radar Establishment, *Microelectronics and Reliability*, (Pergamon Press, 1965), Vol 4, p 195.
20 *Ibid*, p 196; Golding, A, *The Semiconductor Industry in Britain and the United States*, (Univ of Sussex, 1971), pp 351–360.
21 AVIA 26/1908. RRE Rept No 3028, Rept on a visit to the USA on micro-miniaturisation components and techniques by G W A Dummer, May 1960; AVIA 26/1904. RRE Tech Note No 659, Rept on a visit to the USA to study the latest developments in the microminiaturisation of electronic circuits by J W Glanville, 2 June 1960.
22 Perry, W J and Sumney, L, The Very High Speed Integrated Circuit Programme. *Review of US Military R & D,* Ed Tsipis, K & Jasen, P, (Pergamon Brassey's, 1984).
23 Jacobs, J F, *Annals of the History of Computing*, Vol 5, No 4, Oct 1983; Dineen, G P & Frick, F C, Electronics and National Defence: A Case Study.
24 Jacobs, *op cit*. Discussion on SAGE at Mitre Corpn, 26 Oct 1982.
25 AIR 20/9981. Renewal of Control and Reporting System, Air Council mtg concls, 8 Jan 1959.
26 AIR 20/10295. Organisation for Linesman, 1960–61, Memo by C-in-C Fighter Cmd, 10 Mar 1961.
27 Tomlin, *op cit*, 5 Jan 1992.
28 Holloway, D, Technology Management and the Soviet Military Establishment, IISS, *Adelphi Papers*, No 76, 1971, pp 16–27.
29 Hemsley, Brig J, *Soviet Troop Control*, Brassey's (UK) London 1982.
30 Brookner, E, Phased Array Radars, *Scientific American*, Vol 252, No 2, Feb 1985; Schleher, D C *Introduction to Electronic Warfare*, (Artec House, 1986), p 295.
31 Scanlan, M J B, (Ed), *Modern Radar Techniques*, p 5 *et seq.*
32 Bullock, C, Military Surveillance Radars, Now and Tomorrow, *Interavia* 7, 1982.

33   Latham, C, Martello – A Modern Three Dimensional Surveillance Radar, *The GEC Jnl of Research*, Vol 3, No 2, 1985, pp 104–13.
34   Highcock, J, Sideways-looking airborne radar, *RRE Jnl*, No 51 Apr 1964.
35   *Ibid.*
36   Johnson, S L, Millimetre Wave Radar: The New ECM/ECCM Frontier, *Microwave Jnl*, May 1984.
37   Ramsay, D A, The Evolution of Radar Guidance, *The GEC Jnl of Research*, Vol 3, No 2 1985, pp 92–103.
38   Jones, R V, Infrared Detection in British Air Defence, 1935–38, *Infrared Physics*, Vol 1, No 61, pp 153–162.
39   Hudson, R D & J W, The Military Applications of Remote Sensing by Infra Red, *Procs IEEE*, Vol 63, No 1, Jan 1975.
40   Hughes, M A, A Review of the Use of Optical/IR Techniques in the Guidance and Control Systems for Tactical Weapons, One Day Symp, Roy Aero Soc, 26 Apr 1988.
41   Seidel, R W, From Glow to Flow: A History of the Military Laser R & D, *Hist Studies in the Phys and Biol Sciences, Vol 18, Pt I, 1987.*
42   *Ibid.*
43   De Leon, P, The Laser-guided Bomb: A Case History of a Development. A Report prepared for the USAF Project Rand, June 1974.
44   Hall, R C, *op cit*; Draper, C S, *The Evolution of Aerospace Guidance Technology at MIT,* 1935–51; Mackenzie, D, *Inventing Accuracy. A Historical Sociology of Nuclear Missile Guidance*, (MIT Press, London 1990).
45   AVIA 54/2124. Corporal, Brit Joint Staff Miss, Washington, to Min of Supp, Corporal and its further evolution *vs* Sergeant, 30 Apr 1957.
46   AVIA 65/726. VTO Aircraft Research; Sir Stuart Mitchell, Controller Gen GW (Electronics) at DRPC mtg, 25 Mar 1954; AVIA 65/950. Technical Aspects of Red Rose, possible use of US Gyro HIG-4 until satisfactory British gyro is produced, 18 Sept 1956.
47   Mackenzie, *op cit*, pp 307–339.
48   Hall, *op cit*. US Army Air Corps Jet Propulsion Research Project GAL-CIT: Memoir by F J Malina. For the British side, see DSIR 23/16816, Solid and Liquid Propellants.

Chapter 3 Communications: The Key to Command – and the Threat

1   *Procs Instn of Electrical Engineers (IEE)*, Vol 132, No 1, Feb 1985.
2   Everitt, W L, Telecommunications – the resource not depleted by use. A historical philosophical resumé, *Procs Instn of Electrical and Electronic Engineers (IEEE)*, Vol 64, No 9, Sept 1976.

3 *Procs IEEE,* Special issue on packet communications networks, Vol 66, Nov 1978, Introdn.

4 *Ibid,* Roberts, G R, The Evolution of Packet Switching.

5 *Ibid.*

6 Ricci, F R and Schutzer, D, *US Military Communications. AC³I Force Multiplier,* (Computer Science Press, 1986).

7 *Ibid,* p 199 et seq; Everitt, *op cit,* p 1296.

8 Ricci and Schutzer, *op cit,* Section on importance of EW.

9 Herzfield, C M, Command, Control and Communications, New Conventional Weapons and East–West Security, Pt III, IISS *Adelphi Papers,* No 145, pp 40–1.

10 AIR 2/10574, Introduction of UHF into the RAF; VCAS note on VHF-RT Policy for RAF, 4 Jan 1949.

11 AIR 20/6925, UHF and VHF, 2 Jul 1954.

12 Macfarlane, Sir G, The recent evolution of defence communications in the UK. *Procs IEE Comms* Publn No 139, p 262.

13 Brick, D B and Ellersick, F W, Future Air Force Tactical Communications, *IEEE Trans on Comns,* Vol Com-28, No 9, Sept 1980, App A, JTIDS.

14 Feigl, H, The Impact of new Maritime Technologies, IISS *Adelphi Papers,* No 122, 1976.

15 Ball, C R and Conley, R E, Navy Communications Overview, *IEEE Trans on Comns,* Vol Com – 28, *op cit,* p 1573.

16 Ricci and Schutzer, *op cit,* Comns with Submarines.

17 Bell and Conley, *op cit,* p 1575.

18 *Op cit,* p 1578.

19 Macfarlane, Sir G, *op cit,* p 260.

20 *Ibid,* Hezlet, Sir A, *The Electron and Sea Power,* (London, 1975), pp 281–3.

21 *IEEE Spectrum,* Communications and Navigation, Sept 1987.

22 *Ibid.*

23 Warner, P, *The Vital Link. The Story of Royal Signals 1945–1985,* (London 1989), pp 237–9.

24 *Ibid,* p 239.

25 *Ibid,* pp 323–5.

26 *Ibid,* pp 313–6.

27 *Ibid,* p 323.

28 *Ibid,* pp 326–9.

29 *Ibid,* p 248.

30 Ward, and Turner, *op cit.*

31 Warner, P, *op cit,* pp 323–4 and pp 329–30.

32 Kolodziej, *op cit,* p 226.

33 Mannel, W M, Future Communications Concepts in Support of US Army Command and Control, *IEEE Trans on Comns* Vol Com-28 *op cit,* p 1544.

34 *Ibid*, p 1543.

35 *Ibid*, p 1548.

36 Hemsley, *op cit.*

37 Hemsley, *op cit*, Chap 7.

38 Schleher, D C, *op cit*, C3CM.

39 Grant, P M *et al.*, Introduction to electronic warfare, *IEE Proc* Vol 129, Pt F, No 3, Jun 1982, pp 113–4.

40 Price, R, Further Notes and Anecdotes on Spread-Spectrum Origins, *IEEE Trans on Comns*, Vol Com-31, No. 1 Jan 1983, pp 89–90.

41 Scholtz, R A, The Origins of Spread-Spectrum Communications. *IEEE Trans on Comns*, Vol Com-30, No 5 May 1982, *passim.*

42 Warner, P, *op cit*, pp 253–4.

43 *Ibid*, p 248.

Chapter 4 To Seek, To Find

1 Clausewitz, C von, *On War*. Eds Howard, M and Paret, P (Princeton Univ Press, 1976), Chap 6, p 117.

2 Hinsley, H *et al*, *British Intelligence in World War 2*, *op cit*, pp 278–9 and 496–9.

3 Fitts, R E Ed., *The Strategy of Electromagnetic Conflict*, (Peninsula Publishing California), Chap 4.

4 AIR 20/7020, Re-equipment Photo Reconnaissance, Dep Director Pol (AS)1 to Asst Chief of Air Staff (P), 20 Aug 1949 and *passim*. Discussion of cameras and photographic interpretation in Katz, A H. Some notes on the history of aerial reconnaissance. Pt I, Apr 1966 (Rand Corporation California).

5 *Ibid*, Asst Chief of Air Staff (P) to Vice Chief of Air Staff, Jun 1951.

6 AIR 2/11432, Photographic Recce Aircraft Policy, 1954, *passim*; Crew, E D, Air Recce in the RAF: past, present and future, *Aeronautical Jnl*, (Roy Aero Soc., Oct 1969).

7 AVIA 65/334, Development of Recce Radar – Blue Shadow, 1952, *passim*; AIR 2/11962, Victor Long Range PR Aircraft Policy, 2 Oct 1956.

8 AIR 2/11962, *op cit*. Note on future, composition and organisation of long range V Recce element, 11 Jul 1957; see also Brookes, A J, *Photo Recce*, (London, 1975), Chap 12.

9 Rich, B R, The Skunk Works' Management Style – It's No Secret, 77th Wilbur and Orville Wright Memorial Lecture, Roy Aero Soc., *Aerospace*, Mar 1989.

10 Price, A, *Instruments of Darkness, The History of Electronic Warfare*, London 1977, p 254 et seq.

11 Fitts, R E, *op cit*, pp 58–63.

12 Greenwood, T, Reconnaissance, Surveillance and Arms Control, IISS *Adelphi Papers* No 88, 1972, Chap 3.

13 AVIA 65/332, Reconnaissance Satellite, May 1955 – Oct 1959.

14 *Ibid*, Note by King-Hele, 26 Mar 1957.

15 Greenwood, T, Reconnaissance and Arms Control, *Scientific American*, Vol 228, No 2, Feb 1973.

16 *Ibid.*

17 Hafemeister, D, Advances in verification technology, *Bull. of the Atomic Scientists*, Jan 1985, pp 35–40.

18 Barnaby, F, *The Automated Battlefield*, (London, 1986), p 26.

19 Meyer, S M, Soviet Military programmes and the 'New High Ground', *Survival*, Sept/Oct 1983, pp 204–15.

20 WO 32/13816, Organisation and Establishment of the Scientific Advisers to the Army Council, *op cit*, P Johnson to Director Signals Development, 27 Oct 1955.

21 Richardson, D, Technological Eyes for Flying Spies, *Military Technology and Economics*, No 20, 1980.

22 Oxlee, G J, Aerospace Reconnaissance and its Exploitation, *Aeronautical Jnl*, Roy Aero Soc., Nov 1982.

23 Crew, E D *op cit.*

24 Hudson, J P, The Military Appications of Remote Sensing by Infrared, *op cit*, p 121.

25 *Ibid*. p 125; FLIR gaining wider service acceptance, *Aviation Week and Space Technology*, 7 May 1973.

26 Falconer, N, Why an RPV? *Royal United Services Inst Jnl*, Vol 126, No 2, Jun 1982, p 64–6.

27 WO 163/389, Weapons Policy Cttee, 1953–55 War Office Policy Statement No 11 (2nd Revise) Arty Tactical G W, pp 5–6.

28 Armitage, Sir M, *Unmanned Aircraft*, (Brassey's (UK), 1988), p xi and *passim*.

29 *Ibid* p 86; see also Alberts, D J, Deterrence in the 1980s: Pt II The Role of Conventional Air Power, IISS *Adelphi Papers* No 193, 1984, pp 26 and 52.

30 Hooton, T, Castor and Phoenix. The British Army's eyes for the 1980s, *Military Technology*, Vol VIII, No 10, 1984.

31 Dennis, R W and Aplin, J D, Phoenix: real time target acquisition and battlefield surveillance system, avionics in the future land-air battle. One day conference, The Royal Aeronautical Society, 12 Dec 1990.

Chapter 5 Moves and Counter-moves in Land Warfare

1 Hunt, K, The Alliance and Europe: Pt II: Defence with Fewer Men, IISS *Adelphi Papers* No 98, 1973, p 14.

• SOURCES •

2 Sutton, B, *et al.*, Deep Attack Concepts and the Defence of Central Europe, *Survival*, Mar/Apr 1984.

3 *Ibid.*

4 WO 32/12087, The Universal Tank, 20 Jun 1946.

5 WO 32/14417, Centurions in Korea, 1952–53.

6 WO 32/14002, Heavy Tank FV214 Conqueror, 1949–53.

7 DEFE 10/420, DRPC Sub-Committee on Anti-Tank Measures, 5 Oct 1950.

8 WO 321/15322, New Medium Gun Tank No 2, December 1954; AVIA 55/46 Fighting Vehicle Production Advsy Cttee, Dec 1950–Dec 1952; WO 291/1431, AORG: The Heavy Gun Tank No 2 FV215, 15 Apr 1955.

9 Ogorkiewicz, R M, *The Technology of Tanks* Vol I, (London 1991), pp 39–40.

10 *Ibid*, p 41.

11 *Ibid*, p 50.

12 *Ibid*, pp 35–6.

13 *Ibid*, Vol II pp 259–262.

14 WO 32/13039, Research on Armour 1947; AVIA 55/46, *op cit.*

15 Ogorkiewicz, *op cit*, Vol I p 87.

16 *Ibid*, pp 73–6.

17 *Ibid*, p172.

18 *Ibid*, pp 174–7.

19 *Ibid*, pp 156–60.

20 *Ibid*, Vol II pp 400–2.

21 *Ibid*, Vol I pp 56–7.

22 WO 32/13039, Research on Armour, Engineer-in-Chief to Scientific Adviser, Army Council, 6 Oct 1947.

23 Ogorkiewicz, *op cit*, Vol II, pp 371–4.

24 *Ibid*, pp 374–6.

25 WO 32/11051, Post-War Research and Development: Wheeled Vehicles, 1944.

26 Ogorkiewicz, *op cit*, Vol I, Chap 9, *passim.*

27 AVIA 54/1781, Project J. Anti-Tank Weapon, 1957.

28 AVIA 65/904, Blue Water Development Policy; Draft letter from Controller Muns to DCIGS, 26 Jan 1959.

29 AVIA 54/1786, ATGM Research and Development; Note on RAE Team, 30 Jun 1953.

30 Ogorkiewicz, *op cit*, Vol I, pp 219–21.

31 *Ibid*, Vol I p 32.

32 WO 32/13571, 3.5 in rocket launchers and ammo for platoon/battalion anti-tank weapons, 21 Jul 1950.

33 Cordesman, A H, and Wagner, A R, *The Lessons of Modern War* (Westview Press/Mansell Publishing Co, 1990), Vol I, pp 64–66.

34 DEFE 7/277, Anti-Tank defence: obstruction, No 1 Working Party, 24 Apr 1951; AVIA 54/1196, Land Mine Detection Sub-Cttee 1951; Sloan, C E E, *Mine Warfare on Land*, (Brassey's (UK), London 1986).

35 Hafner, R, British Rotorcraft, *Jnl Roy Aero Soc*, Vol 70, Jan 1966; *op cit*, p 235.

36 AVIA 55/90 Use of Helicopters. Note by J A J Bennett, Fairey Aviation, 11 Aug 1945.

37 WO 32/13064, Helicopters Policy (Army) 11 Jun 1953, Cloake, J, *Templer: Tiger of Malaya*, (London 1985), p 245.

38 Taggart, A W M, Helicopter Air Power, *Aerospace*, No 1988 p 12; AIR 2/11428 Inter-Service Cttee, Policy for Helicopters, Cochrane (VCAS) to CAS, 1 Feb 1952.

39 DEFE 7/107, Supply and Control of Helicopters for use by the Army, Oct 1954; WO 32/15177, Cargo Helicopters, 137th Mtg of Army Council, 25 May 1954.

40 Zincone, R, LHX in the future battlefield and its contemporaries – Friend or Foe, Halford Memorial Lecture, *Aerospace*, Feb 1989, p 19.

41 Dudgeon, M G, Chinook in the RAF Today, *Aerospace* Feb 1989, p 11.

42 WO 163/211, Weapons Development Cttee, 1951–57, Discussion on SSMs for Field Army, 16 Dec 1952.

43 AVIA 65/950, Technical Aspects of Medium Range Guided Weapon – Red Rose, 1955–57; AVIA 65/904, Blue Water Development Policy, 1953–59.

44 Ward and Turner, *op cit.*

45 *Ibid.*

46 Buckland, R, Stabilisation of Guided Artillery Shell – spin v. fin, Guidance and Control Systems for Tactical Weapons, Roy Aero Soc Symp, 26 Apr 1988; Tsipis and Jasen, *op cit.*

47 Bellamy, C, *The Future of Land Warfare,* (London 1987), Chap 5.

48 AVIA 54/1916, Ground-to-Air Guided Weapons, Future Development Policy 1954; AVIA 54/1254, Red Shoes Development Policy 1952–55; AIR 20/7224, Guided Weapons for the Air Defence of the UK, 1949; AIR 2/12285, Yellow River Development, 1953.

49 AIR 19/949, Surface-to-Air Guided Weapons. Memo by Christopher Hartley (DD Ops GW) on Red Shoes and Red Duster; WO 291/1504, The Air Defence of the Field Army, Dec 1955.

50 According to Sir Robert Watson-Watt, Leslie Bedford, Obit, *The Times*, 26 Dec 1989.

51 AIR 19/949, *op cit*, Peter Masefield (Bristol Aviation) to George Ward, 14 Aug 1957.

52 AVIA 65/488, Scientific Advisory Cttee Misc Papers, 31 Aug 54.

53 Barron, C and Twinn, J E, The Birth of a System, *Aerospace*, Nov 1987, p 17.

54 Cordesman and Wagner, *op cit*, Vol III, p 295.

55 Jones, R V, The Falklands: An Unplanned Contingency in Air Defence, Talk to Electronic Security Cmd, USAF, 1983, p 9.

56 Safron, M, *Israel: The Embattled Ally*, (Bellknap Press, Cambridge, 1978). p 311.

57 Liddell Hart, B, *Thoughts on War*, (London 1944), p 262.

58 WO 32/15033, Development of Small Arms and Ammunition 1952–53; WO 32/10579, Infantry Weapon Development, 1947.

59 Ezell, E C *The Great Rifle Controversy. The Search for the Ultimate Infantry Weapon through Vietnam and Beyond* (Stackpole Books, Harrisburg, PA, 1984), *passim.*

60 WO 195/13571, Advisory Council on Scientific Research and Technical Development, Min of Supply; Ballistic Air Resistance Sub-Cttee, Spin yaw resonance theory applied to sporadic shorts in mortar bombs; WO 32/12781, Position of the 4.2 in mortar in the Army, 1948–49.

61 Ward and Turner, *op cit.*

62 WO 32/13816, *op cit*, 29 Oct 1955.

63 WO 291/1456, Army Opnl Res Gp Memo No. H12. Rept on a vsit to discuss recent developments in battle area surveillance, May–June 1956.

64 WO 32/11616, Radar tank detection by tanks, 1946–53.

65 AVIA 54/1485, Responsibility for infra-red development in the Army, 1953.

66 Hudson, *op cit*, p 108.

67 WO 32/12236, Development of TV for Army use. Rept on visit to Specialised Armour Development Establishment, 27 Mar 1947; Lampton, M, Micro-Channel Image Intensifier, *Scientific American*, Vol 245, No 5, Nov 1981.

68 Canby, S, The Alliance and Europe: Part IV, Military Doctrine and Technology, IISS *Adelphi Papers* No 109, 1974/75, p 23.

69 WO 32/12236, *op cit*, Note by O H Wansbrough Jones, Jan 1947.

70 Weimer, P K, A Historical Review of the Development of Television Pickup Devices (1930–1976), *IEEE Trans on Electron Devices*, Vol Ed-23, No 7, Jul 1976, pp 741–3.

71 Hartcup, G, *Camouflage*: *A History of Concealment and Deception in War*, (Newton Abbot 1979), Chap 8.

72 WO 163/389, Weapon Policy Cttee, 1953–5, War Office Policy Statement No 67 (2nd Revise), Deception and Concealment Equipment.

73 Ashcroft, G, Military Logistic Systems in NATO: The Goal of Integration, Part I: Economic Aspects, IISS *Adelphi Papers* No 62, p 2, 1969.

74 *Ibid*, Part II: Military Aspects, *Adelphi Papers* No 68, 1970.

75 Mackenzie, J J G and Reid B H (Eds), *The British Army and the Operational Level of War*, (London 1989). Gilbertson, M A, Development of Logistics in the British Army.

76 Cordesman and Wagner, *op cit*, Vol III, Analysis of the Lessons of Limited Armed Conflicts.

77 Liddell Hart, *op cit*, p 285.

Chapter 6 Chemical and Biological Warfare

1 Haber, L F, *The Poisonous Cloud*, (Oxford 1986, p 277).

2 WO 193/712, Chemical Warfare Policy, 1942–45.

3 *Ibid*.

4 WO 208/2183, Investigation into Tabun and Sarin products and Anabasine, Jul–Oct 1945.

5 WO 208/2186, German CW Int. from Combined Int. Objectives Sub-Cttee, 1944–45.

6 WO 291/1473, The Impact of CW on personnel wastage in a war in Western Europe before 1957, 1953.

7 WO 195/10429, Appreciation of potential CW value of nerve gases based on information up to 30 Jun 1949.

8 AIR 20/8731, CW, War Reserves, 15 Feb 1949; WO 195/9354, Mins Chem Defence Advsy Bd, 1 May 1947.

9 WO 195/9074, Advsy Council on Scientific Research and Technical Development, Chem Defence Advsy Bd, 21 Jun 1946.

10 AIR 20/8731, *op cit*, Offensive CW Policy, 6 Apr 1949.

11 AIR 20/8734, War Reserves, CW, 24 Sept 1951.

12 *Ibid*, Vice Chiefs of Staff mtg, 8 Feb 1952.

13 WO 163/390, Weapons Policy Cttee, 1955–57, New Chemical Warfare Agents by E A Perren, 19 Jan 1956; WO 195/14086, Nerve gas trials at CDEE with human observers.

14 WO 163/390, op cit.

15 Langer, E, Chemical and Biological Warfare, *Survival,* Vol IX, No 4, Apr 1967.

16 *IISS Strategic Survey, 1987–88*, Chemical Weapons and Arms Control p 57.

17 WO 163/389, Weapons Policy Committee, 1953–55, War Office Policy Statement No 32 (3rd Revise) Chemical Warfare.

18 *Ibid*.

19 AIR 20/8731, *op cit*, 11 Jun 1948.

20 *IISS Strategic Survey, 1987–88*, *op cit*, p 58.

21 SIPRI, *Chemical Disarmament. New Weapons for Old*, 1975; Robinson, J P, *Binary Nerve Gas Weapons*, Chap 2.

22 Hemsley, J, *The Soviet Biochemical Threat to NATO*, (London 1987), p 19; Soviet Chemical Warfare Capabilities, *Int Def Rev*, Jan 1981.

23 Robinson, J P, *SIPRI Chemical and Biological Warfare Studies*, 1985.

24 *Ibid.*

25 WO 163/389, *op cit.* Decontaminating materials; WO 195/13437, New Service Respirator, Oct 1955; T225/865 Production of Respirators, 18 Sept 1959.

26 WO 195/14041, Development of an automatic alarm for nerve gases, 1957; WO 195/10037, Chemical Defence Advsy Bd. Work done in 1948; WO 195/13243, Miniature Automatic Detectors, May 1955.

27. Geissler, E (Ed), *Biological and Toxic Weapons Today*, SIPRI, (Oxford Univ. Press, 1986).

28 WO 195/9240, Biology Cttee of the Chemical Defence Advsy Bd; Roskill, S, *Hankey, Man of Secrets* Vol III, (London, 1974), p 321.

29 Lewis, J, Churchill and the 'Anthrax Bomb', *Encounter*, Vol LVIII, No 2. Feb 1982.

30 CAB 79/78, COS Mtg, 26 Jul 1944.

31 WO 208/3974, Investigation of BW Targets, Jun 1945.

32 Ibid, Interrogation of Dr Kurt Blome, 1945.

33 WO 195/9354, Mins, Chemical Defence Advsy Bd, 1 May 1947.

34 WO 195/13780, Visit to Microbiological Research Estab., Porton, 5 Jul 1956.

35 Geissler, *op cit*, p 13.

36 WO 195/13534, Note on the recent work of the Crops Division at Camp Detrick, Dec 1955.

37 AIR 20/8729, Crop Destruction, 1947–55, Note by WP4, Dec 1947.

38 WO 195/13534, *op cit.*

39 SIPRI, *The Problem of Chemical and Biological Warfare* Vol 1, The Rise of CB Weapons, (1971), p 224 and pp 185–210.

40 AIR 20/8735, Airborne Chemical Trials, 29 Jan 1953.

41 AIR 20/8729, *op cit*, May 1952–Oct 1953.

42 Robinson, J P, *Chemical and Biological Warfare Developments*, (SIPRI 1985), pp 53–55.

43 SIPRI, *The Problem of Chemical and Biological Warfare* Vol 1, (1971), *op cit*, pp 185–210.

44 Vachon, G K, Chemical Weapons and the Third World *Survival*, Mar/Apr 1984.

45 Karsh, E, The Iran Iraq War: A Military Analysis, IISS *Adelphi Papers* No 220, p 56. Cordesman and Wagner, Vol II *op cit,* gives a figure of 45,000 casualties for both sides.

Chapter 7 Survival of the Manned Aircraft

1 DEFE 7/975, History of Development and Production of the Hunter, 1950–6; DEFE 13/63 Production position of Swift and Hunter aircraft, May–Dec1954; AVIA 54/755, Venom FB I Air Council Paper, 1951.
2 AVIA 65/233. Swept Wings Advsy Cttee, 1948–53, 1st mtg, 21 May 1948 and 14th mtg, 21 Jul 1950.
3 AVIA 54/1528, Barnes Wallis Flying Body with wings adjustable for sweepback and rotation, 1946–1955; AVIA 65/549, R & D Programme for VG Aircraft Finance and Policy, H Garner to H L Dryden, Nat Advsy Cttee for Aeronautics, 4 May 1950: 'We are giving Wallis a free hand in the development of his ideas'.
4 AIR 20/7578, The Air Defence of Great Britain. A New Approach by Barnes Wallis, 1953.
5 DEFE 7/279, Aircraft Research and Development, Brundrett to Minister of Defence (Macmillan), 22 Feb and 27 Apr 1955.
6 T225/812, VG Aircraft Swallow, 1953-55; Hall (RAE), Note on Swallow, Spring 1954.
7 *Ibid*. Note by Wansbrough Jones on Wallis Project, Oct 1953.
8 DEFE 7/279, *op cit*, Brundrett to Macmillan, 27 Apr 1955.
9 T225/812, *op cit*, Hall's note.
10 *Ibid*, Treasury minute, 18 Nov 1958.
11 AVIA 65/735, Research and development programme on VG aircraft, finance and policy, 1955–58; Rept by P A Hufton (RAE) on visit to Langley Field to Sir W Cawood (MoS), 4 Dec 1958.
12 AIR 20/10732, T/SR Aircraft. Operational Requirement Policy, 25 Jul 1957 and Note for DRPC, 26 Aug 1957.
13 AVIA 65/725, Tactical Bomber Aircraft (T/SR2), Finance and Policy, 1957.
14 *Ibid*, Min, 7 Aug 1957.
15 Zuckerman, Lord, *Monkeys, Men and Missiles*, op cit, p 211.
16 Salisbury, M W, The Significance of T/SR2. 37th R I Pierson Memorial Lecture, Roy Aero Soc, 18 Oct 1989.
17 Heath, B O, The MRCA Project, *Aeronautical Jnl*, Vol 74, Roy Aero Soc, Jun 1970, pp 444–56.
18 Cox A and Kirby S, *Congress Parliament and Defence*, (London 1986) pp 222–8. See also Price, A, *Panavia Tornado*, (London 1988).
19 AVIA 65/726, VTO Research Aircraft to Specification ER 143T, 1953; T226/809, VTO Aircraft, 1954.
20 T226/809, *op cit*, Treasury minute, 26 May 1954.
21 Mason, F K, *Harrier*, London 1986, pp 34–38.
22 AVIA 65/1537, VTOL/STOL Fighter. Technical Development, Planning and Progress, 1958–60, A V M Kyle to Handel Davies, 9 May 1958.

23 T226/809, *op cit*, Air Min to Treasury, 18 Sept 1959.

24 Mason, *op cit*, p 45.

25 Cordesman and Wagner, *op cit*, pp 309–14.

26 Mason, R A, *Air Power. An Overview of Roles*, (Brassey's (UK) London), 1987, p 44.

27 Brassey's *Weapons Technology*, 2nd edn, 1978.

28 Gunston, B, *All Weather Attack Aircraft of the West*, (London, 1974), pp 221–3.

29 ADM1/2473, Assessment of Aden to Air-to-Air Weapon, 1953; Wallace, G F, *The Guns of the RAF*, 1939–45 (London, 1972).

30 Air Ministry Publication 3368, *The Origins and Development of Operational Research in the RAF* (HMSO, 1963), p 141.

31 Nordeen, L O., *Air Warfare in the Missile Age*, (Smithsonian Instn Press, Washington DC, 1985), App 1.

32 AVIA 65/659, Radar AI Mark 18, Technical Development and Procs of Steering Cttee, 1952–53; AVIA 65/556, AI for single-seat fighters, 1953–56.

33 ADM1/24434, Project Metcalf, Sidewinder, Jan 1952–Jun 1953.

34 Nordeen, *op cit*, p 45.

35 T225/866, Blue Jay Production Firestreak, 1954–59; AVIA 65/1561, Firestreak, Production and Financial Policy, 1954; AVIA 65/342, Blue Jay R & D Trials Policy Oct 1951–Sept 1955.

36 AVIA 54/1230, Red Dean G W, Development Policy, 1951.

37 Mason, R A, *op cit*, p 34.

38 Karter, H and Fry, J Cooperation in Development and Production of NATO Weapons: An Evaluation of Tactical Missile Programs, *Inst for Defense Analyses*, Dec 1980, Table D–1.

39 AVIA 54/1236, Blue Boar G W Development, 1948–53; AIR 20/7124, Blue Boar, 1949–52.

40 AIR 2/10700, Short Range Expendable Bomber Policy, 1950–3, note by Cochrane, Feb 1951.

41 *Ibid*, Tuttle to Director Royal Artillery, Feb 1951.

42 AIR 2/10704, Short Range Expendable Bomber Policy, 1953–54, DRPC Mtg, 12 Oct 1954.

43 Huisken, R, *The Origin of the Strategic Cruise Missile* (Praeger, New York, 1981).

44 Gottemoeller, R E, Land-attack Cruise Missiles, IISS *Adelphi Papers* No 226, 1987–88, pp 6–7 and 10–11.

45 Nordeen, *op cit*, App II, p 230.

46 Perkins, K, (Ed). *Weapons and Warfare*, (Brassey's (UK) 1987), p 27.

47 Nordeen, *op cit*, App II, p 231.

48 *Ibid*.

49 *The Times*, Hero in a Small Back Room, 29 Jan 1991.

50 Nordeen, *op cit*, App II, p 230.

51 Attributed to Adm Sergei Gorshkov.

52 AIR 8/2032, Renewal of Control and Reporting System, 1955–56; AIR 20/9979–80, Renewal of Control and Reporting system, 1955.

53 AIR 2/12116, 1951–2, Embry to Cochrane, 24 Apr 1962.

54 AVIA 65/552, Low Level Early Warning Working Party, 1952; AVIA 65/21, Blue Joker, 1953–59; AIR 20/9815, Blue Joker, 1960; Blue Joker; Smith, J H, An Exotic Radar of the Fifties, RRE.

55 Grey, C G and Barnett, R W, (Eds) *Sea Power and Strategy*, (London 1989, p 263).

56 ADM 219/338, Director of Naval Ordnance, Visit to US Research Estabs., 1948.

57 AIR 20/9605, Airborne Early Warning, 1948–1952, Rept of AEW Mission to USA to study Cadillac, May–Jun 1949.

58 ADM1/22298, The Shape of Things to Come, 1945.

59 AIR 20/7860, 1453 Flight AEW: Policy, 1952–55.

60 ADM1/23261, Utilisation and Effectiveness of Skyraider Aircraft Operations, 1952–53.

61 House, T A and Leacy, A C, Airborne Early Warning Nimrod, Chadwick Memorial Lecture, Roy Aero Soc, *Aerospace*, Jan 1979.

62 Gunston, *op cit*, p 106.

63 DEFE 2/1716, Radio Warfare. The epigraph to Notes on Radio Warfare in Combined Operations was drawn from *The Times* Personal Column for 5 Apr 1950: 'Unidentified continuous vibratory noise in the atmosphere. Will those who hear this write Box P366, *The Times*, EC4'.

64 DEFE 2/1716, *op cit*, Memo on policy for radio warfare in Naval aircraft, 3 Aug 1950.

65 Nordeen, *op cit*, App II, p 228.

66 Mason, *op cit* p 95.

67 Price, *op cit*.

68 Mason, *op cit*, pp 73–6.

69 Nordeen, *op cit*, App II, p 228–9; Grant, *Introduction to Electronic Warfare*, op cit, pp 123–4.

70 ADM 220/836, Presentation of the Carcinotron by CSF, 31 Jan 1958; Kompfner, R, The Invention of Traveling Wave Tubes, *IEEE Trans on Electron Devices*, Vol. Ed-23, No 7, Jul 1976; Schleher, *op cit*, p 469.

71 Sweetman, B, *Stealth Aircraft*, (Airlife Publishing Ltd, 1986), passim; Lindsey, G, *The Tactical and Strategic Influence of Stealth Technology*, CQRI, 1989.

72 Fitts, *The Strategy of Electromagnetic Conflict, op cit*, pp 233–4.

73 DEFE 13/33, Air Defence (UK), GW and AA Command, Selwyn Lloyd (Minister of Supply) to PM (Churchill), 27 Nov 1954.

Chapter 8 The Sea War in Three Dimensions

1 Lindsey, G R, Tactical Anti-submarine Warfare: The Past and the Future, IISS *Adelphi Papers* 122, Power at Sea, I. The New Environment, 1976.

2 ADM 205/102, First Sea Lord's Records, 1954. Long Term Plan for Navy, *Quo Vadis* by Second Sea Lord, 23 Mar 1954.

3 ADM 1/24536, Report on Characteristics of USS *Antietam*, 16 Sept 1953; ADM 1/23203, Prog Rpt for DPRC on Naval Aviation, 16 May 1952.

4 Howard, M, Order and Conflict at Sea in the 1980s, IISS *Adelphi Papers* 124, Power at Sea III. Competition and Conflict, 1976.

5 Hezlet, *op cit*, p 27–2.

6 ADM 1/22871, Ship-to-Air Guided Weapon, 1951.

7 AVIA 54/1216, Seaslug, G W Development Tech Cttees, 1954–56; AVIA 54/1222, *op cit*.

8 Cordesman and Wagner, *op cit*, Vol III, p 295.

9 Walsh, J, Military Radar Systems. History, Current Position and Future Forecast, *Microwave Jnl*, Vol 21, No II, 1978.

10 *The Sunday Times*, 'Video Game' defence fails a vital test, 10 Jul 1988.

11 Cordesman and Wagner, *op cit*, Vol II, pp 573–84.

12 Cornall, P, Naval Guns in the Anti-Air Warfare Role, Trends in Maritime Weapons, One Day Conference, Roy Aero Soc., 21 Mar 1990. For the effect of modern armaments on ship design, see 'Warship 90', Roy Inst Naval Architects Symp on the future for surface warships.

13 AIR 20/6830, Bombs Bomb Gear, Depth Charges and Rocket projectiles, 27 May 1953.

14 ADM 1/24117, Surface Ship Torpedo Requirements, 31 Jul 1953.

15 Bagley, W H, Sea Power and Western Security: The Next Decade, IISS *Adelphi Papers* No 139, p 18.

16 Adam, J, USS *Stark*: What really happened? IEEE *Spectrum*, Sept 1987.

17 Rowe, P L, An Advanced ESM System for Ship Defence, Procs of military microwaves 1978 conference, pp 3–8.

18 Adam, *op cit*.

19 Short, R D, Stingray, The First Autonomous Underwater Guided Weapon, *Aerospace*, Nov 1989, p 16.

20 Hackmann, *op cit*, pp 271–4.

21 Hackmann, *op cit*, pp 346–9.

22 Hackmann, *op cit*, pp 338–9.

23 Hackmann, *op cit,* p 351.

24 ADM 1/20933, Helicopters in Anti-submarine Warfare, 1946–47, Tactical Employment of A.S Helicopters, 28 Nov 1946.

25 ADM 1/24148, 9th Rept by British helicopter crews participating in USN evaluation of helicopter dipping sonar, 1 Dec 1951.

26 ADM 1/20414, Submarines: Possibilities as Fighters, 29 Nov 1947.

27 Hackmann, *op cit*, p 353.

28 AIR 65/268, Tactical use of the passive directional radio sonobuoy, 6 Mar 1950; AVIA 65/661, Development of Sonobuoy System, MK IC, 9 Feb 1955.

29 ADM 1/24435, Pentane: Suitability for use as an air-launched weapon, 1951–52, Note by E C Williams, Director of O R., 6 Aug 1952.

30 Daniel D C *Anti-Submarine Warfare and Super Power Strategic Stability*, (London 1986).

31 Lindsey, G R, Tactical Anti-Submarine Warfare: The Past and the Future, op cit, p 34; Lythall, B W, The Future of Submarine Detection, *Naval Forces*, Vol II, No 2, 1981.

32 Daniel, *op cit*; Lythall, B W, Underwater Detection: Passsive or Active? *Naval Forces*, Vol IV, No 5, 1985.

33 AIR 15/885, Advsy Cttee on ASW: Policy, note on MAD; DEFE 8/23, Maritime Air Defence, 1950.

34 AIR 19/635, Cherwell to Sec of State for Air, 3 Mar 1953; AIR 15/885, *op cit*, 11 Nov 1957.

35 DEFE 8/23, *op cit*.

36 DEFE 9/22, Underwater Weapon Development, 29 Aug 1947.

37 ADM 1/24121, Staff acceptance of Fancy S R Ferry, 1952–54.

38 ADM 1/24435, *op cit*, Director of Torpedo, Anti-Submarine and Mine Warfare, 3 Jul 1952.

39 *Ibid*, Supt Torpedo Expt and Design to Director of Underwater Warfare, 23 Jul 1952.

40 Short, *op cit*, p 13.

41 ADM 1/24164, Interim Mackle Working Party Report, 1952.

42 ADM 1/22396, Anti-Submarine Weapons: Arming of Anti-Submarine Vessels, 1951–53, Minute by Director of Underwater Warfare, 21 Nov 1951.

43 ADM 1/24158, Underwater Detection Establishment Reports, Sept 1953.

44 Moore and Hall, *op cit*, p 94.

45 Grove, E J, *Vanguard to Trident. British Naval Policy Since World War 2*, (London 1987, p 313).

46 Moore and Hall, *op cit*.

47 Hackmann, *op cit*, p 321.

48 *Ibid*, p 337.

49 ADM 1/24729, Insulated Chamber Combustion. Decrease in Engine Noise, 1953.
50 Lindsey, Tactical and Strategic Influence of Stealth Technology, *op cit.*
51 *The Times*, Run silent, run deep, Comment by Capt R Sharpe RN (Retd), 21 Mar 1988.
52 DEFE 9/22, *op cit*, Note by Director of Underwater Warfare, 1947; ADM 1/24125, The Mining Threat, 1952.
53 ADM 1/24171, Enemy Pressure Mines (Intelligence), 1952.
54 Stafford, C S, Trends in Maritime Weapons-Mines, Trends in Maritime Weapons, *op cit.*
55 ADM 1/24422, Clearance of Pressure Mines, Aug 1951.
56 ADM 1/24451, Evaluation of Minesweeping Operations off Korea by US Pacific Fleet, 1951–52.
57 Hackmann, *op cit,* p 344.
58 Stafford, *op cit,.*
59 *Ibid,* p 5.5.
60 Lindsey, Tactical Anti-Submarine Warfare, *op cit*, pp 38–9.

Conclusion

1 Norman, Research and Development in Defence, *op cit.*
2 Coakley, T P (Ed). *C³I. Issues of Command and Control*, (Nat Def Univ, Washington, D.C. 1991). Covers all aspects of this important subject with personal contributions from military and civilian leaders.
3 Lambert, M (Ed), *Jane's All the World's Aircraft, 1991–92*, p 27.

SELECT BIBLIOGRAPHY

Arcangelis, M de, *Electromagnetic Warfare: from the Battle of Tsushima to the Falklands and Lebanon Conflicts*, (Blandford, Poole, 1985).

Amman, R *et al*, *The Technological Level of Soviet Industry*, (Yale Univ. Press, London 1987).

Armitage, M J and Mason, R A, *Air Power in the Nuclear Age, 1945–84*, (Macmillan, London, 1985).

Armitage, M J, *Unmanned Aircraft*, (Brassey's (UK), London, 1988).

Barnaby, F, *Automated Battlefield*, (Sidgwick & Jackson, London, 1986).

Bellamy, C, *The Future of Land Warfare*, (Croom Helm, London, 1987).

Benecke, T H & Quick, A W (Eds), *History of German Guided Missile Development*, (AGARD, Verlag E. Apelhaus & Co., Brunswick Germany, 1956).

Brookner, E, *Radar Technology*, (Artech House, Dedham, MA, 1978).

Brown, N *The Future of Air Power*, (Croom Helm, London 1986).

Coakley, T P (Ed), *C³I. Issues of Command and Control*, (National Defense Univ, Washington, DC 1991).

Cordesman, H & Wagner, A R, *The Lessons of Modern War*, Vols I–III, (West View Press, Mansell Publishing Co Ltd, London, 1990).

Cox, A W, *Sonar and Underwater Sound*, (D C Heath, Lexington, MA, 1974).

Cox, A & Reppy, J (Eds), *The Genesis of New Weapons. Decision Making for Military R & D*, (Pergamon, 1980).

Creveld, M van, *Supplying War*, (Cambridge Univ Press, 1977).

Daniel, D C, *Anti-submarine Warfare and Super Power Strategic Stability*, (IISS, Macmillan, London, 1986).

Devereux, A. *Messenger Gods of Battle, Radio, Radar, Sonar. The Story of Electronics in War*, (Brassey's (UK), London 1991).

Emme, E M (Ed), *The History of Rocket Technology*, (Wayne Univ Press, Detroit, 1964).

Eylan, C L, *The Fiber Optics Source*, (Philips Publishing Inc, MD, 1986).

Ezell, E C, *The Great Rifle Controversy: The Search for the Ultimate Infantry Weapon from World War II throughout Vietnam and Beyond*, (Stackpole Books, Harrisburg, PA, 1984).

Fagen, M D (Ed), *A History of Science and Engineering in the Bell System*, Vol II, *National Service in War and Peace, 1925–75,* (Bell Lab Inc, NJ, 1978).

Feld, B T, *et al* (Ed), *Impact of New Technologies on the Arms Race*, (MIT Press, Cambridge, MA, 1971).

Fitts, R E (Ed), *The Strategy of Electromagnetic Conflict*, (Peninsula Publishing, Los Altos, CA, 1980).

Geissler, E (Ed), *Biological and Toxic Weapons Today*, (SIPRI, Oxford Univ Press, 1986).

Gough, J *Watching the Sky*, (HMSO London, 1993).

Gutteridge, W & Trevor, T (Eds), *The Dangers of New Weapon Systems*, (Macmillan, London, 1983).

Hackmann, W, *Seek and Strike, Sonar, Anti-submarine Warfare and the Royal Navy* (HMSO. London 1984).

Hall, R C, *History of Rocketry and Astronautics*, American Astronomical Soc Hist Series, Vol 7, Pt II, (AAS Publns, San Diego, 1986).

Harrison, P G *et al*, *Military Helicopters*, (Brassey's (UK), London, 1985).

Hemsley, J, *Soviet Troop Control,* (Brassey's (UK), London, 1982).

Hezlet, A, *The Electron and Sea Power,* (Peter Davies, London, 1975).

Hodges, A, *Alan Turing. The Enigma,* (Burnett Books, London, 1983).

Kemp, G, and Pfaltzgraff, R L, *The Other Arms Race, New Technologies and the Emerging Geo-Strategic Environment*, (Lexington Books, 1975).

Kolodziej, E A, *Making and Marketing Arms: The French Experience and its Implications for the International System*, (Princeton Univ Press, 1987).

Lee, R G, *Introduction to Battlefield Weapons Systems and Technology*, 2nd Edn, (Brassey's (UK), London 1985).

Lee, W T & Staar, R F, *Soviet Military Policy since World War 2*, (Hoover Instn Press, Stanford Univ, CA, 1986).

Lewis, J, *Changing Direction. British Military Planning for Post-war Strategic Defence, 1942–47*, (Sherwood Press, London, 1988).

Mackenzie, J J G & Reid, B H, *The British Army and the Operational Level of War*, (Tri-Service Press, 1989).

Mendelsohn, E (Ed), *Science, Technology and the Military*, (Kluwer, Dordrecht, 1988).

Nordeen, L O Jr, *Air Warfare in the Missile Age*, (Smithsonian Instn Press, Washington, D.C., 1985).

Ogorkiewicz, R M, *The Technology of Tanks*, Vols I–II, (Janes, London, 1991).

Peebles, C, *Guardians. Strategic Reconnaissance Satellites*, (Ian Allan, London, 1987).

Perkins, K (Ed), *Weapons and Warfare*, (Brassey's UK), London, 1987).

Price, A, *Air Battle Central Europe*, Free Press, New York, 1986).

Richardson, D, *Electronic Warfare*, (Salamander Books, London, 1985).

Randell, B (Ed), *Origins of Digital Computers, (Sprenger Verlag, Berlin, 1973)*.

Ricci, F R & Schutzer, D, *US Military Communications: A C^3I Force Multiplier*, (Computer Science Press, USA, 1986).

Schleher, *Introduction to Electronic Warfare*, (Artec House, Dedham, MA, 1986).

Simpkin, R, *Race to the Swift*, (Brassey's (UK), London, 1986).

Speirs, E M, *Chemical Weaponry, A Continuing Challenge*, (Macmillan, 1989).

Stockholm International Peace Research (SIPRI), *The problem of Chemical and Biological Warfare*, Vol I, (Stockholm, 1971).

Sweetman, B, Stealth Aircraft: Secrets of Future Air Power, (Air-life Publishing Ltd, London, 1986).

Thompson, J, *The Lifeblood of War. Logistics in Armed Conflict*, (Brassey's (UK), London, 1991).

Warner, P, *The Vital Link: The Story of Royal Signals, 1945–1985*, (Leo Cooper, London 1989).

Wood, D, *Project Cancelled*, (Janes, 2nd Edn, London, 1976).

Zuckerman, S, *Scientists and War. The Impact of Science on War, Military and Civil Affairs*, (Hamish Hamilton, London, 1966).

Zuckerman, S, *Monkeys, Men and Missiles*, (Collins, London, 1988).

INDEX

First World War, use in, 169–170
German interest in, 11
Medical countermeasures, 185
Nerve gases, 171–6
Respirators, 182, 184
Second World War, 171–3
Soviet threat, 176, 181–2
Tear gas, 191
Third World, use of, 191–2
V agents, 176–7
Weapons, 177–181
Cherwell, Lord, 269–270
Chobham armour, *see* Tanks
Churchill, Winston, 171, 270
Cierva, Juan de la, 131
Clausewitz, C. von, 87
Clegg, J., 34
Cochrane, Air Chief Marshal Sir R.,
    199, 222, 228
Communications, radio:
 Air:
 JTIDS, 65
 Land:
 Ace High, 71
 Bruin, 13–4
 Clansman, 71, 75, 77
 Hobart, 71, 73
 Intacs, 77, 79
 Larkspur, 65
 Mallard, 73
 NICS Management Agency, 71
 Sea:
 Integrated Communications
     System Phase 3, 62
 Matelo, 59, 60
 Soviet, 79–80, 85
 Technology:
 Multiple information channels, 54
 Multiplexer, 56
 Packet Switching, 54–6
Communications, Command and
    Control (C³), 57, 58, 288;

Blades, 83
Ptarmigan, 73–77
RITA, 77, 80
Tri-Tac, 77
Wavell, 75
Compagnie de Télégraphie Sans Fil,
    240
Computers:
 British:
 Ace, 20
 Colossus, 15–16, 287
 EDSAC, 20
 U.S.:
 AN/FSQ–7, 30
 EDVAC, 20
 ENIAC, 16, 20
 Whirlwind, 30
 MIDAC, 32, 100
 Soviet, 32–3
 Ryad, 33, 80
Construcciones Areonauticas, 226
Copperhead, *see* Lasers
Coppock, S., 113
Cotton, S., 87
Cuba crisis, 83, 91

Dassault, Paul, xxvi
Dautry, Raoul, xxvi
Davis, Colonel J. (US), 47
Deception, 163
Defence expenditure, xxvii, 291
Demountable Rack Offloading and
    Pick-up System, 164
Distance measuring equipment, 140
DNA, 188
Dodds, Professor E.C., 187
Dornberger, General W., 2
Draper, C.S., 49, 51
Dummer, G.W.A., 27–8, 32
Duncan, Major General N.W., 113
Dyhernfurth, 172

Mountbatten, Admiral Lord Louis, 205
Mullard's, 25, 259
Multi–role Combat Aircraft, *see* Aircraft Types Tornado
McNamara, Robert, S., xxix–xxx, 201

Nancekuke, 175
National Physical Laboratory, 20
Newman, J.F., 176
Newman, Prof Maxwell, 15, 21
Night vision, aids to, 160–1, 289
see also Infra-red
Nixon, President Richard, 191
Noise suppression, see Sonar countermeasures
Norman, Sir R., 287
North American Aviation, 47
North Atlantic Treaty Organisation (NATO):
AirLand Battle strategy, 71, 110, 181, 249, 294
Artillery policy, 137–8
Basic Military Requirement System, 210
Chemical Warfare Policy, 175–6, 181
Flexible Response, 71, 110
Identification System, 243
MRCA Development and Production Agency, 206
Mutual Weapons Development Programme, xxx, 210
Project System, 210
Notvedt, H., 262

Ohain, H. von, 6, 196
Okinawa, Battle of, 232
Operational analysis/research, xxx, 17–18, 21, 149, 157
Optical guidance, aids to, 38

Oto Melara, 257
Otto fuel, 271

Parsons, J., 4
Permutter, 113
Philco Radio Corp, 232
Photographic interpretation, 90
Photographic Reconnaissance (manned aircraft):
Cameras, 89–91
Charge-coupled devices, 97–8
Digital image processing, 97
Strategic, 88–91
Tactical, 100–102
Photographic Reconnaissance (unmanned aircraft):
Israeli RPVs, 105–6
Western RPVs, 103–5, 107, 242
U.S. policy, 103
W. German RPVs, 107
Plessey, 28, 32, 73
Powers, F.G., 91
Pratt & Whitney, 202

Quadripartite Standing Working Group, 73

Racal, 258
Radar:
General:
Anomalous propagation, 33
Doppler, 5, 34, 157, 159, 207
Millimetric, 35
Missile guidance, 35–7
Radar cross section, 91, 242
Airborne:
Airborne early warning, 231–5
Airborne Warning and Control System, 233–5, 244, 254, 291
Aircraft Interception, 207, 216
AN/APS 20, 232
ASV, 270

324

Second Tactical Air Force, 215
Royal Canadian Navy:
Ships
Athabaskan, 1
Royal Corps of Transport
Intermediate Replenishment
Groups, 164
Royal Navy:
Admiralty
Director of Underwater Weapons,
270
Director of Aeronautical and
Engineering Research, 278
ECM, 236
Ships
Ark Royal, 64
Bideford, 1
Eagle, 248
Egret, 1
Hermes, 64
Royal Navy: *Ships (cont)*:
Osprey (Anti-submarine School),
261
Sheffield, 64, 257, 259
Triumph, 248
Tyne, 247
Vanguard, 247–8
Wilton, 282
Submarines
Affray, 263
Sidon, 271
Royal Radar Establishment, 28, 31
Royal Signals, 73
Royal Signals and Radar
Establishment, 77
Ruhrstahl armament makers, 2, 3
Russell, Admiral Sir G., 247

Salonimer, D., 46
Satellites:
Communications, 54
Skynet, 64

Electronic Reconnaissance, 98
Reconnaissance, 94–100
Satellite-assisted navigation, 64
Soviet, 98–100
Schnorkel: German use of, 12
Soviet use of, 232
Sandys, D., 204
Schrader, G., 171–2
Self Identification Feature, 243
Semiconductors, *see* Integrated cir-
cuits
Services Electronic Research
Laboratory, 28, 240
Shannon, C., 17, 83
Ship design:
Effect of armaments on, 258, 293
Flight decks, 266
Propulsion, 284
Shockley, W., 21, 23–4
Short Bros, 151, 209
Signals Research and Development
Establishment, 72
Sikorsky, I., 131, 264
Six Day War (1967), 114, 227, 241
Shunk Works, 91
Sonar:
Active (shipborne) 261–3, 268
Dunked, 263–4
Towed, 263–4
Submarine-borne, 265–6
Passive, 268–9
Light Airborne Multi-purpose
System, 269
Countermeasures, 277–8
Sound Surveillance Underscan,
268–9
Speer, A., 2, 172
Stack, J., 200
Stamp, Lord, 187
Stealth, 241–2, 292
Stoessel Commission, 181
Submarines: